TIMBER MANAGEMENT: A QUANTITATIVE APPROACH

TIMBER MANAGEMENT: A QUANTITATIVE APPROACH

Jerome L. Clutter
University of Georgia

James C. Fortson
University of Georgia

Leon V. Pienaar
University of Georgia

Graham H. Brister
University of Georgia

Robert L. Bailey
University of Georgia

KRIEGER PUBLISHING COMPANY
MALABAR, FLORIDA

Original Edition 1983
Reprint Edition 1992

Printed and Published by
KRIEGER PUBLISHING COMPANY
KRIEGER DRIVE
MALABAR, FLORIDA 32950

Library of Congress Cataloging-In-Publication Data
Timber management : a quantitative approach / Jerome L. Clutter ..
  [et. al.].
      p.   cm.
   Originally published: New York : Wiley, 1983.
   Includes bibliographical references and index.
   ISBN 0-89464-747-4
   1. Forest management. 2. Timber. 3. Forests and forestry-
-Mensuration.
SD393.T55 1983b
634.9'28--dc20
                                                92-11878
                                                     CIP

10   9   8   7   6   5

To Christine, Carolyn, Henrietta,
Alison, and Brenda

Preface

Several considerations motivated us to prepare this book. Most important of these is the increasing importance and profitability of timber production enterprises. Significant increases in stumpage prices and the availability of new and diverse markets for previously nonmerchantable material have led to market values for forestland which would have been thought impossible only a few years ago. Capital investment in forest management has also accelerated dramatically. Investment institutions of many types now actively compete with the forest products industry for the purchase of forestland and, like the forest products industry, many of them engage in capital-intensive timber management programs. Significant investment in forestry programs is also occurring in developing countries. In many cases, these investments support afforestation projects that are designed to help the countries involved deal with problems created by the world energy situation. In short, governments, corporations, and individuals have developed a new recognition of the economic benefits that can be produced through the intelligent and aggressive management of forestlands for timber production. A principal objective of this book is to present, for both students and practicing professionals, a clear and reasonably complete treatment of the planning and decision-making methodology used in the practice of intensive timber management.

A second factor that stimulated us was the immense improvement in quantitative planning and analysis tools that has taken place during the past 25 years. In 1957, only a few of the most prominent research universities in the United States possessed electronic computers, and the few available, in spite of their tremendous purchase and operating costs, had very limited speed and capacity. Today, efficient computers can be purchased "off-the-shelf" and immediately put into operation in the office or the home at a fraction of the purchase cost for a modest automobile. This technological change has increased our capacity for computational work by several orders of magnitude and simultaneously decreased the per-unit cost of computation by several magnitudes. As a result, spectacular improvements in quantitative procedures have taken place in almost all subject matter areas. Forestry is no exception and our professional journals have, over the past two decades, reported revolutionary changes in mensurational methods, financial analysis techniques, and forest-level planning methods.

However, these recently developed techniques have not as yet been collected in a single volume for easy access by students and interested practitioners. Hence, a second objective of the book is to provide a comprehensive review of recent developments in the quantitative methodology of timber management.

The third motivation for our efforts was of a more personal nature. Our collective forestry careers include approximately 100 years of professional experience with timber management activities. We have worked, on-site, for employers in seven countries scattered across four continents. Within the United States, we have engaged in professional timber management work in all of the significant forest regions and in most of the individual states where timber is a commercially important product. Our employers have included governmental land management agencies, private corporations, and universities. Some time ago, we developed a hope that this collective body of experience would provide a solid background for a book that would be of interest to foresters in those parts of the English-speaking world where timber production is an activity of interest. More recently, we also concluded that if our experience was indeed to aid us in preparation of this book, we had best get on with the project before we forgot too much more of what we had learned over the years.

The organization of the book is intended to facilitate its use as both a textbook and a reference work. Sections marked with an asterisk can be omitted without deleting material that is necessary for subsequent sections. Some marked sections are written at a considerably higher mathematical level than most of the book and are intended for specialists in the areas involved. All nonasterisked sections of the book assume no more mathematical competence than that required for passage of an introductory freshman-level course in differential calculus. The book is subdivided into three component parts. Part 1 consists of Chapters 1 through 4 and is concerned with those aspects of forest mensuration that are directly related to growth and yield prediction at the stand level. The level of presentation assumes a prior elementary mensuration course involving basic tree measurement techniques. Chapters 5 and 6 comprise Part 2, which provides a basic coverage of forest finance, taxation, and risk evaluation. No prior training in these topics is assumed. Parts 1 and 2 have been designed for totally independent presentation. Either one can be taught or studied without prior exposure to the other. Part 3 consists of Chapters 7 through 10 and assumes a knowledge of the concepts developed in both Parts 1 and 2. Some prior exposure to the formulation and solution of linear programming problems is desirable background for the topics presented in Chapter 10. The subject matter contained in Part 3 is concerned with timber management analysis and decision-making. The methods presented in Part 3 deal, to a large extent, with the same problems previously considered in books on forest regulation. However, the present methodology differs so radically from traditional forest regulation approaches that we are hesitant to place a "Forest Regulation" title on the contents of Part 3.

We believe that various sections of the book can be usefully included in several professional forestry courses. At the University of Georgia, Part 2 is included in the content of a senior-year resource management course required of all professional students. The mensuration and timber management courses that are required for undergraduate timber management majors include material from the nonasterisked sections of Chapters 1 through 4 and 7 through 10. Advanced courses in forest management planning and mensuration/timber management draw heavily on the asterisked sections that appear throughout the text.

Our task as authors would be left incomplete if we failed to identify the assistance provided by our friends in this undertaking. First, we are indebted to the many students at the University of Georgia who, in the process of being exposed to various drafts of this book, provided useful suggestions that were subsequently included in the finished product. Graduate research assistants Paule Bernier and Galen Grider toiled diligently, cheerfully, and effectively at such onerous tasks as preparation of illustrations, identification of literature citations, and proofreading. Their assistance is gratefully acknowledged. Special thanks are due to Russell Milliken, who helped us to complete a last-minute revision of Chapter 6, which incorporated tax law changes resulting from passage of the Economic Recovery Tax Act of 1981, and to Richard Field whose careful review of Chapter 10 provided sage advice concerning possible improvements.

The entire office staff of the School of Forest Resources has provided us with prompt and efficient typing services, and we hereby express our sincere thanks to all concerned with preparation of our various preliminary drafts. The final manuscript was meticulously typed by Barbara Hawks and Judy Jarrett to whom we owe a special debt of gratitude for their competence, conscientiousness, and continued good nature in the presence of so many co-authors.

Finally, we wish to express our sincere thanks to Dean L. A. Hargreaves and Dean Emeritus A. M. Herrick for their continued support and for creating and maintaining an environment where serious academic endeavor is not only tolerated but encouraged.

J. L. Clutter
J. C. Fortson
L. V. Pienaar
G. H. Brister
R. L. Bailey

Contents

TIMBER MANAGEMENT: A QUANTITATIVE APPROACH

PART 1

GROWTH AND YIELD PREDICTION

1

Estimating the Volumes and Weights of Individual Trees

Throughout this book, the basic management unit considered is the timber stand. Subsequent chapters will develop methodology for estimating present and future stand values and will discuss procedures for determining the optimum timing and intensity of harvests and other silvicultural practices that can be applied at the stand level. However, any stand is an aggregation of trees, and the *stand volume* or *weight* is defined as the sum of the volumes or weights of the individual trees that comprise the stand. All methods for estimating stand volume or weight must therefore involve, at least in their developmental stages, a prediction of individual tree volumes or weights and the summation of these quantities to obtain per-acre stand volumes or weights. As a result, some consideration of the methodology involved in predicting individual tree volume or weight is appropriate before we present the techniques used for estimating stand volume or weight.[1]

---

[1] Direct measurement of individual tree volume or weight is also an important mensurational topic, and the development of individual tree volume or weight predictors requires direct measurement of volume or weight data. Good coverage of this topic has been provided by Spurr (1952), Husch et al. (1982), and Avery (1975).

The "volume (or weight) of an individual tree" is a phrase that requires careful definition. Any tree is composed of a bole or stem, a root system, and the branches and leaves that collectively make up the crown. However, a forester speaking of individual tree volume or weight is almost invariably referring to the volume or weight of the commercially marketable portion of the tree. In areas where boiler fuel is produced by whole-tree chipping, this merchantable portion could include the entire stem and the crown. In most cases, however, the merchantable portion of the tree is some lower part of the stem. A single merchantable stem often contains logs or bolts that will provide raw material for several processing facilities. Large trees may yield poles or plywood bolts from the lower portion of the stem, sawlogs from the mid-portion, and pulpwood bolts from the uppermost section. Small trees may be utilized as pulpwood or, less commonly, for such products as fence posts, mine props, or fuelwood.

Many different procedures have been used and are being used to quantify the contents of the merchantable stem. These procedures can be usefully subdivided into two groups.

1.   Procedures based on direct volumetric or weight measurement of the merchantable stem.

2.   Procedures involving an implied conversion to some end product.

The direct volumetric or weight measurement procedures express stem contents in such units as outside-bark or inside-bark cubic-foot volume, and outside-bark or inside-bark green weight. A common unit for direct expression of volume is the *cunit*, which is defined as 100 cubic feet of solid wood (without bark).

The quantification procedures based on implied end-product conversion express the stem contents in terms of some product that could be produced from the merchantable stem. The two units used most commonly to quantify stem contents with these approaches are *board feet* and *cords*. When stem content is expressed in board feet, the usual intent is to estimate the amount of lumber that would subsequently be produced after felling and bucking the tree into sawlogs. Various log rules can be employed to estimate this volume.[2] With cord measure, an estimate is being made of the size of the pile that would result if the tree stem were felled and bucked into bolts, with the bolts then stacked in an orderly fashion.[3] For example, if a tree has a merchantable volume of 0.45

[2] A bewildering variety of log rules have been used for estimating the board-foot content of standing trees. Freese (1973) reports the existence of 95 log rules (bearing 185 different names) in the United States and Canada alone.

[3] The traditional definition of a *cord* is a stack of wood containing 128 cubic feet of wood, bark, and airspace. This definition involves an implied conversion of the merchantable stem into a pile of stacked bolts. In many current marketing situations, the cord has been redefined as so many pounds, green-weight, of wood and bark. With this definition, the cord is a direct weight measurement and its use is equivalent to expressing stem content in green-weight tons.

cords, felling the tree, bucking it into bolts, and piling the bolts would be expected to produce a pile containing $0.45 \times 128 = 57.6$ cubic feet of wood, bark, and airspace. It should be remembered that, in those areas where the cord became adopted as the standard unit of measure for standing trees, this adoption resulted from the fact that the bolts produced at harvest were bought and sold on a stacked-measure basis (i.e., payment proportional to the size of the pile). It is difficult to provide any justification for expressing the volume of standing trees in cords in situations where wood is marketed on something other than a stacked-measure basis.

The use of end-product units as a measure of the amount of raw material is uncommon outside the forest products industry. Raw cotton, for example, is not bought and sold in "shirt" units, nor is crude oil marketed with gallons of gasoline as the measurement unit. In single-product market situations, the use of end-product units is not illogical and it is easy to understand how certain areas of the country adopted board-feet and cord measure as the standard expressions of stem content. However, it is also clear that continued total reliance on these units has led to such questionable practices as buying and selling sawlogs in cords and expressing the contents of veneer bolts in board feet. The current trend is toward decreasing the usage of end-product units as expressions of stem content. Experience has shown that incorporation of a single end-product conversion factor into the raw material measurement unit does not provide adequate accuracy in the estimates of resulting end-product outputs. Each mill inevitably develops its own conversion factors and it is more logical to apply these factors to simple, direct volume or weight units[4] than to some derived and approximate end-product unit.

1.1 PREDICTING STEM CONTENT

Stem content (Y) is usually considered to be a function of tree dbh (D), some measure of tree height (H), and an expression of tree form (F). The relationship involved is written symbolically as

$$Y = f_1(D, H, F) \tag{1.1}$$

Stem content can be expressed in volume or weight terms or as an estimate of end-product output from some manufacturing process. The measure of tree height can be either total height or height to some specified upper-stem merchantability limit. The most commonly used measures of stem form are ratios of diameters at specified heights to tree dbh. Such ratios are known as *form quotients* (Spurr, 1952). One example of a form quotient is the Girard form class

---

[4] If these factors are developed separately by dbh classes, very precise estimates of end-product output are usually obtained.

which is defined as inside-bark diameter at the top of the first 16-foot log, divided by dbh (outside bark). This measure of form has been extensively used in North American forestry practice. Another expression of form known as the *cylindrical form factor* is important from a conceptual standpoint. This measure is defined as the ratio of total stem volume (V) to the volume of a cylinder with diameter equal to tree dbh and height equal to the total height of the tree. For a tree population where the cylindrical form factor is relatively constant regardless of tree size, the relationship

$$V = kD^2H \tag{1.2}$$

will hold, where k is a constant of proportionality. This equation form has not been widely used for volume and weight estimation, but it is occasionally suitable in situations where the objective is prediction of total stem volume (or weight) and the range of tree sizes is relatively limited.

Most practitioners prefer to use volume and weight estimating equations that do not involve any measure of form. Such equations have the functional form

$$Y = f_2(D, H) \tag{1.3}$$

and their application involves only the measurement of dbh and height. Formulas of this type are generally preferred over equations involving form measures for several reasons.

1. Measurement of upper-stem diameters is time-consuming and expensive.[5]
2. Variation in tree form has a much smaller impact on tree volume or weight than height or dbh variation.
3. With some species, form is relatively constant regardless of tree size.
4. With other species, tree form is often correlated with tree size, so that the dbh and height variables often explain much of the volume (or weight) variation actually caused by form differences.

Historically, the instrument used to express relationships of the type shown in equations (1.1) and (1.3) was called a *volume table*. If the relationship involved form, the volume table was typically a set of printed tables with each individual table containing entries for a given form quotient value. Within the individual

---

[5] We are aware of the fact that many practitioners obtain form measures by ocularly estimating upper-stem diameters and we freely admit that some of these practitioners are quite expert in this task. However, we also believe that the number of people who think they can accurately estimate upper-stem diameters is disturbingly larger than the number of people who can, in fact, actually produce estimates of reasonable accuracy.

tabulation, tree volumes were tabled by dbh values (usually as rows) and height values (usually as columns). For a volume relationship of the type shown in equation (1.3) where no form measurement was involved, a single tabulation by dbh and height values sufficed to express the relationships involved. Construction of these volume tables was accomplished by measuring the volumes of sample trees selected from the population of interest and by relating these volumes to dbh, height, and form (if desired) through a graphical process involving the construction of harmonized curves (Chapman and Meyer, 1949; Bruce and Schumacher, 1950). The development of the science of statistics and the advent of electronic computers have now made such a graphical approach obsolete, and regression equations are now fitted to the sample tree data to produce formulas that explicitly state the relationship between predicted tree volume and the predictor variables used. (Solutions of such formulas can, of course, still be presented in tabular form.) Conventionally, any volume-predicting equation is referred to as a volume table, and the term *volume table* is usually defined as a function, table, or graph that can be used to estimate the volume of a standing tree from such tree characteristics as dbh, height, and form.

Some equation forms commonly used for individual tree volume and weight estimation are shown in Table 1.1. All of these are special cases of the general functional forms shown previously as equations (1.1) and (1.3). An equation illustrating each of the various forms listed in Table 1.1 is shown here.

1. Prediction of total-stem volume for a composite of species in the Lake States (Gevorkiantz and Olsen, 1955).

$$Y = 0.002291D^2H \tag{1.4}$$

where

Y = total-stem cubic-foot volume, inside bark (i.b.)
H = total height

2. Prediction of merchantable-stem volume for old-field slash pine plantatins in the Georgia middle coastal plain and the Carolina sandhills (Bennett et al., 1959).

$$Y = -1.045389 + 0.002706D^2H \tag{1.5}$$

where

Y = merchantable cubic-foot volume, outside bark (o.b.) to a 4-inch top (o.b.)
H = total height

TABLE 1.1

Equation Forms Commonly Used for Estimation of Individual Tree Volumes and Weights

Name	Equation Form
1. Constant form factor	$Y = b_1 D^2 H$
2. Combined variable	$Y = b_0 + b_1 D^2 H$
3. Generalized combined variable	$Y = b_0 + b_1 D^2 + b_2 H + b_3 D^2 H$
4. Logarithmic	$Y = b_1 D^{b_2} H^{b_3}$
5. Generalized logarithmic	$Y = b_0 + b_1 D^{b_2} H^{b_3}$
6. Honer transformed variable	$Y = D^2/(b_0 + b_1 H^{-1})$
7. Form class	$Y = b_0 + b_1 D^2 H F$

$$Y = \text{some measure of stem content}$$
$$D = \text{dbh}$$
$$H = \text{some measure of tree height}$$
$$F = \text{an expression of tree form}$$
$$b_0, b_1, b_2, b_3 = \text{constants}$$

3. Prediction of total-stem volume of plantation-grown loblolly pine in the lower Piedmont of Georgia (Romancier, 1961).

$$Y = -3.2914302 + 0.06956815 D^2$$
$$+ 0.05175864 H + 0.00125878 D^2 H \tag{1.6}$$

where

Y = merchantable cubic-foot volume (o.b.), excluding stump, to a 3.6-inch top (i.b.)

H = total height

4. Prediction of total-stem volume for Douglas-fir in British Columbia (Brackett, 1973).

$$Y = 0.002198 D^{1.739925} H^{1.133187} \tag{1.7}$$

where

Y = inside-bark, cubic-foot volume including top and stump

H = total height

5. Prediction of total-stem volume for red pine in eastern Canada (Newnham, 1967).

$$Y = 0.284 + 0.002237 D^{1.8627} H^{1.1031} \tag{1.8}$$

where

Y = total volume (o.b.), in cubic feet

H = total height

6. Prediction of total-stem volume for red pine in Canada (Honer, 1965).

$$Y = D^2/(0.691 + 363.676H^{-1}) \qquad (1.9)$$

where

Y = total-stem cubic-foot volume (i.b.)

H = total height

7. Prediction of merchantable-stem volume in board feet, Scribner rule, using Girard form class (Parker, 1972).

$$Y = 20.91130 + 0.37250D^2HF \qquad (1.10)$$

where

Y = merchantable-stem volume in board feet, Scribner rule

H = merchantable height in number of 16-ft logs and half-logs (e.g., 2.5 logs)

F = Girard form class expressed as a proportion (e.g., 0.78)

Equation forms 1, 4, and 6 in Table 1.1 are generally used only for the prediction of total-stem cubic-foot volumes or total-stem weights. Equation forms 2, 3, 5, and 7 are somewhat more flexible and have been applied to the prediction of total-stem cubic-foot volumes and weights, merchantable-stem cubic-foot volumes and weights, and merchantable-stem volumes measured in board feet or cords. A variety of equation forms not shown in Table 1.1 has also been used in various studies for individual tree volume and weight prediction.

Until quite recently, the prediction of merchantable volumes to varying merchantability limits was usually accomplished by fitting a separate regression equation for each merchantability limit involved. Thus, for a single tree population, three different formulas would be involved for, say, prediction of merchantable volumes to 4-inch, 3-inch, and 2-inch tops. Several recent studies have produced volume and weight prediction equations that utilize the merchantability limit as an independent variable (Honer, 1964; Burkhart, 1977; Queen and Pienaar, 1977; Brister et al., 1980). With an equation of this type, predicted volumes to various merchantability limits can be obtained using a single equation. The following equations are typical examples of a variable-top merchantable volume prediction system (Brister et al., 1980).

$$V_t = 0.00616D^{2.05779}H^{0.74679} \qquad (1.11)$$

$$V_m = V_t(1 - 0.61529d^{3.66827}D^{-3.47361}) \qquad (1.12)$$

where

V_t = total-stem cubic-foot volume (o.b.)

D = dbh

H = total height

d = merchantable top diameter (o.b.)

V_m = merchantable volume to a d-inch merchantable top

These equations apply to slash pine plantations in the lower coastal plain of Georgia and Florida. The solution of equation (1.11) for a tree with $D = 10$ inches and $H = 60$ feet is $V_t = 14.97$ cubic feet. Subsequent solutions of equation (1.12) with d set equal to 4 inches, 3 inches, and 2 inches estimate the 4-inch, 3-inch, and 2-inch top merchantable volumes to be 14.47, 14.80, and 14.93 cubic feet, respectively. Studies by Queen and Pienaar (1977) and Flowers (1978) have shown that this approach can also be successfully employed for the prediction of merchantable weight.

1.2 TAPER RELATIONSHIPS

Taper is the term used to describe the decrease in stem diameter with increasing height up the stem. Taper equations express the expected stem diameter, either outside or inside bark, as a function of height above ground level, total tree height, and diameter at breast height. Such equations are useful adjuncts to the merchantable volume equations discussed in the previous section. Merchantable volume equations estimate the volume to a specified upper-stem diameter, but utilization standards often involve log length specifications in addition to a minimum diameter limit. Veneer bolts, for example, must meet rigid size specifications that reflect the characteristics of the particular lathes that will be used in the manufacturing process. Suppose the specifications for veneer bolts call for a length of 8.5 feet with a minimum top diameter of 9.6 inches. How many veneer bolts could, on the average, be cut from standing trees of some specified dbh and total height? If an appropriate taper equation is available, this question is easily answered by solving the taper equation for the diameters at the tops of successive 8.5-foot bole sections. The number meeting the minimum diameter limit is easily established and, since the small-end diameter of each qualifying bolt is known, the veneer yield from the tree can be estimated with considerable precision.

No single taper equation can be expected to adequately describe tree form for all species and, in many cases, a single equation will not be adequate to cover all the stand conditions in which a single species may be grown. As a result, many different forms of taper equations have been developed and they have been used for various purposes. Bennett and Swindel (1972) produced the following taper equation for old-field slash pine plantations.

$$d = 0.8544D\left(\frac{H - h}{H - 4.5}\right) + 0.002988(H - h)(h - 4.5)$$

$$- 0.00004822H(H - h)(h - 4.5)$$

$$+ 0.00001938(H - h)(h - 4.5)(H + h + 4.5) \qquad (1.13)$$

where

D = dbh

H = total height

d = predicted diameter (i.b.) at height h feet above the ground ($4.5 \leqslant h \leqslant H$)

It is obvious that this equation can be used to predict upper-stem diameters and to develop information on log and bolt sizes that could be produced from trees of any specified dbh and total height. The equation could also be used to estimate the volume of the stem between dbh and the top of the tree. This could be done by subdividing the stem into a number of short sections and separately calculating the volume of each section, or it could be accomplished by using standard methods of integral calculus. The fact that a taper function can be used to generate a volume function has long been recognized, and the relationships between taper functions and volume equations have been explored in considerable detail (Behre, 1923; Demaerschalk, 1972). In some instances, volume equations are obtained by first developing a taper function and then generating the volume equations from the taper function (Bruce et al., 1968).

Clutter (1980) essentially reversed the process just described by pointing out that any variable-top merchantable volume equation implicitly defines an associated taper function. For example, if merchantable outside-bark tree volume is correctly given by equations (1.11) and (1.12), it can be shown that the outside-bark taper is defined by the equation

$$d = 0.77525D^{0.84868}H^{-0.44764}(H - h)^{0.59942} \qquad (1.14)$$

where

D = dbh

H = total height

d = outside-bark diameter at height h feet above the ground

It is possible to invert equation (1.14) and obtain a formula for determining the height at which a given outside-bark diameter occurs. The appropriate equation is

$$h = H - 1.52912d^{1.66827}D^{-1.41582}H^{0.74679} \qquad (1.15)$$

The current trend toward production of multiple products from a single tree stem has created an increased interest in the development of suitable taper functions. Readers interested in recent research on taper function methodology are referred to publications by Max and Burkhart (1976), Demaerschalk and Kozak (1977), and Cao et al. (1980).

1.3   CALCULATING PLOT VOLUMES

Individual tree volume prediction equations can be used in a variety of ways to obtain estimates of stand volume per acre. A consideration of the possible variations with fixed-radius plot sampling is sufficient to illustrate the principal concepts involved. When a sample of fixed-radius plots is established in a stand or other forest population, a calculated volume for each plot will usually be desired. For any particular plot, this volume is simply the sum of the individual tree volumes for the trees located within the plot. If a suitable individual tree volume prediction equation is available, the required predictor variables can be measured for each tree and estimated volumes can then be individually calculated for all trees and summed to obtain the plot volume. If desired, the result can be converted to a per-acre basis. Volumes for research plots and monumented inventory plots are often obtained in this way.

In many forest inventory situations, it is inefficient to measure all predictor variables for every tree in each plot because of the differential measurement costs involved. The dbh measurements can be obtained at little expense in almost any timber type. Height measurements are considerably more expensive to collect under the best of conditions, and in tall dense stands the accurate measurement of heights can be very difficult. Form quotient measurements are usually the most expensive of all to collect. As a result, plot volumes are generally obtained by measuring all trees on the plot for dbh and subsampling for heights and, if necessary, form measurements.

Consider first the situation where no form measurement is included in the volume equation, so that predicted volume is a function of dbh and height only. In this case, dbh is measured for every tree on the plot, while heights are obtained on only a subsample. Data from the height sample trees are then used to establish a height/diameter regression relationship. Many different regression model forms have been used to express this relationship, but the most commonly used model is probably[6]

$$\ln (H) = b_0 + b_1 D^{-1} \tag{1.16}$$

or in exponential form

$$H = e^{b_0 + b_1 D^{-1}} \tag{1.17}$$

where

H = individual tree height

D = dbh

e = base of natural logarithms

After the regression coefficients b_0 and b_1 have been estimated from the height sample tree data, the right-side of equation (1.17) can be substituted for H in the volume equation. After this substitution, volume is estimated as a function of dbh only, and the resulting expression is referred to as a *local volume table*. For example, consider a plot where the volume equation

$$V = 0.00616 D^{2.05779} H^{0.74679} \tag{1.18}$$

is appropriate for estimation of the individual tree volumes. Data from a sub-sample of height-measurement trees on this plot are used to fit a simple linear regression of the form shown in equation (1.16). The resulting regression formula is

$$\ln (H) = 4.29989 - 1.92669 D^{-1} \tag{1.19}$$

so that height can be estimated as

$$H = \exp (4.29989 - 1.92669 D^{-1}) \tag{1.20}$$

Substitution of the right-hand side of equation (1.20) in equation (1.18) gives the local volume table equation

$$V = 0.00616 D^{2.05779} [\exp (4.29989 - 1.92669 D^{-1})]^{0.74679} \tag{1.21}$$

---

[6] Throughout this book, the notation ln (X) will be used to indicate the natural (base e) logarithm of an argument X. The common (base 10) logarithm is indicated as log (X).

which can be used to calculate a predicted volume for each tree on the plot. When this procedure is used, a separate height/diameter regression can be calculated for each plot or a single regression can be calculated for all plots in the same stand if stand conditions show little variability. Data from different stands should never be pooled to calculate a single regression of height as a function of dbh.

An alternative to the height/diameter regression approach involves use of the height sample tree data to fit a volume/basal area regression relationship. With this procedure, the volume prediction equation is applied to the diameter and height data from the height-measurement sample trees to obtain a predicted volume for each sample tree. These predicted volumes are then used to fit a regression of the form

$$V = b_0 + b_1 B \tag{1.22}$$

where

V = predicted sample tree volume

B = sample tree basal area

Since equation (1.22) estimates volume as a function of dbh only, it constitutes a local volume table equation that can be used to calculate a predicted volume for each tree on the plot. It is worth noting that the plot volume can be obtained in one solution of the equation, since

$$\sum_{i=1}^{n} V_i = \sum_{i=1}^{n} (b_0 + b_1 B_i)$$

$$= nb_0 + b_1 \sum_{i=1}^{n} B_i \tag{1.23}$$

where

V_i = predicted volume of the ith tree on the plot

B_i = basal area of the ith tree

$\sum_{i=1}^{n} V_i$ = plot volume

$\sum_{i=1}^{n} B_i$ = plot basal area

In many inventory situations, the dbh values for the nonsample trees are not individually recorded, and the tree frequencies are simply tallied by 1- or 2-inch dbh classes. This may be done on a plot-by-plot basis, or the tally may simply

TABLE 1.2

An Example Stand and Stock Table

dbh Class (inches)	Number of Stems per Acre	Average Volume per Tree (cubic feet)	Class Volume (cubic feet/acre)
5.5–6.5	85	4.8	408.0
6.5–7.5	146	6.8	992.8
7.5–8.5	121	9.2	1113.2
8.5–9.5	77	12.0	924.0
9.5–10.5	35	15.1	528.5
10.5–11.5	13	18.6	241.8

Note: Total volume per acre = 4208.3.

be accumulated over all plots in the stand. In either case, the tally is usually adjusted to a per-acre basis to give a tabulation of numbers of trees per acre by dbh class. Such a tabulation is referred to as a *stand table*. The local volume table equation developed from sample tree data can be applied to the stand table data to obtain a tabulation of per-acre volumes by dbh class. This tabulation constitutes a *stock table*. Table 1.2 contains an example of a stand and stock table. The per-tree volumes have been calculated from the diameter class midpoints using equation (1.21).

The previous discussion assumes that, if the individual tree volume prediction equation is used, it does not involve any form measurement as a predictor variable. When form quotient measurements are involved, the problem of developing a local volume table is more complex. Some practitioners approach the problem by measuring a subsample of trees for form quotient (often the same trees that are measured for height) and by averaging the form quotient values to obtain a mean form quotient that is then assumed to apply to all trees on the plot. Derivation of a local volume table then proceeds along either of the lines previously described. However, if form quotient is correlated with tree size (as is often the case), a simple averaging of form quotients can introduce a sizable bias into the volume calculation process. A better approach is to measure form quotient on the same sample trees that are measured for height and then calculate predicted volumes for these trees from the dbh, height, and form measurements. These predicted volumes can then be used to fit a volume/basal area local volume table equation of the type shown in equation (1.22).

1.3.1 Tarif Tables

Tarif table techniques are logical extensions of the previously noted within-stand linear relationship between individual tree volumes and their associated basal areas. These techniques constitute an alternate stand volume computation procedure to the local volume table methods already described. Although the use of tarif table techniques is of fairly recent origin in the United States, extensive experience with such systems had been gained in England and Australia prior to World War II (Jolly, 1950; Hummel, 1955; Hummel et al., 1962; Gray, 1966; Carron, 1971).

Turnbull and Hoyer (1965) used felled sample tree measurements to develop a tarif system for West Coast Douglas-fir. This system has been extended for application to other species native to the Pacific Northwest and it is now applied extensively within that region for computation of stand volumes. The central theme of the Turnbull-Hoyer tarif system (and, indeed, of any tarif system) is the volume/basal area line

$$V = b_0 + b_1 B \tag{1.24}$$

where, for the Turnbull-Hoyer tarif system,

V = merchantable cubic-foot volume, inside bark, to a 4-inch top (o.b.)

B = individual tree basal area

It is assumed that a tree with a dbh of 4 inches ($B = 0.087$ square feet) has no merchantable volume, in which case the lines for three typical stands take the form shown in Figure 1.1. Since all volume/basal area lines intersect the X axis at 0.087 square feet of basal area, the tarif number is simply a slope index for the line to which it refers. By definition, tarif number (T) equals predicted volume for a tree of 1.0 square feet of basal area. The regression equation can be written as

$$V = b_1(B - 0.087)$$

so that

$$T = b_1(1.0 - 0.087)$$

and

$$b_1 = T/0.913$$

Thus, if the tarif number is known, tree volume can be estimated from tree basal area as

$$V = \frac{T}{0.913}(B - 0.087) \tag{1.25}$$

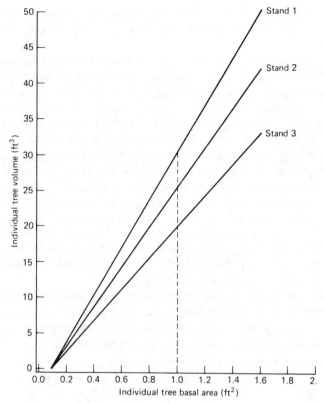

Figure 1.1 Volume/basal area lines for three typical even-aged stands.

Numerous authors (e.g., Hummel, 1955; Lewis, 1957; Gray, 1966) have noted a strong relationship between tarif number and stand height. A quantification of this relationship is usually referred to as a *tarif access table*. In practice, a number of sample trees are measured for height and then mean height is calculated. The tarif number associated with this mean height is determined from the access table, and individual tree volumes are then calculated using equation (1.25). Access tables and tabulations of predicted 4-inch-top volumes for this system have been published by Turnbull et al. (1963) and have been updated by Brackett (1973). Conversions to other merchantable top volumes are also included.

*1.4 DEVELOPING STEM CONTENT PREDICTION EQUATIONS

Stem content prediction equations are developed through a fairly straightforward application of standard statistical methodology. Data from sample tree measurement are used to fit linear or nonlinear regression equations.[7] Programs for carrying out the necessary statistical computations are available in most computer installations.

The data collection phase of the equation development process requires specification of the tree population involved, followed by selection and measurement of appropriate sample trees. The sample trees are usually selected purposively (rather than randomly) to achieve a good coverage across the ranges of the predictor variables involved. The selected trees should be spatially dispersed throughout the geographic range of the population involved; however, sampling efficiency is usually best served by locating appropriate stands at geographically dispersed locations and measuring several sample trees in each stand. Each sample tree is usually measured for dbh prior to being felled. After felling, total height, form quotient (if desired), merchantable height (if desired), and the measurements needed for stem content determination are obtained. As an alternative to felling the sample trees, upper-stem diameters can be measured on standing sample trees with a dendrometer (Grosenbaugh, 1963). This procedure has limitations, since only outside-bark measurements can be obtained and no weight data can be collected from standing trees.

Before the regression analysis can be performed, data from the sample trees must be summarized in appropriate form. This involves the determination of stem content from the measurements made on each sample tree. If the desired measurement of stem content is board-foot volume, scaling diameters at the top of each log can be determined, the board-foot volume of each log can be estimated from an appropriate log rule, and the volume of the tree can be obtained as the sum of the volumes of the component logs. Alternatively, the logs could be transported to a sawmill and the actual lumber volume produced from the tree could then be used as the tree volume.

If the desired measure of stem content is cubic feet, the volume is usually calculated by either physically or conceptually subdividing the stem into component bolts. Diameter measurements at the upper and lower end of each bolt (either inside-bark or outside-bark) are then used to calculate the bolt volume using Smalian's formula:

$$V = \tfrac{1}{2}(A_u + A_\ell)L \qquad\qquad\qquad (1.26)$$

where

V = bolt volume in cubic feet

A_u = upper-end, cross-sectional area in square feet

---

[7] Linear regression techniques are discussed in Appendix C; in particular, Section C.6 of Appendix C contains a brief introduction to nonlinear regression procedures.

A_ℓ = lower-end, cross-sectional area in square feet

L = bolt length in feet

The tree volume to any specified merchantable top limit can then be obtained by summing the volumes of the component bolts in the specified stem section. If total-stem volume is desired, the volume of the uppermost stem section is usually calculated using the formula for the volume of a cone. Most practitioners use a fixed bolt length (5 feet is frequently used). However, some prefer to measure the distances required for each 1-inch change in diameter.

Several approaches are possible when weight is the desired measure of stem content. If the sample trees are not too large, green weight with bark can be directly obtained in the field by weighing the bolts (either individually or collectively) on a platform scale. The ratio of green weight without bark to green weight with bark can be estimated in the field by cutting fixed-width disks from the lower ends of the bolts and then collectively weighing the disks before and after the bark is removed from them. It is also possible to obtain tree weight data entirely from measurements made on sample disks. With this approach, a sample disk (wood and bark) is cut from the lower end of each bolt and weighed in the field before significant moisture loss can occur. Subsequent laboratory measurements of green volume with bark, green volume without bark, and wood oven-dry weight are then obtained for each disk and used to calculate green-weight density (D_g) and dry-weight density (D_d) where

$$D_g = \frac{\text{Green weight of wood and bark}}{\text{Green volume with bark}} \qquad (1.27)$$

and

$$D_d = \frac{\text{Oven-dry weight of wood only}}{\text{Green volume without bark}} \qquad (1.28)$$

The green weight (wood and bark) of any bolt can then be estimated as

$$W_g = \frac{L}{6}(A_\ell D_{gu} + 2A_\ell D_{g\ell} + 2A_u D_{gu} + A_u D_{g\ell}) \qquad (1.29)$$

while the estimate of dry weight (wood only) is obtained as

$$W_d = \frac{L}{6}(A'_\ell D_{du} + 2A'_\ell D_{d\ell} + 2A'_u D_{du} + A'_u D_{d\ell}) \qquad (1.30)$$

where

W_g = green weight of the bolt

A_ℓ = cross-sectional area of wood and bark at the lower end of the bolt

A_u = cross-sectional area of wood and bark at the upper end of the bolt

$D_{g\ell}$ = green-weight density at the lower end of the bolt

D_{gu} = green-weight density at the upper end of the bolt

L = bolt length

W_d = dry weight of the bolt

A'_ℓ = cross-sectional area of wood only at the lower end of the bolt

A'_u = cross-sectional area of wood only at the upper end of the bolt

$D_{d\ell}$ = dry-weight density at the lower end of the bolt

D_{du} = dry-weight density at the upper end of the bolt

Equations (1.29) and (1.30) are obtained by integration over the bolt length with the assumption that both cross-sectional area and weight density vary linearly along the bolt.

When the computation of stem content has been completed for each sample tree, the data can be summarized as shown in Table 1.3. (If measurement of form quotient is omitted, the last column of Table 1.3 would be deleted.) With the notation used in Table 1.3, S_i, D_i, H_i, and F_i represent the stem content, dbh, height, and form quotient, respectively, for the ith sample tree.

Seven equation forms commonly used for the prediction of individual tree volumes and weights were introduced in Table 1.1. Fitting any one of these

TABLE 1.3

Sample Tree Data Set Structure for Development of Stem Content Prediction Equations

Sample Tree Number	Stem Content	dbh	Height	Form Quotient
1	S_1	D_1	H_1	F_1
2	S_2	D_2	H_2	F_2
3	S_3	D_3	H_3	F_3
⋮	⋮	⋮	⋮	⋮
n	S_n	D_n	H_n	F_n

models to data of the form shown in Table 1.3 is a relatively straightforward computation problem. There are, however, several complicating questions that can arise in any regression analysis situation.

1. Which model or models should be selected for initial fitting?
2. Should the form of the model be modified because the variance of the dependent variable is not constant over all observations?
3. Can any of the variables included in the initial model be deleted to give a simpler model?
4. If several candidate models are fitted, what procedure should be used to select the final regression equation?

Current procedures for dealing with these problems are described in Appendix C. These procedures are appropriate for linear regression analyses that are undertaken to develop stem content prediction equations and are also applicable to all other linear regression applications subsequently discussed in this book.

The unequal variance problem identified as question 2 above is worthy of special discussion in the context of fitting stem content prediction models. Whenever a direct measure of stem content is used as the dependent variable in a regression model, it is likely that the assumption of constant variance for the dependent variable throughout the ranges of the independent variables will not be satisfied. This arises from the fact that the stem content variability of large trees is generally greater than the stem content variability of small trees. When the variance of the dependent variable is not a constant, the model must be modified by dividing all variables by a *weighting factor*, which is proportional to the standard deviation of the dependent variable. Transforming the variables in this way produces a new model in which the dependent variable has a constant variance.[x] Experience with tree populations (e.g., Cunia, 1964; Smalley and Bower, 1968) has shown that one of the following two variance assumptions will usually be satisfied.

1. The standard deviation of stem content is proportional to D^2H.
2. The standard deviation of stem content is proportional to $\sqrt{D^2H}$.

We now develop techniques appropriate for fitting the combined variable model of Table 1.1 under either of these two variance assumptions.

The combined variable model can be written as

$$S_i = b_0 + b_1 D_i^2 H_i \tag{1.31}$$

---

[x] See Section C.2 in Appendix C.

If variance assumption 1 holds, this model must be divided by $D_i^2 H_i$ to give

$$\frac{S_i}{D_i^2 H_i} = b_0 \left(\frac{1}{D_i^2 H_i} \right) + b_1 \tag{1.32}$$

which is equivalent to a regression model of the form

$$Y_i = \beta_0 + \beta_1 X_i \tag{1.33}$$

where

$$Y_i = S_i / D_i^2 H_i \quad \text{and} \quad X_i = 1/D_i^2 H_i$$

A simple linear regression analysis can be carried out to estimate the parameters β_0 and β_1. The value obtained for $\hat{\beta}_0$ is the best estimate of b_1, and the $\hat{\beta}_1$ value is the best estimate of b_0 in equation (1.31).[9] Sometimes a regression analysis involving equation (1.33) will show that the null hypothesis

$$H_0 : \beta_1 = 0$$

cannot be rejected. This simply means that the estimate of the intercept value in equation (1.31) is not significantly different from 0. It should be noted that the dependent variable used in equation (1.33) is, except for multiplication by a constant, the cylindrical form factor. It is logical to expect the variance of this form factor to be more stable than the variance of size per se.

If variance assumption 2 holds (standard deviation proportional to $\sqrt{D^2 H}$), equation (1.31) is divided by $\sqrt{D^2 H}$ to give

$$S_i / \sqrt{D_i^2 H} = b_0 \left(\frac{1}{\sqrt{D_i^2 H_i}} \right) + b_1 \sqrt{D_i^2 H_i} \tag{1.34}$$

or

$$Y_i = \beta_1 X_{1i} + \beta_2 X_{2i} \tag{1.35}$$

where

$$Y_i = S_i / \sqrt{D_i^2 H_i}$$

$$X_{1i} = 1/\sqrt{D_i^2 H_i}$$

$$X_{2i} = \sqrt{D_i^2 H_i}$$

---

[9] The notation $\hat{\theta}$ indicates the estimated value of the parameter θ.

The parameter estimates for the original model, equation (1.31), are obtained as $\hat{b}_0 = \hat{\beta}_1$ and $\hat{b}_1 = \hat{\beta}_2$.

The recommended techniques for fitting each of the seven volume and weight prediction models (originally presented in Table 1.1) are summarized in Table 1.4. For each model, the following items are given.

1. The original form of the model.
2. Common variance assumptions.
3. The regression model associated with each variance assumption.
4. The relationship between the parameter estimates from the regression model and the original model.

Before this chapter is concluded, some consideration should be given to the procedures involved in the development of variable-top volume prediction equations of the type shown in equation (1.12). The general form of such an equation is

$$V_m = V_t(1 - b_1 d^{b_2} D^{b_3}) \tag{1.36}$$

where

V_t = total-stem volume or weight

D = dbh

d = merchantable top diameter

V_m = merchantable-stem volume or weight to a d-inch merchantable top

The data set used in fitting such an equation will include several observations from each sample tree.[10] One approach is to include, for each sample tree, observations for merchantable volumes to fixed limits such as 6-inch, 4-inch, 3-inch, and 2-inch merchantable tops. Alternatively, an observation could be included for the merchantable stem content that is generated by the accumulation of each successive bolt volume.

The regression model usually used to estimate the parameters of equation (1.36) is

$$Y = \beta_1 X_1^{\beta_2} X_2^{\beta_3} \tag{1.37}$$

---

[10] The use of several observations from the same tree violates the standard regression assumption of independent observations. However, violation of this assumption does not bias the estimates of the model parameters. Significance tests and confidence interval statements will be compromised to some extent, but this effect is believed to be negligible if a reasonably large number ($n \geq 100$) of sample trees is available.

TABLE 1.4

Recommended Techniques for Fitting Volume and Weight Prediction Models

Original Model	Variance Assumption	Regression Model	Parameter Estimates
1. Constant form factor model $S_i = b_1 D_i^2 H_i + \varepsilon_i$	(a) $\sigma \propto D_i^2 H_i$	$Y_i = \beta_0$ where $Y_i = S_i/D_i^2 H_i$	$\hat{b}_1 = \hat{\beta}_0 = \bar{Y}$
	(b) $\sigma \propto \sqrt{D_i^2 H_i}$	$Y_i = \beta_1 X_i$ where $Y_i = S_i/\sqrt{D_i^2 H_i}$ $X_i = \sqrt{D_i^2 H_i}$	$\hat{b}_1 = \hat{\beta}_1 = \dfrac{\sum X_i Y_i}{\sum X_i^2} = \dfrac{\sum S_i}{\sum D_i^2 H_i}$
2. Combined variable model $S_i = b_0 + b_1 D_i^2 H_i + \varepsilon_i$	(a) $\sigma \propto D_i^2 H_i$	$Y_i = \beta_0 + \beta_1 X_i$ where $Y_i = S_i/D_i^2 H_i$ $X_i = 1/D_i^2 H_i$	$\hat{b}_0 = \hat{\beta}_1$ $\hat{b}_1 = \hat{\beta}_0$
	(b) $\sigma \propto \sqrt{D_i^2 H_i}$	$Y_i = \beta_1 X_{1i} + \beta_2 X_{2i}$ where $Y_{1i} = S_i/\sqrt{D_i^2 H_i}$ $X_{1i} = 1/\sqrt{D_i^2 H_i}$ $X_{2i} = \sqrt{D_i^2 H_i}$	$\hat{b}_0 = \hat{\beta}_1$ $\hat{b}_1 = \hat{\beta}_2$
3. Generalized combined variable model $S_i = b_0 + b_1 D_i^2 + b_2 H_i + b_3 D_i^2 H_i + \varepsilon_i$	(a) $\sigma \propto D_i^2 H_i$	$Y_i = \beta_0 + \beta_1 X_{1i} + \beta_2 X_{2i} + \beta_3 X_{3i}$ where $Y_i = S_i/D_i^2 H_i$ $X_{1i} = 1/D_i^2$ $X_{2i} = 1/H_i$ $X_{3i} = 1/D_i^2 H_i$	$\hat{b}_0 = \hat{\beta}_3$ $\hat{b}_1 = \hat{\beta}_2$ $\hat{b}_2 = \hat{\beta}_1$ $\hat{b}_3 = \hat{\beta}_0$

(b) $\sigma \propto \sqrt{D_i^2 H_i}$

$$Y_i = \beta_1 X_{1i} + \beta_2 X_{2i} + \beta_3 X_{3i} + \beta_4 X_{4i}$$

where $Y_i = S_i/\sqrt{D_i^2 H_i}$
$X_{1i} = 1/\sqrt{D_i^2 H_i}$
$X_{2i} = \sqrt{D_i^2}\sqrt{H_i}$
$X_{3i} = \sqrt{H_i}/\sqrt{D_i^2}$
$X_{4i} = \sqrt{D_i^2 H_i}$

$\hat{b}_0 = \hat{\beta}_1$
$\hat{b}_1 = \hat{\beta}_2$
$\hat{b}_2 = \hat{\beta}_3$
$\hat{b}_3 = \hat{\beta}_4$

4. Logarithmic model

$S_i = e^{b_1} D_i^{b_2} H_i^{b_3} e^{\epsilon_i}$

ϵ_i has constant variance.

$$Y_i = \beta_0 + \beta_1 X_{1i} + \beta_2 X_{2i}$$
where $Y_i = \ln(S_i)$
$X_{1i} = \ln(D_i)$
$X_{2i} = \ln(H_i)$

$\hat{b}_1 = \hat{\beta}_0$
$\hat{b}_2 = \hat{\beta}_1$
$\hat{b}_3 = \hat{\beta}_2$

5. Generalized logarithmic model

$S_i = b_0 + b_1 D_i^{b_2} H_i^{b_3} + \epsilon_i$

(a) $\sigma \propto D_i^2 H_i$

$$Y_i = \beta_1 X_{1i} + \beta_2 X_{2i}^{\beta_3} X_{3i}^{\beta_4}$$
where $Y_i = S_i/D_i^2 H_i$
$X_{1i} = 1/D_i^2 H_i$
$X_{2i} = D_i$
$X_{3i} = H_i$

$\hat{b}_0 = \hat{\beta}_1$
$\hat{b}_1 = \hat{\beta}_2$
$\hat{b}_2 = \hat{\beta}_3 + 2$
$\hat{b}_3 = \hat{\beta}_4 + 1$

(b) $\sigma \propto \sqrt{D_i^2 H_i}$

$$Y_i = \beta_1 X_{1i} + \beta_2 X_{2i}^{\beta_3} X_{3i}^{\beta_4}$$
where $Y_i = S_i/\sqrt{D_i^2 H_i}$
$X_{1i} = 1/\sqrt{D_i^2 H_i}$
$X_{2i} = D_i$
$X_{3i} = H_i$

$\hat{b}_0 = \hat{\beta}_1$
$\hat{b}_1 = \hat{\beta}_2$
$\hat{b}_2 = \hat{\beta}_3 + 1$
$\hat{b}_3 = \hat{\beta}_4 + 0.5$

6. Honer transformed variable model

$S_i = D_i^2/(b_0 + b_1 H_i^{-1})$

The variable D_i^2/S_i has constant variance.

$$Y_i = \beta_0 + \beta_1 X_{1i}$$
where $Y_i = D_i^2/S_i$
$X_{1i} = H_i^{-1}$

$\hat{b}_0 = \hat{\beta}_0$
$\hat{b}_1 = \hat{\beta}_1$

TABLE 1.4

(continued)

Original Model	Variance Assumption	Regression Model	Parameter Estimates

7. Form class model

$S_i = b_0 + b_1 D_i^2 H_i F_i + \varepsilon_i$

(a) $\sigma \propto D_i^2 H_i$

$Y_i = \beta_1 X_{1i} + \beta_2 X_{2i}$
where $Y_i = S_i / D_i^2 H_i$
$X_{1i} = 1/D_i^2 H_i$
$X_{2i} = F_i$

$\hat{b}_0 = \hat{\beta}_1$
$\hat{b}_1 = \hat{\beta}_2$

(b) $\sigma \propto \sqrt{D_i^2 H_i}$

$Y_i = \beta_1 X_{1i} + \beta_2 X_{2i}$
where $Y_i = S_i / \sqrt{D_i^2 H_i}$
$X_{1i} = 1/\sqrt{D_i^2 H_i}$
$X_{2i} = F_i \sqrt{D_i^2 H_i}$

$\hat{b}_0 = \hat{\beta}_1$
$\hat{b}_1 = \hat{\beta}_2$

where

$$Y = 1 - (V_m/V_t)$$
$$X_1 = d$$
$$X_2 = D$$

With this formulation, nonlinear least squares methods must be used to estimate the parameters β_1, β_2, and β_3, and it is assumed that the variable V_m/V_t has a constant variance at all combinations of values for d and D. Parameter estimates for the original model are $\hat{b}_1 = \hat{\beta}_1$, $\hat{b}_2 = \hat{\beta}_2$, and $\hat{b}_3 = \hat{\beta}_3$.

An alternative regression model is

$$Y = \beta_0 + \beta_1 X_1 + \beta_2 X_2 \tag{1.38}$$

where

$$Y = \ln[1 - (V_m/V_t)]$$
$$X_1 = \ln(d)$$
$$X_2 = \ln(D)$$

In this case, linear regression procedures can be used, and the variable $\ln[1 - (V_m/V_t)]$ is assumed to have constant variance. Parameter estimates for the original model are obtained as $\hat{b}_1 = \exp(\hat{\beta}_0)$, $\hat{b}_2 = \hat{\beta}_1$, and $\hat{b}_3 = \hat{\beta}_2$.

REFERENCES

Avery, T. E. 1975. *Natural resources measurements*. 2nd ed. McGraw-Hill, New York.

Behre, C. E. 1923. Preliminary notes on studies of tree form. *J. For.* **21**:507–511.

Bennett, F. A., C. E. McGee, and J. L. Clutter. 1959. Yield of old-field slash pine plantations. *U.S.D.A. For. Serv., S.E. For. Exp. Stn. Paper No. 107.*

Bennett, F. A., and B. F. Swindel. 1972. Taper curves for planted slash pine. *U.S.D.A. For. Serv., Res. Note SE-179.*

Brackett, M. 1973. Notes of tarif tree volume computation. *State of Washington, Dept. of Nat. Res., Resource Mgt. Rpt. No. 24.*

Brister, G. H., J. L. Clutter, and T. M. Skinner. 1980. Tree volume and taper functions for site-prepared plantations of slash pine. *So. J. App. For.* **4**(3):139–142.

Bruce, D., R. O. Curtis, and C. Vancoevering. 1968. Development of a system of taper and volume tables for red alder. *For. Sci.* **14**:339–350.

Bruce, D., and F. X. Schumacher. 1950. *Forest mensuration*. 3rd ed. McGraw-Hill, New York.

Burkhart, H. E. 1977. Cubic foot volume of loblolly pine to any merchantable top diameter. *So. J. App. For.* **1**(2):7–9.

Cao, Q. V., H. E. Burkhart, and T. A. Max. 1980. Evaluation of two methods for cubic volume prediction of loblolly pine to any merchantable limit. *For. Sci.* **26**:71–80.

Carron, L. T. 1968. *An outline of forest mensuration*. Australian National University Press, Canberra, Australia.

Carron, L. T. 1971. Volume tariff systems. *Forestry* **XLIV**:145–150.

Chapman, H. H., and W. H. Meyer. 1949. *Forest mensuration*. McGraw-Hill, New York.

Clutter, J. L. 1980. Development of taper functions from variable-top merchantable volume equations. *For. Sci.* **26**:117–120.

Cunia, T. 1964. Weighted least squares method and construction of volume tables. *For. Sci.* **10**:180–191.

Demaerschalk, J. P. 1972. Converting volume equations to compatible taper equations. *For. Sci.* **18**:241–245.

Demaerschalk, J. P., and A. Kozak. 1977. The whole bole system: a conditioned dual-equation system for precise prediction of tree profiles. *Can. J. For. Res.* **7**:488–497.

Draper, N. R., and H. Smith. 1981. *Applied regression analysis*. 2nd ed. Wiley, New York.

Flowers, W. R. 1978. Individual tree weight and volume equations for site-prepared loblolly pine plantations in the coastal plain of the Carolinas, Georgia and north Florida. Masters thesis, School of Forest Res., Univ. of Georgia.

Freese, F. 1973. A collection of log rules. *U.S.D.A. For. Serv., Gen. Tech. Rpt. FPL-1*.

Furnival, G. M. 1961. An index for comparing equations used in constructing volume tables. *For. Sci.* **7**:337–341.

Gevorkiantz, S. R., and L. P. Olsen. 1955. Composite volume tables for timber and their application in the Lake States, *U.S.D.A. Tech. Bull. 1104*.

Gray, H. R. 1966. Principles of forest tree and crop volume growth. *Bull. For. and Timb. Bur., Canberra, No. 42*.

Grosenbaugh, L. R. 1963. Optical dendrometers for out-of-reach diameters: a conspectus and some new theory. *For. Sci. Monograph No. 4*.

Honer, T. G. 1964. The use of height and squared diameter ratios for the estimation of cubic foot volume. *For. Chron.* **49**:324–331.

Honer, T. G. 1965. A new total cubic foot volume function. *For. Chron.* **41**:476–493.

Hummel, F. C. 1955. The volume-basal area line. *For. Comm. Bull. No. 24* (London).

Hummel, F. C., G. M. Locke, and J. P. Verel. 1962. Tariff tables. *For. Rec. For. Comm. No. 31* (London).

Husch, B., C. I. Miller, and T. W. Beers. 1982. *Forest mensuration.* 3rd ed. Wiley, New York.

Jolly, N. W. 1950. The volume line theory in relation to the measurement of the standing volume of a forest (with particular reference to *Pinus radiata*). Woods and Forests Dept., South Australia.

Lewis, E. R. 1957. Errors in stand volume estimation for exotic conifers in New Zealand. *N.Z. For. Res. Notes No. 9.*

Max, T. A., and H. E. Burkhart. 1976. Segmented polynomial regression applied to taper equations. *For. Sci.* **22**:283–289.

Newnham, R. M. 1967. A modification to the combined-variable formula for computing tree volumes. *J. For.* **65**:719–720.

Parker, R. C. 1972. Regression equations for the Mesavage and Girard form-class volume tables. *Va. Polytechnic Inst. and State Univ., Extension Div. Publ. No. 501.*

Queen, W. R., and L. V. Pienaar. 1977. Green and dry stem weight equations for site-prepared slash pine plantations in the coastal plain of Georgia and north Florida. *Univ. of Ga. Plantation Mgt. Res. Coop., Res. Paper No. 1.*

Romancier, R. M. 1961. Weight and volume of plantation-grown loblolly pine. *U.S.D.A. For. Serv., S.E. For. Exp. Stn. Res. Note No. 161.*

Smalley, G. W., and D. R. Bower. 1968. Volume tables and point-sampling factors for loblolly pines in plantations on abandoned fields in Tennessee, Alabama, and Georgia highlands. *U.S.D.A. For Serv., Res. Paper SO-32.*

Spurr, S. H. 1952. *Forest inventory.* Ronald Press, New York.

Turnbull, K. J., G. R. Little, and G. E. Hoyer. 1963. *Comprehensive tree volume tarif tables.* State of Washington, Dept. of Nat. Res.

Turnbull, K. J., and G. E. Hoyer. 1965. Construction and analysis of comprehensive tree-volume tarif tables. *State of Washington, Dept. of Nat. Res., Resource Mgt. Rpt. No. 8.*

2
Evaluating Site Quality

Chapters 2, 3, and 4 focus on methods of predicting the growth and yield of forest stands. These methods are based on the concept that the growth and yield for stands of a given species or species composition are largely determined by four factors.

1. The age of the stand or, in the case of uneven-aged stands, the age distribution.
2. The innate productive capacity of the land area involved.
3. The extent to which the innate productive capacity has been, and is now, fully utilized.
4. Cultural treatments applied (thinning, fertilization, competing vegetation control, etc.)

The second factor listed, innate productive capacity, is referred to as *site quality* and a detailed discussion of this topic constitutes the remainder of this chapter. The third factor, site occupancy, is, to a large extent, synonymous with the concept of "stand density," which is the subject of Chapter 3.

The Society of American Foresters (Ford-Robertson, 1971) defines *site* as "an area considered in terms of its environment, particularly as this determines the type and quality of the vegetation the area can carry." In everyday professional usage, the term *site* is used in a dual sense, as suggested by the SAF (Society of American Foresters) definition. First, the term site carries a connotation of geographic location. The second meaning of the word involves the totality of environmental conditions (biotic, edaphic, and climatic) existing at a particular location. This distinction may seem overly academic since a location cannot exist without an associated environment, and no environment can exist without being located at some particular place. Nevertheless, it should be noted that some usages of the term site relate primarily to its geographic connotation while other employments of the term are intended to stress the environmental meaning.

2.1 SITE QUALITY

In the context of timber management, site quality can be defined as "the timber production potential of a site for a particular species or forest type." The words "good" and "poor" are frequently used modifiers of site quality and simply imply a high productive potential as opposed to a low potential. Although site is, in the short term, constant regardless of species selection, site quality has meaning only with respect to the one or more species that may be considered for management at a particular location. For example, a given site might have an excellent site quality for loblolly pine but a very poor site quality for white ash.

The proper measurement and interpretation of site quality are important tasks for almost all forest managers. Product sizes and values at various ages are largely controlled by site quality and stand density. Certain investments that are fully justified on good sites constitute economic folly on less productive sites. Responses to certain cultural measures often differ dramatically among areas of unequal site quality.

Because of the great practical importance attached to the effective evaluation of site quality, much effort has been devoted to the development of techniques for quantifying site quality. These methods can be classified as follows.

A. Direct methods

 1. Estimation from historical yield records.
 2. Estimation based on stand volume data.
 3. Estimation based on stand height data.

B. Indirect methods

 1. Estimation from overstory interspecies relationships.
 2. Estimation from lesser vegetation characteristics.
 3. Estimation from topographic, climatic, and edaphic factors.

Direct methods of evaluation require the existence, either now or in the past, of the species of interest at the particular location where site quality is to be evaluated. (Past existence is useful only if measurements were made at the pertinent time and kept until the present.) When on-site measurements of the species of interest are not available, indirect methods must be employed. Direct methods almost invariably provide better evaluations of site quality than indirect methods. Each of the site quality measurement methods listed here is discussed in detail in the following sections.

2.2   DIRECT METHODS FOR EVALUATING SITE QUALITY

2.2.1   Estimation of Site Quality from Historical Yield Records

In agricultural enterprises, the site quality of a given field for a particular crop is most commonly measured by simply averaging prior annual yields of the crop in question from that field. Thus, a farmer's reference to a corn field as "ninety bushels per acre" land is an evaluation of the site quality of that land for corn. In cases where the genetic constitution of the crop remains relatively constant, cultural practices are unchanged, and insect and disease vulnerability changes little, it is difficult to imagine a better way to measure site quality.

As experience with intensively managed forests increases, this historical approach to site quality evaluation will become more applicable. There are, however, few areas of the world where such procedures can be successfully employed today. In many areas, intensively managed forests are now being established as unmanaged or extensively managed forests are harvested. Yields from these latter forests are usually more affected by variation in stand density and species composition than by differences in site quality. Even in cases where yields from previous rotations of intensively managed forest have been measured, changes in species selection, establishment density, cultural practices, rotation age, and genetics may severely compromise the utility of site quality evaluations based on the history of one or more previous rotations.

2.2.2   Estimation of Site Quality from Stand Volume Data

For even-aged stands, an obvious alternative to obtaining site quality information from volume yields of one or more previous stands is to estimate site quality from the volume-age relationship in the currently existing stand. However, the volume attained by a stand at any given age can be greatly affected by factors other than site quality, and unless these factors are controlled or adjustments are made to reflect their effects, volumetric production differences among forest stands will have little relationship to true site quality differences. As previously noted, the principal confounding factors are stand density, species composition, genetics, and cultural practices.

In forests where a standard well-established management regime is consistently applied, it is possible to use stand volume information as an indicator of site quality. An excellent example of such a procedure is the system used in the state-owned Monterey pine plantations of South Australia (Lewis et al., 1976). In these forests, planting densities are held constant over all planting areas, the mortality rate is low and varies little among stands of the same age, and the genetic constitution of the planting stock is comparable for all planting areas. Under such tightly controlled conditions, volume production in relation to age is an excellent indicator of site quality. The specific statistic used as a measure of site quality is volume per hectare at age 10, as determined by inventory procedures. One drawback to the use of stand volume as a measure of site quality is the expense involved in obtaining stand volume data.

2.2.3 Estimation of Site Quality from Stand Height Data

For many species, areas of good site quality are also areas where height growth rates are high. In other words, for these species volume-production potential and height growth are positively correlated. For example, consider Figure 2.1

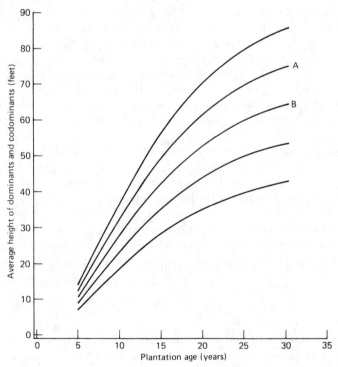

Figure 2.1 Height development curves for site-prepared slash pine plantations in the lower coastal plain of Georgia and Florida. (After Newberry and Pienaar, 1978.)

which shows a family of height development curves for site-prepared slash pine plantations (Newberry and Pienaar, 1978). A stand with a height development pattern similar to curve *A* in Figure 2.1 is considered to be growing on a site with better volume-production potential than a stand with a height development pattern similar to curve *B*.

The practical utility of the volume potential-height growth correlation stems largely from the fact that the height development pattern of the larger trees in an even-aged stand is little affected by stand density and intermediate cutting (except for thinnings from above). For species in which height growth is significantly influenced by stand density variation within the limits encountered in existing or contemplated stands, the estimation of site quality from stand height data will provide poor results unless suitable procedures can be devised for adjusting the relationship to reflect the effect of stand density. Fortunately, for many important timber species, height growth is little affected by variation in stand density, and site quality estimation procedures based on stand height data are by far the most commonly used techniques for evaluating site productivity.

Most height-based methods of site quality evaluation involve the use of site index curves. Any set of site index curves is simply a family of height development patterns with qualitative symbols or numbers associated with the curves for referencing purposes. The most common method of referencing uses the heights achieved at some specified reference age. This reference age, referred to as the *index age* or *base age*, is commonly selected to lie close to the average rotation age. However, for many families of height development curves, it makes little difference in practice what age is selected as the index age. Figure 2.2 shows a set of site index curves constructed from the height development patterns shown in Figure 2.1 by simply labeling each curve with the height value it attains at an age of 25 years. Thus, the site index curves shown in Figure 2.2 have an index age of 25 years. Many users of site index curves erroneously believe that the objective of the site index procedure is prediction of stand height at the index age. The true objective is selection of the height development pattern that the stand can be expected to follow during the remainder of its life. For example, with reference to Figure 2.2, a 15-year-old stand with an average height of dominant and codominant trees of 35 feet is growing on a site with a site index of 50 feet. The important aspect of this information is the expectation that the subsequent average height development in this stand will follow the curve labeled 50. The fact that the stand is expected to have an average dominant-codominant height of 50 feet at 25 years is, in contrast, a relatively insignificant revelation.

Nearly all sets of site index curves published in recent years were derived using statistical curve-fitting procedures, and the height development curves are graphic representations of various mathematical equations. Some illustrations of site index equations are shown here, and site index curves constructed from these equations are found in Figures 2.2 through 2.5. The notation used in these

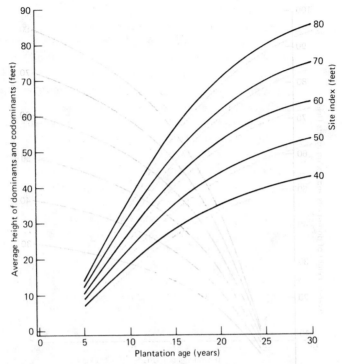

Figure 2.2   Site index curves for site-prepared slash pine plantations in the lower coastal plain of Georgia and Florida. (After Newberry and Pienaar, 1978.)

equations is

S = site index in feet

A = average age[1] (years) of trees measured for site index determination

A_b = average breast-height age (years) of trees measured for site index determination

H = average total height in feet of trees measured for site index determination

---

[1] In natural stands, site index is usually based on total tree age. Site index systems for plantations usually use plantation age.

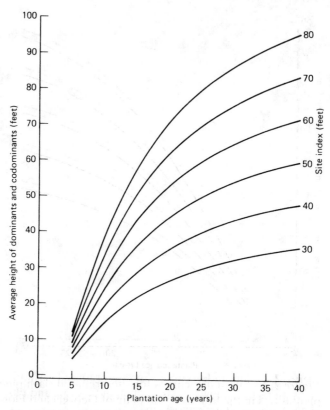

Figure 2.3   Site index curves for planted loblolly pine in the Piedmont Plateau. (After Coile and Schumacher, 1964.)

1. Site-prepared slash pine plantations, Atlantic and Gulf Coastal Plain of Georgia and Florida (index age = 25 years; Newberry and Pienaar, 1978).

$$S = H \{[1 - \exp(-25K)]/[1 - \exp(-KA)]\}^{1/(1-m)} \qquad (2.1)$$

   where

   $K = 0.100354$

   $m = 0.516188$

   Graphs of the corresponding site index curves are shown in Figure 2.2.

2. Loblolly pine plantations, Piedmont Plateau, southeastern United States (index age = 25 years; Coile and Schumacher, 1964).

$$\log(S) = \log(H) + 5.190\left(\frac{1}{A} - \frac{1}{25}\right) \qquad (2.2)$$

   Graphs of the corresponding site index curves are shown in Figure 2.3.

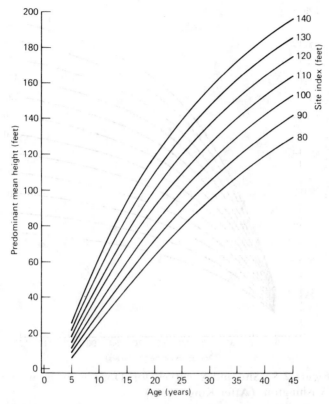

Figure 2.4 Site index curves for Monterey pine plantations in New Zealand. (After Bailey and Clutter, 1974.)

3. Monterey pine plantations, central North Island, New Zealand (index age = 25 years; Bailey and Clutter, 1974).

$$S = 500.26(H/500.26)^{[(A/25)^{0.5258}]} \qquad (2.3)$$

Graphs of the corresponding site index curves are shown in Figure 2.4.

4. Second-growth Douglas-fir, western Washington (index age = 50 years; King, 1966).

$$S = \frac{2500(a_2 + b_2 A_b + c_2 A_b^2)(H - 4.5)}{A_b^2 - (H - 4.5)(a_1 + b_1 A_b + c_1 A_b^2)} + 4.5 \qquad (2.4)$$

where

$a_1 = -0.954038$

$a_2 = 0.109757$

$b_1 = 0.0558178$

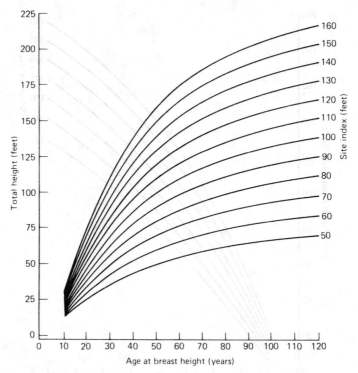

Figure 2.5 Site index curves for Douglas-fir in western Washington. (After King, 1966.)

$$b_2 = 0.00792336$$
$$c_1 = -0.000733819$$
$$c_2 = 0.000197693$$

Graphs of the corresponding site index curves are shown in Figure 2.5.

The above formulas were selected as examples because they illustrate four different equation forms and are applicable to forest types of significant economic importance. Many other mathematical equation forms have been and are now used in site index development work.

An important question in establishing the site index is how to select sample trees for determination of height and age. American practice usually involves the random selection of dominant and codominant trees, followed by measurement of these trees for total height and either total age, plantation age, or breast-height age. Equations (2.1) and (2.2) illustrate site index systems based on plantation age and average height of dominants and codominants. Equation (2.3) uses plantation age and predominant mean height, defined by Beekhuis

(1966) as the average height of the 40 tallest trees per acre. Equation (2.4) is based on an average height obtained by measuring the 10 trees of largest dbh in a total sample of 50 trees. It should also be noted that equation (2.4) utilizes breast-height age rather than total age. The use of breast-height age has obvious practical advantages when increment cores must be used to determine age. In addition, height growth during the first few years following establishment can be significantly affected by herbaceous competition, and the use of breast-height age tends to eliminate this confounding factor. On the other hand, plantation age systems have obvious advantages in artificially regenerated stands where plantation age can usually be determined from office records without recourse to collection of increment cores.

The question of which average height to use in the construction of a site index system also involves fairly obvious trade-offs. Average height of dominants and codominants can be obtained with a minimum amount of time spent on selection of sample trees; however, the definition of dominant and codominant trees is somewhat subjective and some inconsistency among samplers will be encountered. In addition, heavy thinnings from below will have an impact on the average height of dominants and codominants by reducing the proportion of codominants to dominants. This latter consideration and the fact that dominant heights are more stable and less variable (Ker, 1952; Warrack, 1952) suggest that basing site index systems only on the average height of dominants might be advantageous.

Users of site index curves must always deal with the question of how many sample trees to select and measure from a given stand. No simple answer can be given to this question. The sample size used in any given situation should reflect the variability in height and age present in the stand and the expense involved in sample tree measurement. Results from studies of sample tree variability are available in the literature (Ker, 1952; Johnson and Carmean, 1953; Dahms, 1966).

One important, but often overlooked, problem in site index calculation involves the choice of method for calculating the final site index estimate. Two procedures are available.

1. Average the sample tree heights and the sample tree ages (if age is not known from records) and enter the site index equation or the site index curves with these averages to obtain the site index value.

2. For each sample tree, enter the site index equation to obtain a site index value for each tree, and then average the individual tree site index figures to obtain the stand site index estimate.

Which of these procedures is correct depends on the method of construction used in developing the site index equation in use. If the equation was obtained by fitting stand average height/age data, then the first method is appropriate.

However, if the site index equation was developed from individual tree height/ age data, then the second method is preferred. The types of data sets that can be used for construction of site index equations are discussed more fully in Section 2.4.

2.2.4   Estimation of Site Quality from Periodic Height Growth Data

An alternative to basing site quality evaluation on current stand height data is to use information on height growth for some relatively short period during the life of the stand. Techniques using this approach are generally referred to as *growth intercept methods.* Although growth intercept methods could, in theory, be used with any species, they are practical only for species that display distinct annual branch whorls.

Although the details differ in various applications, all growth intercept methods involve the length measurement of a specified number of successive annual internodes, beginning at some well-defined point on the stem. The starting point used is generally near or above breast height, since early height growth is often significantly affected by herbaceous competition. Wakely and Marrero (1958) evaluated a growth intercept method for southern pine based on the measurement of height growth over a 5-year period. The first annual internode included in the measurement is the internode that contains breast height.[2] Values obtained in this way are commonly referred to as *5-year intercepts.* Alban (1972), working with red pine, considered height intercept methods involving varying numbers of internodes and different starting points on the stem and recommended a procedure based on the measurement of five internodes, starting from the first whorl above 8 feet. Growth intercept values can be used directly as measures of site quality (in which case, they are often referred to as *growth intercept indexes*), or they can be used to calculate site index estimates. For example, Beck (1971) developed the following regression to predict eastern white pine site index (50-year index age) from 5-year intercept values.

$$\text{Site index} = 26 + 6.6(\text{5-year intercept}) \qquad (2.5)$$

The measured 5-year intercept values in his sample ranged from 5 to 15 feet. Corresponding predicted site index values are 59 feet and 125 feet.

It is generally believed (Ferree et al., 1958; Wakely and Marrero, 1958; Beck, 1971) that, for young stands, growth intercept values provide just as much

---

[2] It should be noted that the southern pines typically produce more than one branch whorl per year so that, in this case, an annual internode is the distance between the first branch whorl for the year and the first branch whorl for the subsequent year. Methods for identifying internodes of the same year have been described by Wakely and Marrero (1958).

information on site quality as site index values. In older stands, site index values are thought to be more meaningful. However, growth intercept is considerably easier to obtain than site index. Stand age is not needed to calculate growth intercept, and the length of the required number of internodes is usually easier to measure than total tree height. A stand value for growth intercept is obtained by averaging the individual growth intercept measurements from selected sample trees in the stand.

2.3 INDIRECT METHODS FOR EVALUATING SITE QUALITY

2.3.1 Estimation of Site Quality from Overstory Interspecies Relationships

Indirect methods for evaluating site quality must be applied when the species (or forest type) of interest is not present on the land area under evaluation. In situations where other tree vegetation is present, measurements made on this vegetation can sometimes be used to evaluate site quality for the species of interest. Such usage depends on a knowledge of the relationship between certain growth patterns of the species of interest and growth patterns of the species available for measurement. The most common relationship used in such applications is one linking the site indexes for the two species.

In an early application of this procedure, Coile (1948) measured dominant and codominant loblolly and shortleaf pine sample trees on plots in the North Carolina Piedmont where both species were present. For each plot, site indexes for both shortleaf and loblolly pine were calculated from the sample tree measurements, and a regression was calculated using shortleaf pine site index as the independent variable and loblolly pine site index as the dependent variable. The regression equation obtained indicated the following relationship between site indexes for the two species.

$$Y = 1.13X \tag{2.6}$$

where

Y = loblolly pine site index in feet (base age = 50 years)

X = shortleaf pine site index in feet (base age = 50 years)

Olson and Della-Bianca (1959) used a conceptually similar approach to investigate site index relationships among several species and species groups occurring in the Piedmont region of Virginia, North Carolina, and South Carolina. From data collected on 155 plots, regressions were calculated relating the site indexes of other species to yellow-poplar site index. The equations obtained were

$$Y_{sp} = 31.5 + 0.45X$$

$$Y_{wo} = 36.7 + 0.45X$$

$$Y_{bo} = 39.7 + 0.45X$$

$$Y_{so} = 44.5 + 0.45X \qquad (2.7)$$

where

X = yellow-poplar site index in feet

Y_{sp} = shortleaf pine site index in feet

Y_{wo} = white oak-southern red oak site index in feet

Y_{bo} = black oak site index in feet

Y_{so} = scarlet oak-northern red oak site index in feet

All site indexes involved are based on an index age of 50 years.

Considerable research on interspecies site index relationships has also been carried out in the southern Appalachians (Doolittle, 1958).

2.3.2 Estimation of Site Quality from Lesser Vegetation Characteristics

Since many environmental factors affect both overstory and understory vegetation, it is not unreasonable to expect that understory vegetation characteristics could provide information on site quality for tree growth. The species composition of understory vegetation present on a given site is often an excellent indicator of surface soil moisture availability, and the degree of luxuriousness of lower vegetation commonly reflects the fertility of the topmost horizon or horizons present in the soil profile. However, the characteristics of deeper soil horizons may show little impact on understory vegetation but still have great influence on the quality of the site for tree growth. In addition, understory composition and abundance are often drastically altered by disturbing factors such as wildfire or prescribed burning, grazing, and site preparation treatment.

Perhaps the best-known system for determining tree site quality from understory characteristics was developed by Cajander (1926) for the spruce-pine-birch forests of Finland. A brief summary of Cajander's system has been provided by Spurr and Barnes (1980).

A good example of an understory vegetation site evaluation system used in conjunction with intensive forest management practices is the procedure developed by Ure (1950) for use with Monterey pine in the Kaingaroa Plains on the North Island of New Zealand. Ure correlated dominant height data from established Monterey pine plantations with the floristic composition of natural vegetation in adjacent firebreaks where no site preparation or planting had been done. Eight site index groups (base age 20) were defined in the data, with each group having a range of 6 feet, and rules for recognizing the groups from natural vegetation characteristics were established. The complete list of species used in the classification system is too lengthy for inclusion here, but the most important diagnostics involved the frequency of occurrence and the vigor of manuka (*Leptospermum scoparium*) and bracken (*Pteridium esculentum*). For example, the best site class (site index ≥ 111 feet) was typified by a dense growth of manuka and bracken, with the manuka averaging 10 feet in height and the bracken stipes exceeding 4 feet in length. For the fourth-best site class (87 ≤ site index ≤ 92), manuka and bracken were still conspicuous components of the vegetation but were of reduced vigor, with the manuka averaging about 7 feet in height and the bracken stipes reaching lengths less than 4 feet. In the poorest site classes, manuka and bracken occurred only infrequently. Ure's system can be used to predict a site index for native forestland being evaluated for planting and for inexpensively estimating the site index of established plantations if adjacent undisturbed native vegetation is available.

An important forest management tool in the northern Rocky Mountain region of the United States is the Daubenmire habitat-type classification system (Daubenmire and Daubenmire, 1968). Understory vegetation characteristics play an important role in application of the Daubenmire procedures. In the southern United States, the relationship between longleaf pine site index and understory vegetation characteristics has been studied by Hodgkins (1961, 1970).

2.3.3 Estimation of Site Quality from Topographic, Climatic, and Edaphic Factors

An obvious approach to the indirect estimation of site quality is to relate tree growth to measurements of various environmental factors and, when necessary, predict site quality from an evaluation of these environmental factors. All foresters informally develop such relationships in their day-to-day observations, and a list of formal published studies that follow this approach would be lengthy indeed. Here we refer to only a few typical examples.

Many researchers have focused their efforts on relating tree growth to measurable soil properties. Perhaps the best-known work in this area is that of T. S. Coile, much of which is well summarized in Coile (1952). Coile's approach involved the selection of sample locations in the forest population of interest, followed by determination of site index and measurement of a number of soil variables at each location. Multiple regression techniques were then used to derive an equation for predicting site index from observations of the soil variables. A representative example of Coile's equations follows; this one applies to loblolly pine in the Piedmont Plateau region.

$$\log (S) = 2.0188 - 0.399/X_1 - 0.00843X_2 - 0.0198/X_2 \qquad (2.8)$$

where

S = site index in feet (base age = 50 years)

X_1 = thickness of the A horizon in inches

X_2 = imbibitional water[3] value of the B horizon

This equation has a standard error of estimate equal to 11 percent of the predicted site index value. A site index value calculated from an equation such as this is often referred to as the *soil site index*.

One of the earlier soil site index studies dealing with plantations in the United States was carried out by McGee (1961) in old-field slash pine plantations in the middle coastal plain of Georgia. The equation developed is

$$\log (H) = 2.0058 - 5.5907/X_1 + 0.005968X_2 - 0.1445X_2^2$$
$$+ 0.001837X_3 - 0.000032X_3^2 \qquad (2.9)$$

where

H = average height of dominants and codominants in feet

X_1 = plantation age in years

X_2 = thickness of the A_1 horizon in inches

X_3 = depth to a fine-textured horizon in inches

The equation is used to predict site index (25-year base) by substituting 25 as plantation age along with appropriate values for X_2 and X_3. Although this equation explains 87 percent of the log (H) variability, the majority of this (69 percent) is explained by the reciprocal of age variable, with the soil variables accounting for only 18 percent of the variation. Such results are not atypical of soil site index studies which often produce regressions explaining only small proportions of the variability in site index. It has been suggested that these low

---

[3] Imbibitional water value is the difference between the moisture equivalent and adjusted xylene equivalent of a soil. It is thought to be a useful measure of water and air permeability in soils with a high clay content.

R^2 values may be at least partly caused by the large sampling errors often attached to certain soil variable measurements (Ike and Clutter, 1968).

Although much of the best-known early work on soil site index was concentrated in the southeastern United States, numerous applications of the procedures can now be found for most forest regions (e.g., Myers and Van Deusen, 1960; Lewis and Harding, 1963; Carmean, 1970; Steinbrenner, 1975; Alban, 1976).

Many site index prediction equations make use of climatic and topographic variables in addition to, or instead of, soil variables. In mountainous areas, aspect and elevation are often important variables for estimating site index. Use of a climatic variable in predicting site quality is illustrated by the work of Farr and Harris (1979) who related Sitka spruce site index along the North Pacific coast of Canada and the United States to average number of days per year with maximum temperature greater than 5°C.

*2.4   DEVELOPMENT OF SITE INDEX EQUATIONS

The site index equations presented in Section 2.2.3 predict site index from age and height information. In this section we discuss some of the procedures used to derive site index equations. A variety of different equation forms is used with many variations in application, but our discussion includes only a representative sampling of some of the more commonly applied procedures.

Data for the development of site index equations are derived from three sources.

1. Measurement of stand height and age on temporary plots.
2. Measurement of height and age over time with monumented trees or plots.
3. Reconstruction of height/age development patterns for individual trees through stem analysis techniques.

In the first case, temporary plots are located in the population of interest, appropriate trees of the target species are measured for height and age, and average height and age are then calculated for each plot. (In U.S. practice, it is common to restrict sample trees to dominants and codominants. Other selection procedures have been previously discussed.) Temporary plots provide the most inexpensive data for site index equation development, but the use of such data involves the assumption that the full range of site indexes is well represented in all age classes within the sample. If this assumption is false, the resulting prediction equation will generally be seriously biased. Several factors operate to prevent equal representation of all sites in the various age classes. Good sites produce volume more rapidly than poor sites and, therefore, develop a given standing volume at an earlier age. This often leads to the use of shorter rotation ages on better sites. As a result, poor sites are often overrepresented in older age classes. In first-rotation plantation populations planted on land removed from agricultural production, it is typical for the poorest agricultural land to be taken out of cultivation first. In this situation, the older the age class, the poorer the average site quality for that class.

Remeasurement of monumented trees or plots provides the best data for site index equation development. These data may take the form of remeasured heights at known ages for individually monumented sample trees, or the data may consist of average plot heights at known average plot ages. It is economically expensive to obtain data in this way, and the data do not become available until a number of years after the plots are initially established.

Stem analysis of felled sample trees provides data nearly equal in quality to that obtained by remeasurement. Economic costs are high, but data can be obtained fairly immediately. A discussion of the detailed techniques involved in stem analysis can be found in Dahms (1963), Curtis (1964), Heger (1968), Carmean (1972), and Lenhart (1972). Data produced by stem analysis are similar to those obtained by remeasurement of monumented individual trees and consist of heights at known ages for each tree in the sample.

We classify site index equations into three types according to the nature of the height/age curve families they generate. These three types are shown in Figure 2.6. For any two curves in an anamorphic curve family (Figure 2.6a), the height of one at any age is a constant proportion of the height of the other at the same age. In a polymorphic-disjoint curve family (Figure 2.6b), this proportionality relationship does not hold, but the curves do not cross within the age range of interest. For curves in the same polymorphic-nondisjoint curve family (Figure 2.6c), there is no constant proportionality relationship and at least some of the curves intersect within the age range of interest. Remeasurement height/age data or stem analysis height/age data can be used to develop anamorphic, polymorphic-disjoint, or polymorphic-nondisjoint site index equations. With temporary plot height/age data, it is generally only possible to produce anamorphic site index equations.

Although many different techniques have been used to fit site index curves, most of these techniques can be viewed as special cases of three general equation-development methods.

1. The guide curve method.
2. The difference equation method.
3. The parameter prediction method.

*2.4.1 The Guide Curve Method

The guide curve method is used to generate anamorphic site index equations and it represents a fairly straightforward quantification of earlier graphic methods

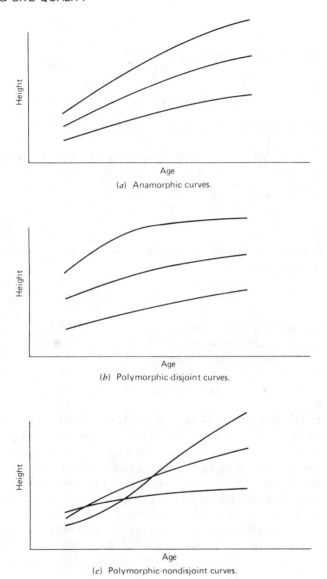

Figure 2.6 Classification of height/age curve families.

for preparing site index curves. A model commonly used with this method is the (ln (height)/reciprocal of age) model originally suggested by Schumacher (1939). This approach assumes a family of height/age curves of the form

$$H_i = K_{0i} e^{\beta_1 A^{-1}}$$ (2.10)

where

H_i = stand or tree height at age A with the ith curve

A = stand or tree age

K_{0i} = constant associated with the ith curve

β_1 = constant with the same value for all curves

It should be noted that such a family of curves is anamorphic since, for any two curves i and j,

$$\frac{H_i}{H_j} = \frac{K_{0i}e^{\beta_1 A^{-1}}}{K_{0j}e^{\beta_1 A^{-1}}} = \frac{K_{0i}}{K_{0j}}$$

which is a constant for all ages. The model shown in equation (2.10) is normally used in logarithmic form as

$$\ln (H_i) = \ln (K_{0i}) + \beta_1 A^{-1} \qquad (2.11)$$

In this form the site index curves are a family of parallel lines with constant slope but varying intercepts. With this linearization, the guide curve method simply involves fitting an equation of the form

$$\ln (H) = \beta_0 + \beta_1 A^{-1} \qquad (2.12)$$

to the height/age data points. In most applications of this model, the height/age data point values have come from the measurement of temporary plots, but data from remeasured trees or plots or from stem analysis could be used. Substitution of the estimated values of β_0 and β_1 into equation (2.12) provides the so-called "guide curve," which is an "average" (ln (height)/reciprocal of age) line for the sample data used. Individual height/age development lines parallel the guide curve. These lines are referenced by selecting an index age (A_0) and labeling each line with the height value attained at age A_0. When the lines are referenced in this way, they are logarithmic forms of the site index curves. The equation for a particular site index line can be obtained by noting that such a line has the form

$$\ln (H) = b_{0i} + b_1 A^{-1} \qquad (2.13)$$

where b_1 is the sample-based estimate of β_1, and b_{0i} is an intercept value uniquely associated with each particular site index. By definition, when $A = A_0$ in this equation, H must be equal to site index, so that

$$b_{0i} = \ln (S) - b_1 A_0^{-1}$$

where S is site index. By substituting in equation (2.13), we obtain

$$\ln (H) = \ln (S) + b_1(A^{-1} - A_0^{-1})$$

or

$$\ln (S) = \ln (H) - b_1(A^{-1} - A_0^{-1}) \tag{2.14}$$

which is the form used to estimate site index from known values of height and age.

An example of this type of site index equation is one obtained by Bennett et al. (1959) for old-field slash pine plantations in the middle coastal plain of Georgia and the Carolina sandhills. Data for their study consisted of plantation age (A) and average height of dominants and codominants (H) measured on 308 temporary sample plots. The guide curve equation obtained was[4]

$$\ln (H) = 4.6646 - 12.4486A^{-1}$$

and the corresponding site index equation is

$$\ln (S) = \ln (H) + 12.4486(A^{-1} - 25^{-1})$$

where 25 years is the index age selected.

An example of the guide curve method with a more complex model form is provided by the work of Newberry and Pienaar (1978) using stem analysis data from slash pine plantations in the lower coastal plain of Georgia and Florida. Each of 320 sample trees provided several observed height/age combinations. The data were combined over all trees, and nonlinear regression methods[5] were used to estimate the parameters θ_1, θ_2, and θ_3 in the following form of the Chapman-Richards function (Richards, 1959; Chapman, 1961).

$$H = \theta_1[1 - \exp(-\theta_2 A)]^{[(1-\theta_3)^{-1}]} \tag{2.15}$$

where

H = tree height

A = tree age

---

[4] Bennett et al. (1959) published their results using base 10 logarithms. We have converted those results to base e logarithm form for presentation here.

[5] A brief introduction to nonlinear regression methodology is included in Section C.6 of Appendix C.

The nonlinear regression analysis generated the parameter estimates

$$\hat{\theta}_1 = 72.51239$$

$$\hat{\theta}_2 = 0.10035$$

$$\hat{\theta}_3 = 0.51619$$

which, when substituted into equation (2.15), produce the guide curve

$$H = 72.51239[1 - \exp(-0.10035A)]^{2.06693} \tag{2.16}$$

When $A = 25$, the calculated H value is 60.8 feet. Hence, this guide curve is the site index curve for a site index value of 60.8 feet (index age = 25 years). Curves for other site index values were obtained from the guide curve equation by holding the shape parameters θ_2 and θ_3 constant and varying the asymptote parameter θ_1 as necessary to achieve the required H value when A equals A_0 (the index age). The equation of the curve for site index S is therefore

$$S = \hat{\theta}_1[1 - \exp(-0.10035A_0)]^{2.06693}$$

so that

$$\hat{\theta}_1 = S[1 - \exp(-0.10035A_0)]^{-2.06693}$$

and

$$H = S\left[\frac{1 - \exp(-0.10035A)}{1 - \exp(-0.10035A_0)}\right]^{2.06693} \tag{2.17}$$

For prediction of site index from height and age, the above equation is algebraically rearranged to

$$S = H\left[\frac{1 - \exp(-0.10035A_0)}{1 - \exp(-0.10035A)}\right]^{2.06693} \tag{2.18}$$

It is a relatively simple matter to show that the above equation defines an anamorphic family of height/age curves.

*2.4.2 The Difference Equation Method

The difference equation method of fitting site index equations requires either monumented plot or tree remeasurement data or stem analysis data. The procedure is quite flexible and can be applied with any height/age equation to produce anamorphic or polymorphic curve families. The initial step in the application of this method is development of a difference form of the height/age equation being fitted. This difference form expresses height at remeasurement (H_2) as a function of remeasurement age (A_2), initial measurement age (A_1), and height at initial measurement (H_1).

As a simple example of this approach, consider the Schumacher (ln (height)/ reciprocal of age) model. Figure 2.7 shows the situation involved geometrically. Point A represents the initial measurement values with coordinates $[1/A_1, \ln (H_1)]$, while the remeasurement values define point B with coordinates $[1/A_2, \ln (H_2)]$. The form of the Schumacher (ln (height)/reciprocal of age) model implies that both these points lie on a line with slope equal to β_1 (see equation 2.11). Thus,

$$\beta_1 = \frac{\ln (H_2) - \ln (H_1)}{(1/A_2) - (1/A_1)}$$

or

$$\ln (H_2) = \ln (H_1) + \beta_1 \left(\frac{1}{A_2} - \frac{1}{A_1} \right) \qquad (2.19)$$

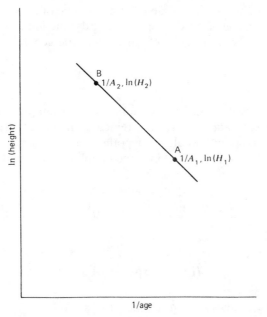

Figure 2.7 Remeasurement points on a Schumacher growth curve.

is the difference equation form of the Schumacher height/age model. With re-measurement or stem analysis data, this equation would be fitted using linear regression procedures with the model

$$Y = \beta_1 X \tag{2.20}$$

where

$Y = \ln (H_2) - \ln (H_1)$

$X = (1/A_2) - (1/A_1)$

After an estimated value for β_1 is computed, a site index equation is obtained from the height/age equation by letting A_2 equal A_0 (the index age) so that H_2 is, by definition site index (S). Equation (2.19) can then be written as

$$\ln (S) = \ln (H_1) + \beta_1 \left(\frac{1}{A_0} - \frac{1}{A_1} \right) \tag{2.21}$$

With more complex height/age models, the difference equation formulation is often somewhat more difficult to develop than in the case of the simple linear model illustrated above, but a usable form can generally be obtained. For example, one possible use of the Chapman-Richards function as a height/age model assumes the existence of a family of curves with the general formula

$$H = \theta_{1i}[1 - \exp(-\theta_2 A)]^{[(1-\theta_3)^{-1}]} \tag{2.22}$$

where each individual height/age curve has its own unique value for θ_{1i}. With initial measurement data (A_1, H_1) and remeasurement data (A_2, H_2) for a tree or a plot, these two points would be hypothesized to lie on the same curve and thus have the same value for θ_{1i}. Since the initial measurement point lies on the curve

$$H_1 = \theta_{1i}[1 - \exp(-\theta_2 A_1)]^{[(1-\theta_3)^{-1}]}$$

and

$$\theta_{1i} = H_1[1 - \exp(-\theta_2 A_1)]^{-[(1-\theta_3)^{-1}]} \tag{2.23}$$

Similarly, for the remeasurement point,

$$H_2 = \theta_{1i}[1 - \exp(-\theta_2 A_2)]^{[(1-\theta_3)^{-1}]}$$

so that

$$\theta_{1i} = H_2[1 - \exp(-\theta_2 A_2)]^{-[(1-\theta_3)^{-1}]} \qquad (2.24)$$

Since the right-hand sides of equations (2.23) and (2.24) are both equal to θ_{1i}, they can be equated to give

$$H_2[1 - \exp(-\theta_2 A_2)]^{-[(1-\theta_3)^{-1}]} = H_1[1 - \exp(-\theta_2 A_1)]^{-[(1-\theta_3)^{-1}]}$$

so that

$$H_2 = H_1 \left[\frac{1 - \exp(-\theta_2 A_2)}{1 - \exp(-\theta_2 A_1)} \right]^{[(1-\theta_3)^{-1}]} \qquad (2.25)$$

which is a difference equation form of the Chapman-Richards height/age function. Given suitable data on A_1, H_1, A_2, and H_2, this equation can be fitted using nonlinear least squares techniques. After parameter estimates are obtained, substitution of the index age (A_0) for A_2 and site index (S) for H_2 gives the site index equation

$$S = H_1 \left[\frac{1 - \exp(-\hat{\theta}_2 A_0)}{1 - \exp(-\hat{\theta}_2 A_1)} \right]^{[(1-\hat{\theta}_3)^{-1}]} \qquad (2.26)$$

Even though the difference equation approach has many desirable characteristics, it does not appear to have been widely used in previous studies. This may be at least partially attributable to the fact that nonlinear least squares procedures have only recently come into widespread use. An example of a published site index equation developed with this approach is the following formula for old-field slash pine plantations in the southeastern coastal plain, as developed by Clutter and Jones (1980).

$$\ln(S) = 3.75044 + 1.4488[\ln(H) + 17.6098/A$$
$$- 4.45483] \exp(-9.26795/A) \qquad (2.27)$$

where

S = site index in feet (index age of 25 years)

A = plantation age

H = average height of dominants and codominants

The above equation was developed by fitting the difference equation model

$$Y = \beta_2 X_2 - \beta_3 + (X_4 - \beta_2 X_1 + \beta_3) \exp(\beta_1 X_3) \qquad (2.28)$$

to plot remeasurement data, where

$Y = \ln(H_2)$

$X_1 = 1/A_1$

$X_2 = 1/A_2$

$X_3 = (1/A_1) - (1/A_2)$

$X_4 = \ln(H_1)$

Equations produced with this model are of the polymorphic-disjoint type.

*2.4.3 The Parameter Prediction Method

The parameter prediction method of fitting site index curves has been used by a number of researchers for fitting polymorphic-disjoint site index equations (King, 1966; Brickell, 1968; Lundgren and Dolid, 1970; Beck, 1971; Carmean, 1972; Graney and Burkhart, 1973; Trousdell et al., 1974). The procedure requires remeasurement or stem analysis data and involves the following three steps.

1. Fitting a linear or nonlinear height/age function to the data on a tree-by-tree or plot-by-plot basis.
2. Using each fitted curve to assign a site index value to each tree or plot.
3. Relating the parameters of the fitted curves to site index through linear or nonlinear regression procedures.

Most of the authors referenced above used the Chapman-Richards function as the basic height/age relationship. The research reported by Trousdell et al. (1974) for loblolly pine in the Atlantic coastal plain of the Carolinas and Virginia provides a typical example of the studies using the Chapman-Richards function. The principal steps involved in this study were as follows.

1. Stem analysis procedures were used to collect height/age data from 44 dominant or codominant trees that were at least 50 years old.
2. The Chapman-Richards function,

$$H = \theta_1[1 - \exp(-\theta_2 A)]^{[(1-\theta_3)^{-1}]} \qquad (2.29)$$

where H equals height in feet at age A and θ_1, θ_2, and θ_3 are parameters to be estimated, was separately fitted to the height/age data for each tree.
3. The fitted curves were solved with $A = 50$ to obtain site index values (S) for each tree.

4. The parameters θ_1, θ_2, and θ_3 were hypothesized to be functions of site index, where

$$\theta_1 = \beta_1 + \beta_2 S$$

$$\theta_2 = \beta_3 + \beta_4 S + \beta_5 S^2$$

$$\theta_3 = \beta_6 + \beta_7 S + \beta_8 S^2$$

5. The Chapman-Richards function was then expressed as

$$H = (\beta_1 + \beta_2 S)\{1 - \exp\left[-(\beta_3 + \beta_4 S\right.$$
$$\left. + \beta_5 S^2)A]\}^{[(1 - \beta_6 - \beta_7 S - \beta_8 S^2)^{-1}]} \qquad (2.30)$$

and refitted to the data to estimate the parameters β_1, β_2, . . . , β_8. The estimating equations obtained for θ_1, θ_2, and θ_3 were

$$\hat{\theta}_1 = 63.1415 + 0.635080 S$$

$$\hat{\theta}_2 = 0.00643041 + 0.000124189 S + 0.00000162545 S^2$$

$$\hat{\theta}_3 = 0.0172714 - 0.002918775 S + 0.0000310915 S^2 \qquad (2.31)$$

For any given site index value, equations (2.31) can be solved to give a particular Chapman-Richards site index curve. By substituting various values of age into the equation and solving for H, we are provided with height/age points for plotting the site index curve. Since each site index curve has different parameter values, the curves are obviously polymorphic.

Although site index curves prepared with this procedure have been generally acceptable from a practical standpoint, the procedure often suffers from certain limitations that do not apply when difference equation methods are used. In particular:

1. When parameter prediction equations such as (2.31) are solved and height/age points are generated for plotting the site index curve, it will generally be found that the site index curve does not pass through height S at the index age, so that the curves must be proportionally adjusted. This is at least aesthetically disturbing. (A procedure for eliminating this problem has been described by Burkhart and Tennent, 1977.)

2. In the previous methods discussed, choice of an index age is made simply for labeling purposes and the specific choice selected has no effect on the shape of the site index curves produced. With the parameter prediction method, choice of the index age affects the parameter estimates of the height/age curves and different curves are obtained for different choices of index age.

3. After equations similar to (2.31) are developed, a height/age equation such as (2.30) can be solved for H, given S and A, and such solutions are used to plot the site index curves. However, for many height/age functions, and the Chapman-Richards function in particular, the equivalent of equation (2.30) cannot be solved explicitly for S, given H and A. In this situation, site index can only be determined by graphic interpolation or by tedious iterative computations.

It should be noted that King's (1966) application of this procedure does avoid this third problem. The basic height/age equation used by King was

$$H = \frac{A^2}{a + bA + cA^2} + 4.5 \qquad (2.32)$$

where H equals tree height at age A, and a, b, and c are coefficients to be estimated from the data. The parameters were related to the sample tree site index "S" (base age 50) using regression analysis, and equations of the form

$$\hat{a} = a_1 + a_2 Z$$

$$\hat{b} = b_1 + b_2 Z$$

$$\hat{c} = c_1 + c_2 Z$$

were calculated where

$$Z = \frac{50^2}{(S - 4.5)}$$

This resulted in a height/age equation of the form

$$H = \frac{A^2}{(a_1 + a_2 Z) + (b_1 + b_2 Z)A + (c_1 + c_2 Z)A^2} + 4.5 \qquad (2.33)$$

For given site index and age values, this equation can be solved for corresponding height values and the solutions can be used to plot site index curves. However, the above equation can also be algebraically inverted to provide an explicit formula for S as a function of H and A. The result is

$$S = 4.5 + \frac{2500(H - 4.5)(a_2 + b_2 A + c_2 A^2)}{A^2 - (H - 4.5)(a_1 + b_1 A + c_1 A^2)} \qquad (2.34)$$

In this form, the equation can be used to obtain site index directly for given height and age values.

*2.4.4 Polymorphic Nondisjoint Site Index Equations

Simplifying generalizations concerning polymorphic-nondisjoint site index equations seem conspicuous by their absence. Few equations of this type are described in the literature and these few have little in common methodologically. There is, however, one characteristic shared by polymorphic-nondisjoint site index systems: All involve one or more variables other than height and age. This fact can be appreciated by noting that, with anamorphic or polymorphic-disjoint systems, specification of a pair of height and age values suffices to define the expected future height development curve for the tree or stand in question. However, in the polymorphic-nondisjoint case, a given height/age point generally lies on more than one height development curve, and some variable other than height and age must be evaluated to indicate which of the curves passing through the point is the expected subsequent path.

A good example of a polymorphic-nondisjoint site index system has been developed by Zahner (1962) for loblolly pine in a region adjoining the Arkansas-Louisiana state line. Zahner's system is composed of three separate site index equations—one for loess soils, one for nonloess soils with a well aerated subsoil, and one for nonloess soils with a poorly aerated subsoil. In using the system to estimate site index for some particular stand, average height of dominants and codominants and stand age must be determined. However, these values alone would not provide a site index estimate. In addition, observations of soil characteristics would have to be made so that the soil could be assigned to one of the three categories noted. As soon as such an assignment is made, a curve is defined that shows the expected future height development pattern for the stand in question. It is purely a matter of semantics whether to call Zahner's system: (a) a polymorphic-nondisjoint system of site index curves that uses soil category in addition to height and age to define the future height development pattern, or (b) a procedure for stratifying the geographical area studied into three land types; for each land type, a separate set of anamorphic site index curves is available. Zahner's own description of his work is closer to type (b) semantics than to type (a).

Newberry and Pienaar (1978), on the other hand, carried out a similar analysis based on six soil groups involving site preparation-soil drainage class combinations. Again, the ultimate outcome involves six separate sets of anamorphic site index curves, but Newberry and Pienaar tend to describe their system as a set of polymorphic-nondisjoint curves.

This semantic duality exists so long as the variable or variables used in addition to height and age are qualitative with a small number of possible values. However, when the additional variable(s) is(are) quantitative and continuous, there is no alternative to viewing the curve system as being polymorphic-nondisjoint. An example of this situation is provided by the work of Alexander et al. (1967) with lodgepole pine. Lodgepole pine is a species in which the height growth of dominants and codominants is markedly affected by stand density. The authors therefore incorporated a measure of stand density (specifically, crown compe-

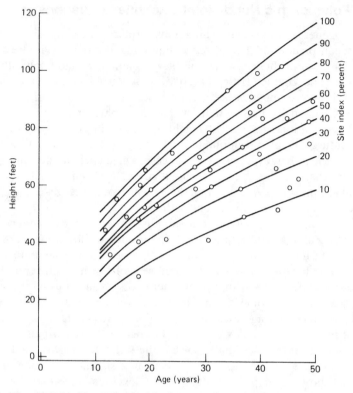

Figure 2.8   Hypothetical index-age-free site index curves.

tition factor) into their height/age equations, and a combination of height/age values alone does not suffice to define the expected future height development pattern. This definition is established only when a crown competition factor value is measured and used in combination with the height and age values. However, it is significant to note that, for any given combination of height and age, there would, at least in theory, be a different expected future growth pattern for every possible value of the crown competition factor.

*2.4.5   An Alternative Method for Labeling Site Index Curves

Pienaar and Clutter[6] have suggested an alternative procedure for labeling site index curves that completely avoids the concept of an index age. The simplest variant of this procedure is illustrated by the hypothetical example shown in Figure 2.8. The small circles in Figure 2.8 represent height/age data from 40

---

[6] Currently unpublished research.

temporary sample plots. It is assumed that the guide curve procedure was used to fit an "average" height/age curve to the data. Once such an average curve has been developed, one of the parameters can be varied to force a height/age curve through each of the data points, and the data points can be ordered according to the relative positions of their height/age curves in the family of 40 associated curves. In Figure 2.8, the curves associated with the 4th, 8th, 12th, . . . , 40th ranked data points have been drawn and labeled with appropriate percentile values. With respect to, for example, the site index 70 curve, it could now be said that, for the population of stands represented by this sample, 70 percent of the stands are estimated to have height/age development curves that lie below the curve labeled as 70. For use in growth and yield prediction, it is probable that conventional site index curves are preferable to such percentage site index curves because site index values expressed in feet of height at some index age will probably be more linearly related to stand volume and growth rate than site indexes expressed as percentiles. Nevertheless, the idea of percentile site index curves is useful in illustrating the fact that index age is not a fundamental or required concept in the use of site index to express site quality.

REFERENCES

Alban, D. H. 1972. An improved growth intercept method for estimating site index of red pine. *U.S.D.A. For. Serv., Res. Paper NC-80.*

Alban, D. H. 1976. Estimating red pine site index in Minnesota. *U.S.D.A. For. Serv., Res. Paper NC-130.*

Alexander, R. R., D. Tackle, and W. G. Dahms. 1967. Site indexes for lodgepole pine, with corrections for stand density: methodology. *U.S.D.A. For. Serv., Res. Paper RM-29.*

Bailey, R. L., and J. L. Clutter. 1974. Base-age invariant polymorphic site curves. *For. Sci.* **20**:155–159.

Beck, D. E. 1971. Polymorphic site index curves for white pine in the southern Appalachians. *U.S.D.A. For. Serv., Res. Paper SE-80.*

Beekhuis, J. 1966. Prediction of yield and increment in *Pinus radiata* stands in New Zealand. *N.Z. For. Res. Inst. Tech. Paper No. 49.*

Bennett, F. A., C. E. McGee, and J. L. Clutter. 1959. Yield of old-field slash pine plantations. *U.S.D.A. For. Serv., S.E. For. Exp. Stn. Paper 107.*

Brickell, J. E. 1968. A method of constructing site index curves from measurements of tree age and height—its application to inland Douglas-fir. *U.S.D.A. For. Serv., Res. Paper INT-47.*

Burkhart, H. E., and R. B. Tennent. 1977. Site index equations for radiata pine in New Zealand. *N.Z. J. For. Sci.* **7**:408–416.

Cajander, A. K. 1926. The theory of forest types. *Acta For. Fenn.* **29**.

Carmean, W. H. 1970. Tree height-growth patterns in relation to soil and site. In Chester T. Youngberg and Charles B. Davey (Eds.), *Tree growth and forest soils*. Oregon State Univ. Press, Corvallis.

Carmean, W. H. 1972. Site index curves for upland oaks in the central states. *For. Sci.* **18**:109–120.

Chapman, D. G. 1961. Statistical problems in population dynamics. In *Proc. Fourth Berkeley Symposium on Mathematical Statistics and Probability*. Univ. Calif. Press, Berkeley.

Clutter, J. L., and E. P. Jones. 1980. Prediction of growth after thinning in old-field slash pine plantations. *U.S.D.A. For. Serv., Res. Paper SE-217*.

Coile, T. S. 1948. Relation of soil characteristics to site index of loblolly and shortleaf pines in the lower Piedmont region of North Carolina. *Duke Univ. School of For. Bull. 13*.

Coile, T. S. 1952. Soil and the growth of forests. *Adv. in Agron.* **4**:329–398.

Coile, T. S., and F. X. Schumacher. 1964. *Soil-site relations, stand structure, and yields of slash and loblolly pine plantations in the southern United States*. T. S. Coile Inc., Durham, N.C.

Curtis, R. O. 1964. A stem-analysis approach to site-index curves. *For. Sci.* **10**:241–256.

Dahms, W. G. 1963. Correction for a possible bias in developing site index curves from sectioned tree data. *J. For.* **61**:25–27.

Dahms, W. G. 1966. Effect of kind and number of measured tree heights on lodgepole pine site-quality estimates. *U.S.D.A. For. Serv., Res. Paper PNW-36*.

Daubenmire, R. F., and J. B. Daubenmire. 1968. Forest vegetation of eastern Washington and northern Idaho. *Wash. Agr. Exp. Stn. Tech. Bull. 60*.

Doolittle, W. T. 1958. Site index comparisons for several forest species in the southern Appalachians. *Proc. Soil Sci. Soc. Amer.* **22**:455–458.

Farr, W. A., and A. S. Harris. 1979. Site index of Sitka spruce along the Pacific coast related to latitude and temperatures. *For. Sci.* **25**:145–153.

Ferree, M. J., T. D. Shearer, and E. J. Stone. 1958. A method of evaluating site quality in young red pine plantations. *J. For.* **56**:328–332.

Ford-Robertson, F. C. (Ed.). 1971. *Terminology of forest science, technology, practice, and products*. Soc. Amer. Foresters, Washington.

Graney, D. L., and H. E. Burkhart. 1973. Polymorphic site index curves for shortleaf pine in the Ouachita Mountains. *U.S.D.A. For. Serv., Res. Paper SO-85*.

Heger, L. 1968. A method of constructing site-index curves from stem analyses. *For. Chron.* **44**(4):11–15.

Hodgkins, E. J. 1961. Estimating site-index for longleaf pine through quantitative evaluation of associated vegetation. *Proc. Soc. Am. For., 1960*, pp. 28–32.

Hodgkins, E. J. 1970. Productivity estimation by means of plant indicators in the longleaf pine forests of Alabama. In Chester T. Youngberg and Charles B. Davey (Eds.), *Tree growth and forest soils*. Oregon State Univ. Press, Corvallis.

Ike, A. F., and J. L. Clutter, 1968. The variability of forest soils of the Georgia Blue Ridge Mountains. *Proc. Soil Sci. Soc. Amer.* **32**:284–288.

Johnson, F. A., and W. H. Carmean. 1953. Sampling error in the estimation of site index. *J. For.* **51**:26–27.

Ker, J. W. 1952. An evaluation of several methods of estimating site index of immature stands. *For. Chron.* **28**:63–74.

King, J. E. 1966. Site index curves for Douglas-fir in the Pacific Northwest. *Weyerhaeuser Forestry Paper 8.*

Lenhart, J. D. 1972. An alternative procedure for improving height/age data from stem analysis. *For. Sci.* **18**:332.

Lewis, N. B., and J. H. Harding. 1963. Soil factors in relation to pine growth in South Australia. *Austral. For.* **27**:27–34.

Lewis, N. B., A. Keeves, and J. W. Leech. 1976. Yield regulation in South Australian *Pinus radiata* plantations. *South Australia Woods and Forest Dept. Bull. No. 23.*

Lundgren, A. L., and W. L. Dolid. 1970. Biological growth functions describe published site index curves for Lake States timber species. *U.S.D.A. For. Serv., Res. Paper NC-36.*

McGee, C. E. 1961. Soil site index for Georgia slash pine. *U.S.D.A. For. Serv., S.E. For. Exp. Stn. Paper 119.*

Myers, C. A., and J. S. Van Deusen. 1960. Site index of ponderosa pine in the Black Hills from soil and topography. *J. For.* **58**:548–555.

Newberry, J. D., and L. V. Pienaar. 1978. Dominant height growth models and site index curves for site-prepared slash pine plantations in the lower coastal plain of Georgia and North Florida. *Univ. of Ga. Plantation Mgt. Res. Coop. Res. Paper No. 4.*

Olson, D. F., Jr., and L. Della-Bianca. 1959. Site index comparisons for several tree species in the Virginia-Carolina Piedmont. *U.S.D.A. For. Serv., S.E. For. Exp. Stn. Paper 104.*

Richards, F. J. 1959. A flexible growth function for empirical use. *J. Exp. Bot.* **10**:290–300.

Schumacher, F. X. 1939. A new growth curve and its application to timber yield studies. *J. For.* **37**:819–820.

Spurr, S. H., and B. V. Barnes. 1980. *Forest ecology.* 2nd ed. Wiley, New York.

Steinbrenner, E. C. 1975. Mapping forest soils on Weyerhaeuser lands in the Pacific Northwest. In B. Bernier and C. H. Winget (Eds.), *Forest soils and forest land management.* Les Presses de L'Universite Laval, Quebec.

Trousdell, K. B., D. E. Beck, and F. T. Lloyd. 1974. Site index for loblolly pine in the Atlantic Coastal Plain of the Carolinas and Virginia. *U.S.D.A. For. Serv., Res. Paper SE-115.*

Ure, J. 1950. The natural vegetation of the Kaingaroa Plains as an indicator of site quality for exotic conifers. *N.Z. J. For.* **6**:112–123.

Wakely, P. C., and J. Marrero. 1958. Five-year intercept as site index in southern pine plantations. *J. For.* **56**:332–336.

Warrack, G. 1952. Comparative observation of the changes in classes in a thinned and natural stand of immature Douglas-fir. *For. Chron.* **28**:46–56.

Zahner, R. 1962. Loblolly pine site curves by soil groups. *For. Sci.* **8**:104–110.

3

Growing Stock and Stand Density

The growth rate achieved by any given forest stand is largely determined by two factors.

1. The innate productive capacity of the site
2. The amount and composition of the growing stock present in the stand.

Methods for evaluating the first factor, productive capacity, are discussed in Chapter 2. Procedures for expressing and quantifying the second factor constitute the subject matter of this chapter.

Specific growing stock characteristics of importance are:

1. The species present.
2. The numbers of trees by species class and size class categories.
3. The spatial distribution of the trees.

All three of these characteristics are subject to control by the forest manager. This control is achieved through the manager's selection of silvicultural and harvest strategies. The strategies selected usually represent attempts to utilize the productive capacity of the site as fully as possible for production of the commercial product mix that best furthers the management objectives of the forest owner.

The degree of crowding present in a stand and the level of site utilization attained are evaluated quantitatively through expressions of *stand density* and *stocking*. Measures of stand density are direct functions of such stand statistics as number of trees per acre or basal area per acre. Stocking measures, on the other hand, involve a comparison of the existing stand with some norm that has been established with a particular product objective in mind (Bickford et al., 1957). The important distinction here is that two foresters evaluating the growing stock in a particular stand should obtain the same values for stand density statistics regardless of their intentions concerning subsequent management of the stand. However, if one intended to manage the stand for sawtimber production and the other envisioned pulpwood production, their assessments of stocking could differ considerably. It should be noted that, while most textbooks and scientific articles draw a distinction between stocking measures and stand density measures, common usage often fails to recognize this difference and many foresters frequently treat the terms stand density and stocking as synonymous.

Some measures of stand density, such as the number of trees per acre, are simply direct functions of measurable stand statistics, while others involve comparisons with previously established limiting relationships (e.g., the maximum number of trees that can be supported at a given age). Measures of stocking are usually expressed in relative terms, such as the basal area or volume per acre in a stand as a percentage of the same variable in a hypothetical stand considered to be the norm for the age and site index involved. Stocking is often expressed qualitatively as a judgment of the adequacy of the growing stock at the present stage of stand development in terms of the overall product goal and the potential of the site. For example, stands are often characterized as understocked, well-stocked, fully stocked, or overstocked. Regardless of the measure used to express density or stocking, the adequacy of the stocking or stand density must be evaluated through its effect on product yields.

Measures of stand density are more precise and generally more useful in analysis and estimation of growth and yield than stocking measures. In application, the utility of any given measure of stand density depends on the objective of the analysis. Certain measures may prove satisfactory when the objective is to estimate aggregate stand yield from measured stand variables. The same measures may be inadequate in an analysis of the subtle effects of various silvicultural treatments on the development of individual tree components in the stand.

It is important to remember that almost all measures of stand density and stocking are dynamic rather than static. Direct measures of stand density such as number of trees per acre or basal area per acre will obviously change as time passes. However, values for stand density measures that involve comparisons with limiting relationships and values for stocking measures will also generally change as the stand ages, with understocked stands becoming more adequately stocked as time passes. It is also possible for stocking levels to be drastically reduced at one or more points in the life of the stand as a result of catastrophic mortality. Typical causes of this type of mortality are storm damage, insect or disease attack, and fire damage.

3.1 STAND DENSITY AND GROWTH

The significance of stand density stems from the fact that, within limits, the greater the amount of growing space per tree, the faster the tree will grow. Therefore, for any given stand, the present average tree size has been determined by the growing space previously occupied by the tree. Control of density at stand establishment, and subsequently by thinning and other silvicultural means, is therefore an important aspect of timber management. Most empirical information concerning the effect of stand density on growth and yield comes from a large number of thinning and spacing studies that have been undertaken around the world with many different species. A small, but representative, subset of these studies is included in the References at the end of this chapter. From these and similar studies, some general conclusions can be drawn concerning the effect of stand density on tree and stand growth.

3.1.1 Height Growth

Empirical evidence from thinning experiments indicates that for many commercially important species height growth is not greatly affected by the manipulation of stand density. The average height of the stand may be changed by thinning, depending on the thinning method, but within wide limits of stand density, height growth seems to be unaffected, especially when the comparison is restricted to dominant and codominant trees.

Spacing experiments generally support this conclusion within moderately wide limits of spacing, but the extent to which the generalization applies depends on the species. The height growth of many hardwood species is significantly less at low densities than at moderate or high levels. Very dense natural stands of western hemlock and lodgepole pine display greatly reduced height growth, and some spacing studies with fast-growing conifers such as Douglas-fir and slash pine have shown significantly greater height growth for 10-by-10 feet spacings than for 6-by-6 feet plantings.

3.1.2 Diameter Growth

Spacing and thinning experiments have consistently shown increases in breast height diameter (dbh) growth with decreasing stand density. Stands with wider spacings or stands previously thinned, in time, have larger average diameters than similar stands with closer spacings or comparable unthinned stands.

Intertree competition affects diameter growth at surprisingly low stand densities, particularly in the case of fast-growing, shade-intolerant species. As a result, very low densities are required to produce maximum diameter growth throughout the life of an even-aged stand. At any given age, there is a lower limit of stand density below which no further increase in diameter growth will result from continued density reduction. At density levels below this lower limit, the trees are growing free of intertree competition and are usually referred to as *open-grown trees*. However, other vegetation present on the site may also affect diameter growth even though tree density is below this competition limit (Grano, 1970). The general effect of spacing on average stand diameter is illustrated in Figure 3.1.

In stands where competition has caused a reduction in diameter growth compared to open-grown trees, the response to increases in growing space resulting from thinning varies with species, age, and quality of the site. Older trees with greatly reduced crowns do not respond as much as younger trees of comparable stem size, and dominant trees which have been relatively less affected by competition respond less to increased growing space in terms of relative diameter growth rate than smaller trees in the same stand. As in the case of average stand height, the average stand diameter may be affected by thinning, depending on

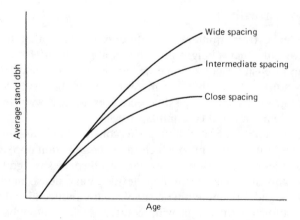

Figure 3.1 An illustration of the development of average stand dbh in plantations established at different spacings.

the thinning method. This thinning effect should not be confused with the effect of density changes on subsequent stand diameter growth.

3.1.3 Stem Form

Differences in stem form resulting from variations in stand density are a matter of potential concern in timber management since their existence complicates the process of accurately estimating individual tree volumes. Spacing experiments have shown that denser stands often have average dominant and codominant trees of the same height but of smaller diameter than less dense stands, while thinning studies have indicated that stem diameter in the lower bole increases relatively faster in thinned stands than in comparable trees in unthinned stands. Such stems will have different taper curves, but not necessarily different stem volumes, as would be implied by a standard volume equation based on breast height diameter and total height. In fact, the effect of stand density on a common measure of stem form, the cylindrical form factor,[1] is not readily deduced from its separate effects on height growth and breast height diameter growth. The volumetric effect of stand density on stem form can best be evaluated by comparing trees of the same diameter and total height (for example, a codominant tree in a less dense stand with a dominant tree of the same total height and diameter in a denser stand). In practice, differences in stem form that result from stand density variation seldom have an economically significant impact on stem volume.

3.1.4 Stand Basal Area and Volume Growth

In assessing the effect of density manipulation on stand basal area and volume growth, it is important to distinguish between the relationships that apply in all-aged stands and those that are appropriate to even-aged situations. An all-aged stand is distinguished by two primary characteristics. First, the stand has no definite beginning or end in time; second, trees of all ages are spatially intermixed within the stand. The general form of the relationship between stand density and net annual cubic volume growth rate for such stands is shown in Figure 3.2. Knowledge of the form of this relationship between growth and the amount of growing stock, or stand density, is important in the management of such a renewable resource. When continued harvests are imposed on the stand, an equilibrium is said to exist if, for each time period, net growth plus ingrowth is harvested. This equilibrium condition produces a stationary reserve growing stock and a constant sustainable harvest. For each level of reserve growing stock,

---

[1] The *cylindrical form factor* is defined as the ratio of stem volume to the volume of a cylinder with height equal to the height of the tree and diameter equal to tree dbh.

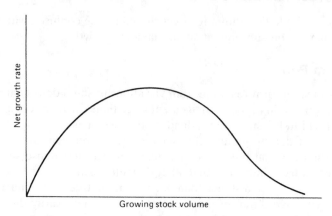

Figure 3.2   General relationship between net volume growth rate and amount of growing stock in all-aged stands.

there is an associated sustainable equilibrium harvest, and for some level of the growing stock, there exists a maximum sustainable equilibrium harvest.

In contrast, any even-aged stand has a definite beginning in time. For some time after stand establishment, the higher the stand density (within limits), the greater the net growth in basal area and total cubic volume. Typical results from spacing experiments in even-aged stands appear in Figures 3.3 and 3.4.

In thinning experiments involving even-aged stands, the effects of stand density variation on growth in terms of basal area or cubic volume have been inconsistent, partly as a result of the confounding effects of age and merchantability limits. A generalized result is shown in Figure 3.5, where gross yield in an unthinned stand is approximately equaled by the cumulative harvests plus the remaining stock in a thinned counterpart. The results of most thinning studies support the general conclusion that thinning does not significantly affect gross cubic volume yield per acre, except where severe overcrowding would greatly restrict root and crown development in an unthinned stand or where stand density is reduced so severely by thinning that the site is clearly underutilized for some time. Although there have been instances where thinning has actually increased total gross stem cubic volume production, the rationale for thinning in timber management is generally based on economic considerations and a reduction of mortality losses rather than on the expectation of increased total production.

3.2   MEASURES OF AVERAGE STAND DENSITY

Measures of stand density can conveniently be grouped as measures of average stand density or as point density measures, depending on whether they express

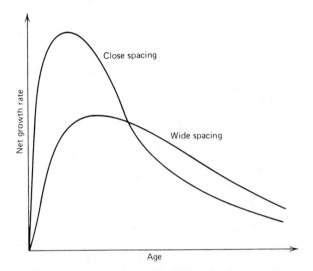

Figure 3.3   An illustration of stand density effects on net growth rate as observed in spacing experiments in even-aged stands.

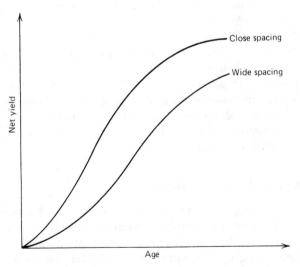

Figure 3.4   An illustration of stand density effects on net yield as observed in spacing experiments in even-aged stands.

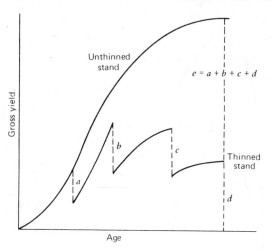

Figure 3.5 An illustration of a gross yield curve in an unthinned even-aged stand and in a thinned counterpart.

average overall crowding or the competitive stress affecting a particular tree (Spurr, 1962). Some of the measures can be directly calculated from data collected in the stand of interest, while others require additional reference to previously determined relationships. In this section, we consider some commonly used measures of average stand density. Methods for expressing point density are considered in Section 3.3.

The degree of crowding in a stand is determined by the number of trees present, their respective sizes, and their spatial distribution. Distribution is not considered explicitly in existing measures of average stand density. For timber management purposes in general, and for the prediction of stand growth and yield in particular, a measure of stand density should be easily and objectively measurable, biologically meaningful, and highly correlated with both stand growth and yield. Some commonly used measures of average stand density are discussed in the remainder of this section.

3.2.1 Number of Trees per Acre

In homogeneous all-aged stands and in unthinned even-aged stands of given age and site quality, the average number of trees per acre is a useful measure of stand density. Number of trees per acre is also meaningful when used for thinned stands if the thinning history is known in full detail. Many plantation yield studies have used number of trees per acre as a measure of stand density in the development of yield equations and tables (Dell et al., 1979).

3.2.2 Basal Area per Acre

The cumulative cross-sectional area, per acre, of tree stems at 4.5 feet above ground level (basal area) is a widely used measure of stand density. Basal area per acre is easily and objectively measured and its value depends on both the number of trees and their respective sizes. It is often used as a relative measure of stocking by expressing the basal area per acre in a given stand either as a percentage of some appropriately chosen norm or as a percentage of average basal area for comparable stands.

As with number of trees per acre, the utility of basal area per acre as an indicator of crowding is limited when the prior stand history is unknown. However, when used in the proper context, such as for a given age and site in unthinned even-aged stands or plantations, or in all-aged stands with a reasonably stable age distribution, basal area has proved useful in yield estimation. Since basal area per acre and the number of trees per acre specify average tree size, the use of both will often give improved yield estimates in comparison to those obtainable with the use of only one of these measures.

The basal area B_i in square feet for a tree of breast height diameter D_i inches is

$$B_i = \pi D_i^2 / 576 \approx 0.005454 D_i^2 \tag{3.1}$$

and the total basal area B for a sample of n trees is

$$B = \sum_{i=1}^{n} B_i = 0.005454 \sum_{i=1}^{n} D_i^2 \tag{3.2}$$

with a mean per-tree basal area of

$$\overline{B} = \frac{1}{n} \sum_{i=1}^{n} B_i = 0.005454 \sum_{i=1}^{n} D_i^2 \Big/ n \tag{3.3}$$

The quadratic mean breast height diameter $\overline{D}_q$ is defined as

$$\overline{D}_q = \sqrt{\frac{1}{n} \sum_{i=1}^{n} D_i^2} \tag{3.4}$$

so that

$$\overline{B} = 0.005454 \overline{D}_q^2$$

and

$$B = 0.005454 n \overline{D}_q^2 \qquad (3.5)$$

In other words, $\overline{D}_q$ is the diameter of the tree of mean basal area.
  It should also be noted that

$$\sum_{i=1}^{n} (D_i - \overline{D})^2 = \sum_{i=1}^{n} D_i^2 - \left(\sum_{i=1}^{n} D_i \right)^2 \Big/ n$$

and

$$\frac{1}{n} \sum_{i=1}^{n} (D_i - \overline{D})^2 = \frac{1}{n} \sum_{i=1}^{n} D_i^2 - \left(\sum_{i=1}^{n} D_i \Big/ n \right)^2$$

so that

$$\sqrt{\frac{1}{n} \sum_{i=1}^{n} D_i^2} = \sqrt{\frac{1}{n} \sum_{i=1}^{n} (D_i - \overline{D})^2 + \left(\sum_{i=1}^{n} D_i \Big/ n \right)^2}$$

or

$$\overline{D}_q = \sqrt{\left(\frac{n-1}{n} \right) s^2 + \overline{D}^2} \qquad (3.6)$$

where s^2 is the sample variance of the D_i values.

3.2.3 Stand Density Index

Stand density index (*SDI*) is a measure of average stand density that can only
be obtained with reference to a predetermined limiting relationship between the
number of trees per acre and the average tree size. Frothingham (1914) used
this relationship in the development of a white pine yield table and Reineke
(1933) later used the same relationship as the basis for a stand density index.
  In fully stocked even-aged stands the limiting relationship between the number
of trees per acre N and the quadratic mean dbh $\overline{D}_q$ often appears linear in
logarithmic coordinates, as shown in Figure 3.6. For any given $\overline{D}_q$, there exists
a limit to the expected number of trees per acre in even-aged stands regardless
of the age or site quality. Stands at the limit are assumed to experience the same

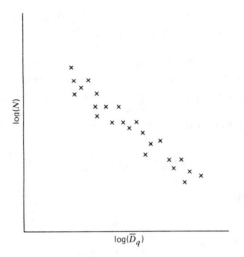

Figure 3.6 The relationship between number of trees per acre and quadratic mean dbh in fully stocked even-aged stands.

degree of crowding. Reineke observed this relationship in even-aged stands of several species, both conifers and hardwoods. For the cases considered, the slope of the limiting line was approximately −1.6.

The limiting relationship is of the form

$$N = \alpha \overline{D}_q^{\beta} \tag{3.7}$$

where α and β are the parameters that define the relationship. For stands in this limiting condition the common degree of crowding is expressed numerically as the expected number of trees per acre when $\overline{D}_q$ is 10 inches, so that

$$SDI = \alpha 10^{\beta} \tag{3.8}$$

where *SDI* is the stand density index. For any stand of known N and $\overline{D}_q$, Reineke defines the stand density index as

$$SDI = N(10/\overline{D}_q)^{\beta} \tag{3.9}$$

which implies that all stands with the same proportion of the limiting number of trees per acre have the same stand density index regardless of average stand dbh. For stands of given $\overline{D}_q$, the stand density index increases proportionally with the number of trees per acre and, therefore, also with the basal area per acre.

The standard procedure for estimating the parameters α and β requires appropriate sample data from fully stocked even-aged stands. Linear least squares estimates of the parameters are obtained from observations of the number of trees per acre and the quadratic mean dbh for each stand using a logarithmic transformation of equation (3.7).

$$\log (N) = \log (\alpha) + \beta \log (\overline{D}_q) \tag{3.10}$$

For example, suppose

$$\hat{\alpha} = 10,119$$
$$\hat{\beta} = -1.5$$

so that the predicted number of trees per acre is given by

$$N = 10,119 \overline{D}_q^{-1.5}$$

and the full-stocking stand density index value is

$$SDI = 10,119(10)^{-1.5}$$
$$= 320$$

For a given stand with $N = 600$ and $\overline{D}_q = 5.0$ inches,

$$SDI = 600(10/5.0)^{-1.5}$$
$$= 212$$

The full-stocking (limiting) number of trees per acre when $\overline{D}_q = 5.0$ inches is

$$N = 10,119(5.0)^{-1.5}$$
$$= 905.07$$

while the number of trees per acre in a full-stocking (limiting) stand with $\overline{D}_q = 15.0$ inches would be

$$N = 10,119(15.0)^{-1.5}$$
$$= 174.18$$

Thus, a stand with $\overline{D}_q$ = 15.0 inches would have the same stand density index as another stand with $\overline{D}_q$ = 5.0 inches and N = 600 trees per acre, if the number of trees per acre is

$$N = (600/905.07) \times 174.18$$

$$= 115.35$$

This is easily verified by computing

$$SDI = 115.35(10/15.0)^{-1.5}$$

$$= 212$$

The limiting relationship between number of trees per acre and quadratic mean dbh in fully stocked stands as expressed in equation (3.7) assumes that the relative rate of mortality in such stands and the relative rate of increase in quadratic mean dbh have the relationship

$$\frac{dN/dt}{N} = \beta\left(\frac{d\overline{D}_q/dt}{\overline{D}_q}\right) \tag{3.11}$$

Before a stand reaches this limiting condition, mortality will be less than in stands of comparable quadratic mean dbh at the limit, and the constant proportionality between the rates will not yet apply. A typical example of a stand approaching full stocking over time is shown in Figure 3.7. Parker (1978) used data from remeasured Monterey pine plots to explore the change in stand density index values over time and reported a new procedure for estimating the slope of the limiting relationship. An approach to stand density control of Douglas-fir plantations by Drew and Flewelling (1979) is based on stand density index as the measure of stand density. In an analysis of the utility of various stand density measures for the prediction of cubic-volume growth in natural even-aged loblolly pine stands, Nelson and Brender (1963) found no advantage for stand density index over the simpler basal area per acre when both were used in combination with information on age and site index.

3.2.4 Tree-Area Ratio

Chisman and Schumacher (1940) proposed a measure of stand density based on the assumption that the land area A occupied by any given tree in a stand can be represented by the equation

$$A = \beta_0 + \beta_1 D + \beta_2 D^2 \tag{3.12}$$

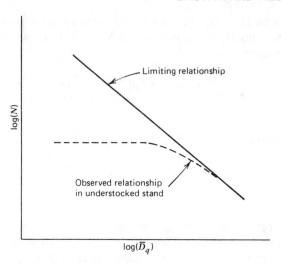

Figure 3.7 The number of trees per acre in relation to quadratic mean dbh in an understocked stand approaching the limit over time.

where D is tree diameter (dbh). The total area occupied by n trees on one acre of land is then

$$\sum_{j=1}^{n} A_j = \beta_0 n + \beta_1 \sum_{j=1}^{n} D_j + \beta_2 \sum_{j=1}^{n} D_j^2 \tag{3.13}$$

where the summation is made over the n trees growing on the acre. Suppose N one-acre sample plots were selected from a population of interest, and on each plot the values n_i, $\sum_{j=1}^{n_i} D_{ij}$, and $\sum_{j=1}^{n_i} D_{ij}^2$ $(i = 1, 2, \ldots, N)$ were obtained, where D_{ij} is the dbh of the jth tree on the ith sample plot and n_i is the number of trees on sample plot i. Estimates of the parameters β_0, β_1, and β_2 are then obtained by minimizing

$$\sum_{i=1}^{N} \left(1 - \hat{\beta}_0 n_i - \hat{\beta}_1 \sum_{j=1}^{n_i} D_{ij} - \hat{\beta}_2 \sum_{j=1}^{n_i} D_{ij}^2 \right)^2 \tag{3.14}$$

These least squares estimates can then be used to evaluate equation (3.13) for any given stand with known n, $\sum_{j=1}^{n} D_j$, and $\sum_{j=1}^{n} D_j^2$. The resultant tree-area ratio $\left(\sum_{j=1}^{n} A_j \right)$ is a measure of stand density relative to the average relationship in the original sample. The idea seems to make better sense if the original sample is restricted to "fully stocked" stands as in the case of stand density index.

Tree-area ratio is a measure of stand density that relies on a predetermined relationship, as does stand density index, but its use is not restricted to even-aged stands. This statistic has seen little use in yield estimation because it does not seem to offer any significant advantages over simpler measures which are obtained directly.

As an example of how to calculate the tree-area ratio, suppose sample plots were measured in fully stocked stands selected from a population of interest. In each plot trees were enumerated and individual tree diameters were measured. These observations led to the following least squares estimates of the parameters.

$$\hat{\beta}_0 = 0.000200$$

$$\hat{\beta}_1 = 0.000100$$

$$\hat{\beta}_2 = 0.0000250$$

The estimated average area occupied by a tree of diameter $D = 10$ inches, for example, is calculated from equation (3.12) as

$$A = 0.000200 + 0.000100(10) + 0.0000250(10)^2$$

$$= 0.0037 \text{ acres.}$$

For a stand with an average of 300 trees per acre whose diameters sum to 2400 and whose squared diameters sum to 19,200, the tree-area ratio (TAR) is calculated as

$$TAR = 0.000200(300) + 0.000100(2400) + 0.0000250(19,200)$$

$$= 0.78$$

3.2.5 Crown Competition Factor

Krajicek et al. (1961) proposed a measure of stand density that is appropriate for both even-aged and all-aged stands. It is based on the horizontal projection of the crown area of trees of given diameter relative to the maximum crown area for open-grown trees of the same diameter and is another measure of stand density based on a predetermined relationship. The relationship between crown width (CW) and diameter (D) for open-grown trees is assumed to be of the form

$$CW = \alpha + \beta D \tag{3.15}$$

If CW is in feet, the crown area CA in square feet is given by

$$CA = (\pi/4)(CW)^2$$

or

$$CA = (\pi/4)(\alpha + \beta D)^2 \qquad (3.16)$$

The maximum crown area (MCA), that is, the crown area for an open-grown tree of diameter D, expressed as a percentage of an acre, is given by

$$MCA = \frac{100(\pi/4)(\alpha + \beta D)^2}{43,560}$$

which is equivalent to

$$MCA = 0.001803(\alpha + \beta D)^2 \qquad (3.17)$$

The parameters α and β are estimated from measurements of crown width and diameter on open-grown trees. An MCA value is then calculated for each tree in a stand, and the sum of all these values, on an acre basis, is the crown competition factor (CCF). The CCF has been used as a measure of stand density in growth and yield estimation (Stage, 1973).

As an example of how to calculate the crown competition factor, suppose a sample of open-grown trees of a given species was measured for average crown width CW in feet and diameter D in inches. From these observations, the parameter estimates obtained by least squares procedures were

$$\hat{\alpha} = 5.0$$
$$\hat{\beta} = 2.0$$

so that

$$CW = 5.0 + 2.0(D)$$

Maximum crown area (MCA) is then given by

$$MCA = 0.001803(5.0 + 2.0D)^2$$
$$= 0.007212D^2 + 0.03606D + 0.045075$$

Computation of the CCF for an example stand is shown in Table 3.1.

TABLE 3.1

Computation of the CCF Value for a Typical Forest Stand

D (inches)	Number of Trees/ Acre	MCA (%)	MCA × Trees/Acre (%)
4	10	0.3047	3.047
5	30	0.4057	12.171
6	50	0.5211	26.055
7	60	0.6509	39.054
8	50	0.7951	39.755
9	30	0.9538	28.614
10	10	1.1269	11.269
			CCF = 160.0%

3.2.6 Spacing Index or Relative Spacing

A density measure based on the average distance between trees and the average height of the dominant canopy was first proposed for plantations by Hart (1928) and was later referred to as a spacing index (Becking, 1954; Hummel, 1954) and then as relative spacing (Beekhuis, 1966). Apparently, this statistic evolved from the observation that stands judged to have desirable stocking shared similar ratios of average distance between trees to average dominant height. Some reflection on this observation led to the suggested use of the ratio as a measure of stand density. Spacing index or relative spacing is defined as

$$RS = \frac{\text{Average distance between trees}}{\text{Average height of dominant canopy}}$$

which, if square spacing is assumed, can be written as

$$RS = \frac{\sqrt{43,560/N}}{H} \tag{3.18}$$

where

N = number of trees per acre

H = average dominant height

Some have argued that triangular spacing is a more realistic assumption for calculating the average distance between trees, but since any triangular-spacing

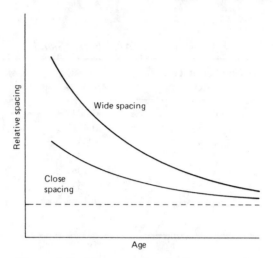

Figure 3.8   Time trends of relative spacing
in stands of different density.

RS value is a constant proportion of the corresponding square-spacing *RS* value,
the distinction is irrelevant as far as a density measure is concerned.

An interesting feature of relative spacing is illustrated in Figure 3.8, which
shows the development through time of relative spacing values in a close-spacing
and a wide-spacing stand. Regardless of site quality and initial age, all stands
of a given species seem to asymptotically approach a common minimum relative
spacing value as they grow older.[2] For any given average dominant height growth
curve, this lower limit establishes a maximum number of trees per acre to be
expected at any given age. It should also be noted that a combination of the
height growth curve and the *RS* time trend line implicitly defines a survival curve
(Parker, 1978). Relative spacing has been used to control density in intensively
managed plantations. For example, thinning regimes have been designed to
attain prespecified values of relative spacing at each thinning, and thinning
intervals have been determined to coincide with specified increments in dominant
height. Yield tables have been developed in which average dominant height
replaces both age and site quality in yield prediction (Beekhuis, 1966).

As an example of the application of the relative spacing index, consider an
even-aged stand that has an average dominant height of 44 feet and 360 trees

---

[2] This statement must be qualified by the observation that different limits may exist for plantations
as opposed to natural stands. Geographic differences may also be present for species with extensive
ranges.

per acre. With square spacing, the relative spacing value is

$$RS = \frac{\sqrt{43,560/N}}{44}$$

$$= 0.25$$

As an illustration of the use of relative spacing in developing thinning specifications, consider a thinning schedule that involves two thinnings. Both are to
leave relative spacing values of 0.275 in the residual stand. The first thinning
will be imposed when average dominant height is 40 feet, and the second thinning
will be made when average dominant height reaches 60 feet. The numbers of
trees per acre to be left after thinning are:

1. When average dominant height is 40 feet,

$$N = 43,560/(40 \times 0.275)^2 = 360$$

2. When average dominant height is 60 feet,

$$N = 43,460/(60 \times 0.275)^2 = 160$$

*3.3 MEASURES OF POINT DENSITY

The data-handling capacity and speed of modern computers have made possible
the development of complex stand growth and yield simulation models. Most
detailed are the so-called single-tree, distance-dependent tree growth simulators
which take into account the actual spatial distribution of trees as well as their
numbers and sizes. Stem maps, in the form of location coordinates, are main-
tained during growth simulation, and individual trees are characterized in terms
of several measures of size and form, which are then projected over time.

Point density measures are attempts to refine average stand density measures
so that the varying degrees of crowding experienced by individual trees in a
stand can be incorporated into the procedure of projecting individual tree growth.
These measures can also be used in the prediction of mortality probabilities
(Keister and Tidwell, 1975), and possibly for the introduction of natural regeneration into the stand during simulation (Spurr, 1962). Measures of point density
for single-tree growth simulators are based on the dimensions of the subject tree
and on the dimensions of, and distances to, competitors. The utility of a measure
is judged in terms of its correlation with observed tree growth and its computational simplicity (Daniels, 1976).

Lemmon and Schumacher (1962) proposed a measure that used Bitterlich's
angle-count method to provide an estimate of basal area per acre in the vicinity
of the subject tree. An obvious shortcoming of this approach is its inability to

take into account the relative sizes of the subject and competing trees and their spatial distribution. Spurr (1962) suggested a method of estimating point density that essentially accumulates the subtended angles for a fixed number of surrounding trees. The measure is expressed in basal area per acre and is obtained by starting with the tree that subtends the largest angle. A basal area per acre estimate is obtained from the distance to the tree and the angle it subtends. A second basal area per acre estimate is obtained by accumulating similar basal area per acre estimates using the two trees with largest subtended angles. The process continues using 3, 4, . . . , and finally n trees. The point estimate of density is then computed as the mean of the n basal area per acre estimates.

Most of the recent studies of intertree competition and tree growth have used a different approach that involves the concept of a competition-influence zone around each tree and assumes that the area, in horizontal projection, over which a tree competes for all site resources can be represented by a circle whose radius is a function of tree size. The competitive stress experienced by a given tree is then assumed to be a function of the extent to which its competition circle overlaps those of neighboring trees (Staebler, 1951). Different functions of tree size for determining the radius of the competition circle and different procedures for approximating or calculating overlap areas and weighting these by relative sizes of competitors have led to a rapid proliferation of competition indexes (Newnham, 1966; Opie, 1968; Gerrard, 1969; Bella, 1971; Arney, 1973; Ek and Monserud, 1974). For example, Gerrard (1969) suggested that competition index be defined as

$$CI_i = \frac{1}{A_i} \sum_{j=1}^{n} a_j \qquad (3.19)$$

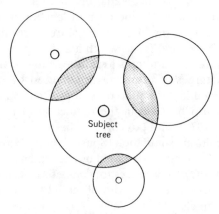

Figure 3.9 An illustration of the competition zone overlap used in the definition of point density measures.

where

CI_i = competition index for subject tree i

A_i = competition circle area for subject tree i

a_j = area of overlap of jth competitor

n = number of competitors

Figure 3.9 is a hypothetical stem map that shows a circular competition-influence zone for each tree and the area of overlap of the competition circle for the subject tree.

Another competition index or measure of point density suggested by Hegyi (1974) is a distance-weighted aggregate of the ratios of competition and subject tree dbh values. Daniels (1976) found this measure to be as highly correlated with loblolly pine dbh and height growth as the more complex indexes based on competition circle overlap. Hegyi's competition index is computed as

$$CI_i = \sum_{j=1}^{n} (D_j/D_i)/DIST_{ij} \qquad (3.20)$$

where

CI_i = competition index for subject tree i

D_j/D_i = dbh of competitor j expressed as a proportion of subject tree i dbh

$DIST_{ij}$ = distance between tree i and competitor j

n = number of competitors

Daniels (1976) defined a competitor as any tree that would be counted by a factor-10 angle gauge centered at the subject tree.

There remains some doubt as to the general utility of point density measures for the prediction of individual tree growth. Individual tree growth prediction models that use point density as a predictor variable frequently are no more precise in their predictions than similar models that do not use point density. It has been suggested that such considerations as microsite differences and root grafting may account for this lack of predictive ability (Stone, 1974).

REFERENCES

Arney, J. D. 1973. Tables for quantifying competitive stress on individual trees. *Can. For Serv., Inf. Rpt. BC-X-78.*

Assmann, E. 1961. *Waldertragskunde*. B.L.V. Verlagsgesellschaft. München.

Bassett, J. R. 1969. Growth of widely spaced loblolly pine. *J. For.* **67**:634–636.

Becking, J. H. 1954. Einige Gesichtspunkte für die Durchführung von verglei-chenden Durchfostungsversuchen in gleichaltrigen Beständen. In *Proc. I.U.F.R.O. Congress,* Rome, 1953.

Beekhuis, J. 1966. Prediction of yield and increment in *Pinus radiata* stands in New Zealand. *N.Z. For. Res. Inst. Tech. Paper No. 49.*

Bella, I. E. 1971. A new competition model for individual trees. *For. Sci.* **17**:364–372.

Bickford, C. A., F. S. Baker, and F. G. Wilson, 1957. Stocking, normality, and measurement of stand density. *J. For.* **55**:99–104.

Braathe, P. 1957. *Thinnings in even-aged stands, a summary of European lit-erature.* Fac. of For., Univ. of New Brunswick.

Chapman, H. H. 1953. Effects of thinnings on yields of forest-grown longleaf and loblolly pines at Urania, Louisiana. *J. For.* **51**:16–26.

Chisman, H. H., and F. X. Schumacher. 1940. On the tree-area ratio and certain of its applications. *J. For.* **38**:311–317.

Collins, A. B. 1967. Density and height growth in natural slash pine. *U.S.D.A. For. Serv., Res. Paper SE-27.*

Crow, A. B. 1952. Thinning methods in slash pine. In *La. State Univ. First Annual For. Symp. Proc.*

Daniels, R. F., and H. E. Burkhart. 1975. Simulation of individual tree growth and stand development in managed loblolly pine plantations. *Div. For. and Wildlife Res., Va. Polytechnic Inst. and State Univ., FWS-5-75.*

Daniels, R. F. 1976. Simple competition indices and their correlation with annual loblolly pine tree growth. *For. Sci.* **22**:454–456.

Dell, T. R., and L. V. Collicott. 1978. Growth in relation to density for slash pine plantations after first thinning. *For. Sci.* **4**:7–12.

Dell, T. R., D. P. Feduccia, T. E. Campbell, W. F. Mann, and B. H. Polmer. 1979. Yields of unthinned slash pine plantations on cutover sites in the west gulf region. *U.S.D.A. For. Serv., Res. Paper SO-147.*

Drew, T. J., and J. W. Flewelling. 1979. Stand density management: an alter-native approach and its application to Douglas-fir plantations. *For. Sci.* **25**:518–532.

Ek, A. R., and R. A. Monserud. 1974. FOREST: A computer model for sim-ulating the growth and reproduction of mixed species forest-stands. *Univ. Wisc. Sch. Nat. Resources Res. Rpt. R2635.*

Enghardt, H. G. 1970. Growth of 40-year-old planted loblolly pine. *Forests and People* **20**(3):38–41.

Frothingham, E. H. 1914. White pine under forest management. *U.S.D.A. Bull. No. 13.*

Gerrard, D. J. 1969. Competition quotient: a new measure of the competition affecting individual forest trees. *Mich. State Univ. Agr. Exp. Stn. Res. Bull. No. 20.*

Gilmore, A. R., and R. P. Gregory. 1974. Twenty years growth of loblolly and shortleaf pine planted at various spacings in Southern Illinois. *Transactions Ill. State Acad. of Sci.* **67**:38–47.

Gingrich, S. F. 1967. Measuring and evaluating stocking and stand density in upland hardwood forests in the central states. *For Sci.* **13**:39–53.

Goebel, N. B., J. R. Warner, and D. H. VanLear. 1974. Periodic thinning in loblolly pine stands: growth, yield and economic analysis. *Clemson Univ. For. Res. Series 28.*

Grano, C. X. 1970. Small hardwoods reduce growth of pine overstory. *U.S.D.A. For. Serv., Res. Paper SO-55.*

Hansborough, T. 1968. Stand characteristics of 18-year-old loblolly pine growing in different initial spacings. *La. State Univ. Agr. Exp. Stn. Hill Farm For. 8.*

Harms, W. R., and A. B. Collins. 1965. Spacing and twelve-year growth of slash pine. *J. For.* **63**:909–912.

Hart, H. M. J. 1928. Stamtal en dunning. *Proefstation Boschwesen, Batavia, Mededelingen 21.*

Hegyi, F. 1974. A simulation model for managed jackpine stands. In *Growth models for tree and stand simulation.* Royal Coll. For., Res. Notes No. 30, Stockholm.

Hummel, F. C. 1947. The Bowmont Norway spruce sample plots (1930–1945). *Forestry* **XXI**:30–42.

Hummel, F. C. 1954. Definition of thinning treatments. In. *Proc. I.U.F.R.O. Congress,* Rome, 1953.

Johnson, E. W. 1973. Relationship between point density measurements and subsequent growth of southern pines. *Auburn Univ. Agr. Exp. Stn. Bull. No. 447.*

Keister, T. D. 1971. A measure of intraspecific competition experienced by an individual tree in a planted stand. *La. State Univ. Agr. Exp. Stn. Bull. No. 652.*

Keister, T. D. 1972. Thinning slash pine plantations results in little growth or economic gain after 40 years. *La. State Univ. For. Note 102.*

Keister, T. D., and G. R. Tidwell. 1975. Competition ratio dynamics for improved mortality estimates in simulated growth of forest stands. *For. Sci.* **20**:46–51.

Krajicek, J. E., K. A. Brinkman, and S. F. Gingrich. 1961. Crown competition—a measure of density. *For. Sci.* **7**:35–42.

Lemmon, P. E., and F. X. Schumacher. 1962. Stocking density around ponderosa pine trees. *For. Sci.* **8**:397–402.

Livingston, K. W. 1964. Slash pine at Auburn, a case history. *Auburn Univ. Agr. Exp. Stn. For. Dept. Series No. 1.*

Mann, W. F. 1971. Early yields of slash pine planted on a cutover site at various spacings. *U.S.D.A. For. Serv., Res. Paper SO-69.*

Mann, W. F., and T. R. Dell. 1971. Yields of 17-year-old loblolly pine planted on a cutover site at various spacings. *U.S.D.A. For. Serv., Res. Paper SO-70.*

Mann, W. F., and H. G. Enghardt. 1972. Growth of planted slash pine under several thinning regimes. *U.S.D.A. For. Serv., Res. Paper SO-76.*

Marsh, E. K. 1957. Some preliminary results from O'Connor's correlated curve trend (CCT) experiments on thinnings and espacements and their practical significance. *Commonwealth For. Conf. 1957.*

Mulloy, G. A. 1946. Thinning red pine. *Canada Dom. For. Serv., Silv. Res. Note 79.*

Mulloy, G. A. 1947. Empirical stand density yield tables. *Canada Dom. For. Serv., Silv. Res. Note 82.*

Nelson, T. C., and E. V. Brender. 1963. Comparison of stand density measures for loblolly pine cubic-foot growth prediction. *For. Sci.* **9**:8–14.

Newnham, R. M. 1966. Stand structure and diameter growth of individual trees in a young red pine stand. *Can. Dept. For. Rural Develop., Res. Notes* **22**:4–5.

Opie, J. E. 1968. Predictability of individual tree growth using definitions of competing basal area. *For. Sci.* **14**:314–323.

Parker, R. C. 1978. *Investigations into the limits of stand density.* Ph.D. dissertation, School of Forest Res., Univ. of Georgia.

Phipps, H. M. 1973. Effects of thinning on young shortleaf pine plantations in Indiana. *U.S.D.A. For. Serv., Res. Paper NC-93.*

Reineke, L. H. 1933. Perfecting a stand-density index for even-aged forests. *J. Agric. Res.* **46**:627–638.

Reukema, D. L. 1970. Forty-year development of Douglas-fir stands planted at various spacings. *U.S.D.A. For. Serv., Res. Paper PNW-100.*

Russell, T. E. 1958. Spacing—its role in the growth of planted slash pine. *Southern Lumberman* **197**(2465):115–117.

Shepard, R. K. 1974. Growth of thinned and non-thinned loblolly pine stands. *La. Agri.* **17**(4):10–12.

Smith, L. F. 1967. Effects of spacing and site on the growth and yield of planted slash pine. *U.S.D.A. For. Serv., Res. Note SO-63.*

Spurr, S. H. 1962. A measure of point density. *For. Sci.* **8**:85–95.

Staebler, G. R. 1951. Growth and spacing in an even-aged stand of Douglas-fir. Masters thesis, Univ. of Michigan.

Stage, A. R. 1973. A model for the prognosis of forest stand development. *U.S.D.A. For. Serv., Res. Paper INT-137.*

Stone, E. L. 1974. The communal root system of red pine: growth of girdled trees. *For. Sci.* **20**:294–305.

Tennent, R. B. 1975. Competition quotient in young *Pinus radiata. N.Z. J. For. Sci.* **5**:230–234.

Wakeley, P. C. 1969. Single commercial thinnings in variously spaced slash and loblolly pine plantations. *U.S.D.A. For. Serv., Res. Paper SO-48.*

Ware, L. M., and R. Stahelin. 1948. Growth of southern pine plantations at various spacings. *J. For.* **46**:267–274.

Williston, H. L., and T. R. Dell. 1974. Growth of pine plantations in North Mississippi. *U.S.D.A. For. Serv., Res. Paper SO-94.*

4

Predicting Growth and Yield

Timber management shares many similarities with production management in manufacturing. In both activities, given levels of inputs to the process result in certain outputs and either a profit or loss for the firm. Optimal decisions concerning the levels of inputs, the timing and intensity of interventions, and other modifications of the process by management require accurate predictions of output at all relevant combinations of these levels, timings, intensities, and process modifications. In the case of timber management, these predictions have traditionally taken the form of yield tables—tabular records showing expected volume of wood (board feet, cords, cubic feet, cubic meters, etc.) per unit of land area (acre, hectare) by combinations of measurable characteristics of the forest stand (age, site quality, stand density). Today, most yield prediction systems are expressed as mathematical equations or systems of interrelating equations rather than as tables, so that computers can be used to generate predictions for any desired combinations of inputs. The predicted volumes, when multiplied by values per unit of volume, provide estimates of total value per acre at various levels of the input variables. The use of these estimates, with the appropriate economic analysis models, generates decisions concerning the optimum ages to harvest (rotation ages), levels of planting density, and timings of thinnings or other management activities. These timber management decisions are analogous to decisions regarding numbers of shifts to work, raw materials to use, and process alterations in a manufacturing situation.

One unique aspect of forest yield, however, which distinctly separates it from most production processes is the growing stock-inventory relationship. In forest management, the "factory" is also the "product" and a balance must be achieved between production and storage. Holding too much growing stock as inventory may reduce the economic efficiency of the production process by tying up excessive capital. On the other hand, too little growing stock reduces the effectiveness of the production process because the "factory" or stand will not be making full use of the available growth potential. A yield prediction model must be capable of evaluating these interrelationships if it is to be useful in the decision-making process.

Since stands of trees are biological systems, measures of their cumulative growth usually exhibit the common sigmoid curve shape when plotted over age (Figure 4.1). The inflection point of a sigmoid yield curve, commonly called the *age of culmination of current annual increment*, generally occurs at younger ages on higher site index land. Average stand diameter, a yield statistic of considerable practical significance, is strongly correlated with stand density (Figure 4.2). Higher numbers of trees per acre are associated with lower average diameters. Quadratic mean diameter $(\overline{D}_q)$, number of trees per acre (n), and basal area per acre (B) are related by the equation

$$\overline{D}_q = \sqrt{\frac{B/n}{0.005454}} \tag{4.1}$$

Thus, average diameter increases with increasing basal area for the same number of trees (Figure 4.3). The size-class distribution of diameters is primarily dependent on the age structure of the stand. All-aged stands tend to have reversed J-shaped diameter distributions (Figure 4.4), while even-aged stands exhibit mound-shaped distributions with varying degrees of left or right skewness (Figure 4.5).

4.1 CLASSIFICATION OF YIELD PREDICTION MODELS

Available yield models reflect different silvicultural practices, modeling philosophies, and levels of mathematical complexity. Groupings of yield models can therefore be based on a variety of characteristics. Target populations to which predictions apply can be usefully grouped as follows.

1. Natural forests
    (a) Uneven-aged
    (b) Even-aged

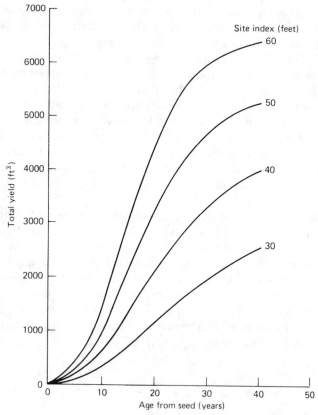

Figure 4.1   Total yield per acre of entire stem (outside bark) of all trees for shortleaf pine planted at 6-by-6 foot spacing. (After Smalley and Bailey, 1974.)

2. Plantations
    (a) Thinned
    (b) Unthinned

The earliest yield predictions for natural forests applied only to stands called *fully stocked* or *normal* as judged against some concept of the desirable above-ground mass of trees (Bickford et al., 1957). German foresters first used this approach in the early nineteenth century and it subsequently formed a basis for many yield prediction methods. Data for the yield estimates came from stands selected as having normal stand density, and various procedures were applied to adjust the estimates for non-fully-stocked situations. The subjective nature of normality definitions together with the development of improved analysis methods, which use absolute measures of stand density such as basal area and

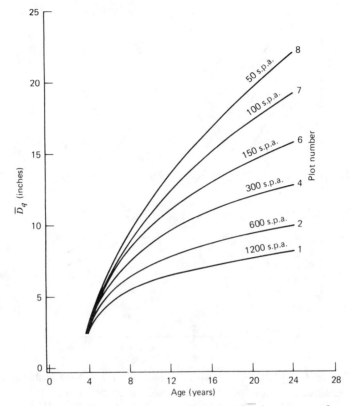

Figure 4.2 Quadratic mean diameter $(\bar{D}_q)$ over age for
6 stems-per-acre planting densities (s.p.a.) of slash pine
in the Transvaal, South Africa. (After Pienaar, 1965.)

number of trees per acre as predictor variables, have obviated the normality
approach (Nelson and Bennett, 1965). The following sections develop variable
density growth and yield prediction methods in some detail. Particular emphasis
is placed on techniques applicable to plantations.

Yield prediction models can be categorized by the complexity of the mathematical approach involved:

A. Models in tabular form

B. Models as equations and systems of equations
    1. Direct prediction of unit-area values
    2. Unit-area values obtained by summation
        (a) Equations for classes of trees
        (b) Equations for individual trees

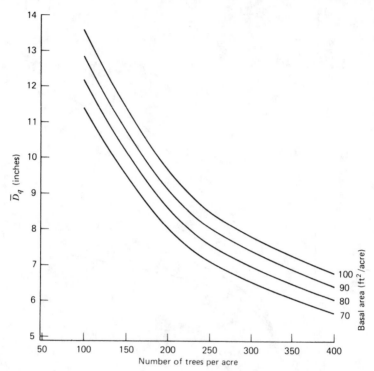

Figure 4.3 Average quadratic diameter ($\overline{D}_q$) over number of trees per acre for four levels of basal area per acre.

Yield models presented in tabular form only are seldom used today.

A wide variety of yield equation approaches has been presented in the literature and new developments appear each year. The complexity of these approaches has varied from the simplicity of a single regression equation, expressing yield per acre as a function of age, site index, and basal area, to the detailed intricacy of equation systems that simulate the growth of each individual tree in a stand as a function of its own characteristics, the characteristics of neighboring trees, and the distances to neighboring trees.

Data requirements for the different approaches vary widely as well. Direct prediction equations for yields can be developed from inventory data collected on temporary plots. Equations or systems of equations that explicitly or implicitly predict growth require at least some remeasured plot data. Elaborate single-tree growth models are the most demanding of data. For so-called distance-dependent individual tree models (Munro, 1974), extremely detailed and expensive data are necessary. These include diameter and height growth of individual trees, between-tree distances, and, in some cases, the crown dimensions of each tree.

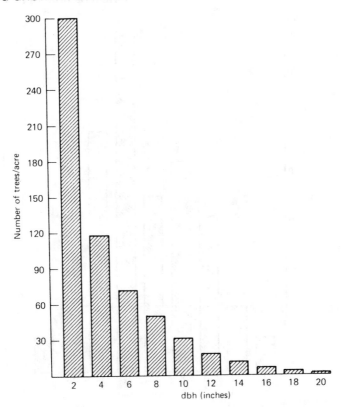

Figure 4.4 Average stand diameter distribution for all-aged, upland stands of oak. (After Schnur, 1937.)

Yield models vary considerably in the amount of detail included in projections. An estimate of per-unit area total volume or weight yield must always be produced. Where a single product is involved, such as pulpwood, a single prediction of tons or cubic feet of recoverable solid wood may be sufficient. However, few forests are managed for only one wood product. In addition, harvesting costs per unit of volume usually vary with tree size. Thus, it is sometimes necessary and generally desirable to have a yield prediction system that provides estimates of the numbers of trees (stand table) and volumes (stock table) by tree diameter classes. Some prediction systems also include methodology for subdividing the diameter class volumes into product class components such as sawtimber and pulpwood (e.g., Bennett and Clutter, 1968).

In summary, it should be reemphasized that yield models for even-aged stands relate per-acre standing volume to measures of age, site quality, and stand density. The manager uses the relationships given by such models to make intelligent decisions concerning manipulation of the controllable variables—age

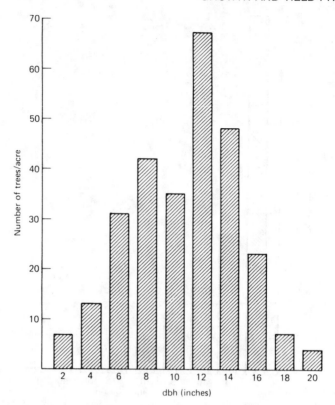

Figure 4.5 Typical diameter distribution for an even-aged stand of upland hardwoods. (After Gingrich, 1978.)

and stand density. (As noted in Chapter 2, site quality will, in some cases, also be subject to managerial modifications.) Information from appropriate yield models is a necessary input for the selection of rotation ages, initial planting densities, and thinning schedules.

4.2 PREDICTING CURRENT YIELD

This section presents several examples of methods for predicting current yields; the prediction of future yields is considered in Section 4.3. The distinction between the two cases is more complex than a casual comparison of the words "current" and "future" would suggest. The basic difference is that current yield predictions do not involve a projection of stand density, while predictions of future yield do involve such a projection, either explicitly or implicitly. To illustrate this point, consider the following situations.

1. A stand has a known age, site index, and current basal area. Estimation of the current per-acre volume in this stand from the known values is a prediction of current yield.

2. It is specified that plantations will be established on land of a given site quality and will be grown to a particular rotation age. It is also specified that a particular number of trees will be available for harvest at rotation age. Even though the estimate of rotation-age yield applies to a future point in time, it is, in the terminology defined here, a current yield prediction since the stand density (in this case, number of trees per acre) is assumed to be known at the point in time for which the yield estimate is desired.

3. An existing stand has a known site index, age, and current stand density. An estimate of yield 10 years hence is desired. Since the yield 10 years hence will be a function of the age, site index, and stand density at that time, the estimation of this yield must take into account the change in stand density that will occur during the next 10 years. This situation therefore involves a prediction of future yield.

We subdivide the systems for predicting current yields into two categories. In the first of these, the solution of the equations (or equation) that comprise the system provides estimates of volume per unit area. Systems of this type are referred to as *explicit prediction systems*. Systems in the second category are called *implicit prediction systems*. With implicit prediction, solution of the equations involved produces basic information on stand structure. Yield estimates implied by the predicted structure are then calculated from further computations based on the stand structure information.

4.2.1   Explicit Prediction of Current Yield

The first variable-density yield prediction equations were developed during the late 1930s using methodology developed by MacKinney et al. (1937) and Schumacher (1939). The basic form of the Schumacher yield model is

$$\ln (V) = \beta_0 + \beta_1 A^{-1} + \beta_2 f(S) + \beta_3 g(D_s) \tag{4.2}$$

where

V = some expression of per-acre yield

A = stand age

$f(S)$ = some function of site index

$g(D_s)$ = some function of stand density (D_s)

Most of the earliest applications of this model are of limited interest today because they involved measures of stand density based on the normal-stocking concept. Several yield equations based on the Schumacher model are listed here.[1]

1.   Natural slash pine stands, Georgia and North Florida (Bennett, 1970b).

$$\ln (V_1) = 5.98812 - 121.713/S$$

$$- 19.758/A + 0.89683 \ln (B) \tag{4.3}$$

2.   Natural loblolly pine stands, Virginia, South Carolina, and Georgia (Sullivan and Clutter, 1972).

$$\ln (V_2) = 2.8837 + 0.014441S$$

$$- 21.326/A + 0.95064 \ln (B) \tag{4.4}$$

3.   Black spruce on organic soils in Minnesota (Perala, 1971).

$$\ln (V_3) = 1.07542 + 0.61265 \ln (S)$$

$$+ 0.96861 \ln (B) - 9.450/A \tag{4.5}$$

4.   Eastern white pine in Maine, Massachusetts, and New Hampshire (Leak et al., 1970).

$$\ln (V_4) = 4.32976 + 0.01580S$$

$$+ 2.07850 \ln (P) - 32.75770/A \tag{4.6}$$

5.   Old-field slash pine plantations in the middle coastal plain of Georgia and the Carolina sandhills (Bennett et al., 1959).

$$\ln (V_5) = 15.82465 - 41.00593/A$$

$$- 0.04257S + 0.44864 \ln (N) - 357.98712/S \tag{4.7}$$

Notation used in the above equations is defined as

A = stand age (years)

S = site index in feet; 50-year base for equations (4.3) through (4.6) and 25-year base for equation (4.7)

B = basal area per acre in square feet

P = percent of full stocking

---

[1] Several of these equations were developed using log (V) as the dependent variable. They have been transformed to ln (V) form for presentation here.

N = Number of surviving trees per acre

V_1 = per-acre, outside-bark, cubic-foot volume for all trees 4.6 inches dbh and larger to a 4-inch top diameter, outside bark

V_2 = per-acre, total, inside-bark, cubic-foot volume of all trees including stump and top

V_3 = per-acre, total, inside-bark, cubic-foot volume of trees 3.6 inches dbh and larger

V_4 = per-acre, inside-bark, cubic-foot volume for all trees 3.0 inches dbh and larger to a 3-inch top diameter, inside bark

V_5 = per-acre, outside-bark, cubic-foot volume for all trees 4.6 inches dbh and larger to a 4-inch top diameter, outside bark

Numerous investigators have used slightly modified versions of the basic Schumacher yield model. Typical examples are the yield equations published by Langdon (1961) and Vimmerstedt (1962) which have the general form[2]

$$\ln (V) = \beta_0 + \beta_1 A^{-1} + \beta_2 f(S) + \beta_3 g(S/A) + \beta_4 h(D_s/A)$$

where

$g(S/A)$ = some function of the ratio S/A

$h(D_s/A)$ = some function of the ratio D_s/A

A conceptually similar prediction model using a different equation form has been developed by Chambers (1980) for predominantly second-growth, natural stands of Douglas-fir in western Washington. The prediction equation for cubic-foot volume per acre is

$$CVTS = -938.33423 + 2.01933 ASP - 21.28009 AP$$
$$+ 41.4912A - .51870A^2 - 1567.56665P \qquad (4.8)$$

where

$CVTS$ = inside-bark, cubic-foot volume per acre of trees 7.0 inches dbh and larger, including top and stump

A = average breast-height age for site trees

---

[2] In the Vimmerstedt equation, β_2 is equal to 0.

S = base-age-50 site index; see equation (2.4)

B = basal area per acre of trees 7.0 inches dbh and larger

P = $B/[-901.67920 + 301.38721 \log(A) + 296.87085 \log(S)]$

Chambers also provides formulas for calculating conversion factors that can be used to estimate various measures of merchantable volume from the *CVTS* predicted value.

Another example of an explicit prediction yield equation is provided by the following formula for estimating the yield of red pine stands in northwestern Wisconsin (Rose and Ek, 1972).

$$V = 0.00545 SB[1 - e^{-0.01979(A)}]^{1.38940} \tag{4.9}$$

where

V = per acre volume in cords

A = stand age

S = site index (base age = 50 years)

B = basal area per acre in square feet

Some explicit prediction equations estimate yield as a function of basal area and height rather than as a direct function of age, site index, and some measure of stand density. Such formulas are generally referred to as *stand volume equations* because of their functional similarity to individual tree volume equations. Three typical examples of stand volume equations follow.

1. Quaking aspen in north-central Minnesota (Schlaegel, 1971).

$$V_1 = 0.41898 BH_1 \tag{4.10}$$

2. Red pine in Minnesota (Buckman, 1962).

$$V_1 = 0.4085 BH_1 \tag{4.11}$$

3. Lodgepole pine in Montana and Idaho (Cole, 1971).

$$V_2 = -32.79 + 0.46952 BH_2 \tag{4.12}$$

where

V_1 = inside-bark, total-stem, cubic-foot volume per acre of all trees 0.5 inches dbh and larger

V_2 = inside-bark, total-stem, cubic-foot volume per acre of all trees greater than 4.5 feet in height

B = total stand basal area in square feet per acre

H_1 = average height in feet of dominants and codominants

H_2 = average height in feet of dominants

4.2.2 Implicit Prediction of Current Yield

Implicit prediction of current yield is accomplished by using techniques that have come to be known as *diameter distribution methods*. All diameter distribution yield systems predict the numbers of trees per acre by diameter class and the average height for each diameter class. These data are then used in conjunction with an appropriate individual tree volume equation for calculation of the estimated per-acre yield. The equations that generate the predicted diameter class frequencies and average heights generally use stand age, site index, and total number of surviving trees per acre as the predictor variables. (Average height of dominants and codominants is sometimes used in place of site index.) Diameter distribution systems obviously provide more detailed information concerning stand structure than the explicit prediction systems previously discussed. To date, diameter distribution methods have been primarily used for predicting plantation yields (e.g., Bennett and Clutter, 1968; Lenhart and Clutter, 1971; Lenhart, 1972a; Burkhart and Strub, 1974; Smalley and Bailey, 1974; Smith, 1978; Clutter and Belcher, 1978; Dell et al., 1979; Feduccia et al., 1979; Alder, 1979), but some applications in natural stand populations have been reported (McGee and Della-Bianca, 1967; Schreuder et al., 1979).

All diameter distribution yield systems predict values for the parameters of some probability distribution. Most applications use continuous probability distributions. The best-known continuous probability distribution is, of course, the normal distribution which is defined by the probability density function

$$f(X) = \frac{1}{\sqrt{2\pi}\sigma} \exp\left[-\tfrac{1}{2}\left(\frac{X - \mu}{\sigma}\right)^2\right] \qquad (-\infty < X < \infty) \qquad (4.13)$$

This function defines the amount of probability density that is associated with each specific value of the random variable X. To fully specify the distribution, values must be assigned to the two parameters, μ and σ. These parameters are the mean and standard deviation of the normal distribution, but with most distributions the parameters do not have such a simple correspondence to meaningful properties.

The cumulative distribution function of X gives the probability that a value less than or equal to X will occur. A closed-form, analytic expression for the cumulative distribution function of the normal distribution does not exist and solution of a probability statement such as $P(a < X < b)$ requires access to tables of the standard normal distribution (the normal distribution with $\mu = 0$ and $\sigma = 1$).

Various statistical distributions, including the normal, have been used to model diameter distributions. However, nearly all recent work has used the Weibull distribution. The applicability of the Weibull for diameter distribution prediction was first noted by Bailey and Dell (1973). The Weibull is a three-parameter distribution defined by the probability density function

$$f(X) = \frac{c}{b}\left(\frac{X - a}{b}\right)^{c-1} \exp\left[-\left(\frac{X - a}{b}\right)^{c}\right] \qquad (a \leqslant X < \infty)$$

$$= 0, \quad \text{otherwise} \tag{4.14}$$

The parameter a is referred to as the location parameter, b is the scale parameter, and c is the shape parameter. The b and c parameters must always be positive. In general, a can be positive, zero, or negative, but for diameter distribution applications a must be nonnegative. As with the normal, this function defines the amount of probability density associated with each possible value of the random variable X. Although the probability density function for the Weibull looks intimidating, the distribution is really much easier to use than the normal, because a closed-form, analytic expression of the cumulative distribution function exists and is relatively simple in form. For the Weibull distribution, the cumulative distribution function is

$$F(X) = 1 - \exp\left[-\left(\frac{X - a}{b}\right)^{c}\right] \qquad (a \leqslant X < \infty)$$

$$= 0, \quad \text{otherwise} \tag{4.15}$$

Figure 4.6 shows three Weibull distributions. If X is a random variable which has the Weibull distribution, with $a = 2.5$, $b = 3.5$, and $c = 3.0$, the probability that a randomly selected value of X would be less than 5.0 is equal to the shaded area under the middle curve in Figure 4.6. This probability can be computed as

$$P(X < 5.0) = F(5.0) = 1 - \exp\left[-\left(\frac{5.0 - 2.5}{3.5}\right)^{3.0}\right]$$

$$= .30541$$

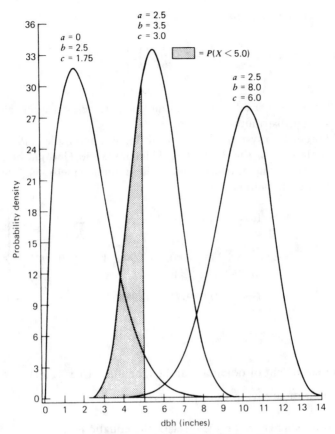

Figure 4.6 Examples of the Weibull distribution.

Similarly, the probability that $4.0 < X < 5.0$ can be calculated as

$$P(4.0 < X < 5.0) = F(5.0) - F(4.0)$$

$$= \exp\left[-\left(\frac{4.0 - 2.5}{3.5}\right)^{3.0}\right]$$

$$- \exp\left[-\left(\frac{5.0 - 2.5}{3.5}\right)^{3.0}\right]$$

$$= .22971$$

This relationship can be generally stated as follows. If a population of values has a Weibull distribution, the proportion of the population with values greater than L and less than U is given by the equation

$$P(L < X < U) = \exp\left[-\left(\frac{L - a}{b}\right)^c\right] - \exp\left[-\left(\frac{U - a}{b}\right)^c\right] \quad (4.16)$$

This equation can be used for calculating diameter class frequencies with all Weibull diameter distribution models.

The yield prediction system developed by Smalley and Bailey (1974) for short-leaf pine plantations in the Tennessee, Alabama, and Georgia highlands is a typical example of diameter distribution yield prediction methods. The equations used to estimate the parameters are

$$\left.\begin{array}{ll} a = -1.9492 + 0.0757H & \text{if } H \geqslant 26 \\ = 0 & \text{if } H < 26 \\ b = -a - 5.2352 - 0.0003N + 1.1955(10)^3/N \\ + 6.2046 \log (H) \\ c = 6.0560 - 0.0391H - 0.0006N \end{array}\right\} \quad (4.17)$$

where

H = average height of dominant and codominant trees (feet)

N = number of surviving trees per acre

Individual tree heights are predicted with the equation

$$\log (H/h) = -0.0207 + (1/D - 1/D_{max})[1.9022 - 0.3861AN(10)^{-6}$$
$$+ 0.001625N/A - 0.8970 \log (N/A) + 0.9578 \log (H/A)] \quad (4.18)$$

where

h = total tree height (feet)

D = dbh (inches)

D_{max} = the midpoint value of the largest occupied 1-inch dbh class

An appropriate individual tree volume equation for this population is

$$V = -0.3482 + 0.0021782D^2h \quad (4.19)$$

where

V = inside-bark, merchantable, cubic-foot volume to a 2-inch top, outside bark (Smalley and Bower, 1968)

To illustrate the use of this system, consider a 20-year-old shortleaf pine plantation with 800 trees per acre and an average height of dominants and codominants equal to 43 feet. The solution of equations (4.17) gives the Weibull parameter estimates

$$a = 1.3059$$

$$b = 4.8483$$

$$c = 3.8947$$

Equation (4.16) can now be written as

$$P_i = \exp\left[-\left(\frac{L_i - 1.3059}{4.8483}\right)^{3.8947}\right] - \exp\left[-\left(\frac{U_i - 1.3059}{4.8483}\right)^{3.8947}\right] \quad (4.20)$$

where

P_i = proportion of trees in diameter class i

L_i = lower limit of diameter class i

U_i = upper limit of diameter class i

The computations involved in estimating the diameter class frequencies are shown in columns (2) through (6) of Table 4.1 Since there is no upper limit on the random variable X in the Weibull probability density function, there will be a small, but finite, probability associated with any upper-tail dbh class. It is therefore necessary in practice to adopt some truncation rule. The rule used in this system can be stated as follows.

When the first upper-tail class with a class frequency less than 0.5 is encountered, set this class frequency to zero and adjust the class frequency of the next smallest class to an amount that makes the cumulative frequency for that class equal to the total number of trees.

Fortunately, this rule is much easier to apply than it is to state. The unmodified computations in Table 4.1 gave a class frequency for the 10-inch class of 0.35 trees per acre. This frequency was therefore made equal to zero, and the frequency originally calculated for the 9-inch class was increased by 3.42 trees per

TABLE 4.1

Diameter Distribution Computations for a 20-Year-Old Shortleaf Pine Plantation with 800 Trees per Acre (N) and an Average Height of Dominants and Codominants Equal to 43 Feet

(1) dbh Class (in.)	(2) Lower Limit (in.)	(3) Upper Limit (in.)	(4) Class Probability P_i	(5) Class Frequency $N \times P_i$ (trees/acre)	(6) Cumulative Frequency (trees/acre)	(7) Class Midpoint (in.)	(8) Average Height (ft)	(9) Per-Tree Volume (ft³)	(10) Class Volume (ft³/acre)
1	1.3059	1.5	.000004	0.00	0.00	1.403	14.0	0.000	0.00
2	1.5	2.5	.004252	3.40	3.40	2.0	21.2	0.000	0.00
3	2.5	3.5	.040316	32.25	35.65	3.0	29.3	0.226	7.29
4	3.5	4.5	.134109	107.29	142.94	4.0	34.5	0.854	91.64
5	4.5	5.5	.255016	204.01	346.95	5.0	38.0	1.721	351.12
6	5.5	6.5	.295882	236.71	583.66	6.0	40.5	2.828	669.32
7	6.5	7.5	.195871	156.70	740.36	7.0	42.4	4.177	654.57
8	7.5	8.5	.064993	51.99	792.35	8.0	43.9	5.772	300.07
9	8.5	9.5	.009113	7.65[a]	800.00[b]	9.0	45.1	7.609	58.21
10	9.5	10.5	.000438	0.00	—	—	—	—	—
Total				800.00					2132.22

[a] Prior to adjustment, this value was 7.29.
[b] Prior to adjustment, this value was 796.58.

acre (800 − 796.58) to make the 9-inch class cumulative frequency equal to 800 trees per acre.

After numerical substitution and algebraic simplification, equation (4.18) takes the form

$$\log (h) = 1.6542 - 0.8424\left(\frac{1}{D} - \frac{1}{9}\right)$$

Solutions of this equation with D set to the diameter class midpoints provide the average height values shown in column (8). A per-tree volume is calculated for each class using the midpoint dbh and the corresponding average height with equation (4.19). Class volumes are obtained by multiplying the per-tree volumes by the corresponding class frequencies, and the estimate of volume per acre is obtained by summing the class volumes.

The determination of estimated yield with any diameter distribution model is computationally tedious and these procedures are generally impractical without the use of a computer or a programmable calculator.

4.3 PREDICTING FUTURE YIELDS

Systems for predicting future yields have generally involved one of three different approaches.

1. Predict volume growth and add this to the estimate of current volume.
2. Predict the stand density (and the values of other input variables, if necessary) that will be present at the projection age and then solve the same equation or equations that are used to estimate current yields.
3. Predict future volume directly using current stand conditions and the length of the projection period as predictor variables.

Methods 2 and 3 are closely related since many method 3 equations are obtained by simply incorporating a stand density projection into an estimating equation for current yield. Methods 2 and 3 have been more widely used than method 1.

A typical example of the first approach is provided by a growth prediction equation developed by Oliver (1979) for thinned plantations of mixed ponderosa and Jeffrey pine. The equation is

$$G = 11.47631 + 1.20045B - 0.00396B^2 \tag{4.21}$$

where

G = cubic-foot periodic annual growth rate

B = current basal area per acre in square feet

Since the equation was developed from 5-year growth data, the model is most appropriately used for 5-year projections. If a plantation currently has 60 square feet of basal area, the estimated growth rate obtained from the solution of equation (4.21) is 69.2 cubic feet per acre per year. The estimated yield 5 years hence would thus be the current estimated volume plus 346 cubic feet per acre (5 times 69.2).

4.3.1   Explicit Prediction of Future Yield

In this section, we consider methods for modifying the explicit prediction current yield estimators of Section 4.2.1 to obtain predictions of future yield. Several alternative approaches follow.

Consider again the yield equation for natural slash pine stands developed by Bennett (1970b). [This equation was previously shown as equation (4.3).] The equation is

$$\ln (V) = 5.98812 - 121.713/S - 19.758/A$$
$$+ 0.89683 \ln (B) \qquad (4.22)$$

When current values of age, site index, and basal area are used in this equation, an estimate of current volume is obtained. If volume at some future projection age is desired, it can be estimated by solving the equation with appropriate values for site index, the future age, and the predicted basal area at the projection age. Appropriate values for the first two variables are simply the current site index and the current age plus the length of the projection period. Thus, the problem of predicting future yield is essentially a matter of predicting future stand density. The equation given by Bennett (1970b) to make this prediction is

$$\ln (B_2) = \left(\frac{A_1}{A_2} \right) \ln (B_1) + 5.1649 \left(1 - \frac{A_1}{A_2} \right) \qquad (4.23)$$

where

A_1 = current age (years)

A_2 = projection age (years)

B_1 = current basal area (square feet)

B_2 = predicted basal area at the projection age (square feet)

Suppose a natural slash pine stand is 35 years old with a site index of 80 feet and 105 square feet of basal area. Substitution of these values into equation (4.22) gives a predicted current volume of 3216 cubic feet per acre. To estimate the projected volume 10 years hence, a predicted basal area 10 years hence is obtained by solving equation (4.23) with A_1 = 35, A_2 = 45, and B_1 = 105. The resulting value is 117.62 square feet per acre. The volume estimate is then obtained using equation (4.22) with A = 45, S = 80, and B = 117.62. The calculated predicted volume is 4037 cubic feet per acre. Bennett also presents a volume projection equation that is a combination of formulas (4.22) and (4.23). This equation is obtained by writing formula (4.22) as

$$\ln (V_2) = 5.98812 - 121.713/S - 19.758/A_2 + 0.89683 \ln (B_2)$$

and then substituting the right side of formula (4.23) for $\ln (B_2)$. The result is

$$\ln (V_2) = 5.98812 - 121.713/S - 19.758/A_2$$
$$+ 4.632\left(1 - \frac{A_1}{A_2}\right) + 0.89683\left(\frac{A_1}{A_2}\right) \ln (B_1) \qquad (4.24)$$

This provides a method for calculating the projected volume from current stand values and the projection age in a single step. However, the process still implicitly involves a prediction of projection age basal area.

A similar approach can be used with the yield equation for old-field slash pine plantations (Bennett et al., 1959) previously given as equation (4.7). This equation predicts yield as

$$\ln (V) = 15.82465 - 41.00593/A - 0.04257S$$
$$+ 0.44864 \ln (N) - 357.98712/S \qquad (4.25)$$

If this equation is solved with current values of age and number of trees per acre, an estimate of current yield is obtained. If, however, it is solved with future values for age and number of trees per acre, an estimate of future yield results. Therefore, the problem of estimating future yield is essentially a matter of predicting the number of trees per acre that will be present at the projection age. Such predictions are obtained with equations known as mortality functions. A mortality function for old-field slash pine plantations has been developed by Clutter and Jones (1980). The equation involved is

$$N_2 = [N_1^{-0.870841} + 0.0000146437(A_2^{1.37454}$$

$$- A_1^{1.37454})]^{[(-0.870841)^{-1}]} \qquad (4.26)$$

where

N_1 = number of surviving trees per acre at age A_1

N_2 = predicted number of surviving trees per acre at age A_2

Consider a 15-year-old, site index 60 plantation with 600 stems per acre. Substitution of these values into equation (4.25) gives a predicted current volume of 1703 cubic feet per acre. To obtain a predicted volume per acre 10 years hence, equation (4.26) is solved with $A_1 = 15$, $A_2 = 25$, and $N_1 = 600$. The resulting estimate of the number of surviving trees at age 25 is 505. Subsequent solution of equation (4.25) with $A = 25$, $S = 60$, and $N = 505$ provides a future yield estimate of 4705 cubic feet per acre.

Chambers (1980) provides a basal area growth equation that makes it possible to use his previously described Douglas-fir yield prediction equation [equation (4.8)] for estimation of future yield. The basal area growth equation is

$$G = 1.77548 + 14.13342\,B/A^2 - 955.048/S^2$$

$$+ 1181.21191/A^2 - 72.90152/B \qquad (4.27)$$

where

G = annual, per-acre, net basal area growth (square feet)

S = site index (based on equation (2.4))

B = basal area per acre of trees 1.6 inches dbh and larger

A = average breast-height age for site trees

Chambers computes periodic basal area growth by iteratively computing annual basal area growth for each year in the period. Consider a 52-year-old Douglas-fir stand with a site index of 110 feet and a basal area of 266 square feet per acre for which an estimated volume 10 years hence is desired. Solution of equation (4.8) using the current stand statistics gives a current volume estimate of 10,468 cubic feet per acre. Iterative computation of the projected basal area 10 years hence is shown in Table 4.2. Each annual projection involves a solution of equation (4.27) with the ending basal area from the preceding year used as the projection base. The result obtained is 296.55 square feet per acre. Equation (4.8) can now be solved with $A = 62$, $S = 110$, and $B = 296.55$ to give the

TABLE 4.2

Iterative Calculation of Basal Area Growth in Douglas-fir

Breast-Height Age (years)	Initial Basal Area (ft²/acre)	Basal Area Growth (ft²/acre)	Ending Basal Area (ft²/acre)
52	266.00	3.25	269.25
53	269.25	3.20	272.45
54	272.45	3.15	275.61
55	275.61	3.11	278.72
56	278.72	3.07	281.78
57	281.78	3.03	284.81
58	284.81	2.99	287.80
59	287.80	2.95	290.75
60	290.75	2.92	293.67
61	293.67	2.88	296.55
62	296.55		

projected volume 10 years hence. The estimate obtained is 12,840 cubic feet per acre.

An estimation of future yield with a stand volume equation is illustrated using Schlaegel's (1971) yield equation for quaking aspen in north-central Minnesota:

$$V = 0.41898 BH \qquad (4.28)$$

When current values of B (basal area per acre) and H (average height of dominants and codominants) are used in the equation, an estimate of current volume is produced. Prediction of future volume is accomplished with the same equation using projected values for B and H. The formulas used to make these projections are

$$\ln (B_2) = 5.3903 - (A_1/A_2)[5.3903 - \ln (B_1)] \qquad (4.29)$$

for basal area and

$$\ln (H_2) = \ln (H_1) + 14.6111(A_1^{-1} - A_2^{-1}) \qquad (4.30)$$

for average height of dominants and codominants where

A_1 = current age (years)

A_2 = projection age (years)

B_1 = current basal area (square feet per acre)

B_2 = projected basal area at age A_2 (square feet per acre)

H_1 = current average height of dominants and codominants (feet)

H_2 = projected average height of dominants and codominants at age A_2

Consider a 40-year-old quaking aspen stand with an average height of dominants and codominants of 70 feet and 90 square feet of basal area. An estimate of future yield 20 years hence is desired. Substitution of the average height and basal area values into equation (4.28) yields a current volume estimate of 2640 cubic feet per acre. Solution of equation (4.29) with A_1 = 40, A_2 = 60, and B_1 = 90 gives a projected basal area at age 60 of 121.10 square feet per acre. The estimated average height at age 60 is obtained by substituting A_1 = 40, A_2 = 60, and H_1 = 70 into equation (4.30). The result is 79.06 feet. Equation (4.28) can now be applied with the projected average height and basal area values, giving

$$V = 0.41898(121.10)(79.06)$$

$$= 4011 \text{ cubic feet per acre}$$

Thus, over the 20-year growth period, estimated volume increases from 2640 cubic feet per acre to 4011 cubic feet per acre. This is equivalent to a predicted periodic increment of 68.6 cubic feet per acre per year.

4.3.2 Implicit Prediction of Future Yield

There is little difference, conceptually, between the procedures just described for explicit prediction of future yield and the steps involved in predicting future yield with a diameter distribution technique. Any diameter distribution method predicts the diameter distribution and heights by diameter class from values for certain stand statistics (e.g., age, site index, stand density, average height of dominants and codominants). If current values of the stand statistics are used in the computations, then the resulting volume prediction is an estimate of current yield. However, if the computations are based on projected values for the stand statistics, an estimate of future yield at the projection age will be obtained.

To illustrate the steps involved in an implicit prediction of future yield, consider another application of the Smalley and Bailey (1974) shortleaf pine model presented in Section 4.2.2. A plantation has been established with a planting density of 900 stems per acre. Site index for the stand is 55 feet (based on an index age of 25 years). What volume per acre can be expected when this stand reaches 20 years of age? Development of this estimate requires solution of equations (4.17) and (4.18) with appropriate projection age values for the predictor variables—stand age (A), average height of dominants and codominants (H), and number of surviving trees per acre (N). Thus, the problem of predicting the future yield is essentially a matter of estimating the average height and number of surviving trees per acre at the projection age of 20 years.

The average height of dominants and codominants at any age can be estimated from the site index value if an appropriate site index equation is available. Smalley and Bower (1971) developed a site index equation for the plantation population considered here. The most convenient form of their equation for current purposes is

$$\log (H) = \log (S) + 2.896448(25^{-0.5} - A^{-0.5}) \qquad (4.31)$$

Solution of this equation with $S = 55$ and $A = 20$ gives a predicted average height of dominants and codominants of 47.0 feet. Prediction of the number of surviving trees per acre at age 20 requires use of an appropriate mortality function. Smalley and Bailey (1974) developed the following mortality function which relates the number of surviving trees to the initial planting density.

$$\log (N) = \log (N_p) - A[0.009958 \log (N_p)$$
$$+ 0.0008078H - 0.009120\sqrt{H}] \qquad (4.32)$$

where

A = projection age

N_p = number of trees planted per acre

H = average height of dominants and codominants at the projection age

N = expected number of surviving trees per acre at the projection age

Solution of this equation with $A = 20$, $N_p = 900$, and $H = 47.0$ gives a predicted value for N of 719 trees per acre. The projected values for H and N can now be substituted into equations (4.17) to obtain the estimated Weibull parameter values. These are

$$a = 1.6087$$
$$b = 4.9778$$
$$c = 3.7869$$

The projection age values for H, N, and A can also be substituted into equation (4.18) which, after algebraic simplification, can then be written as

$$\log (h) = 1.6928 - 0.9150\left(\frac{1}{D} - \frac{1}{10}\right)$$

The computations involved in calculating the future volume estimate are summarized in Table 4.3.

Since all diameter distribution models require a value for the number of surviving trees at the prediction age, the key to the use of such models for predicting future yield is the availability of suitable mortality functions. Some mortality functions are designed to predict the future number of trees per acre from inventory information concerning the number of trees per acre at some previous age. The mortality function developed by Clutter and Jones (1980), previously shown as equation (4.26), is one example of such a mortality function. A second example is the equation developed by Pienaar and Shiver (1981) for site-prepared slash pine plantations in the Georgia–Florida flatwoods.

$$\ln (N_2) = \ln (N_1) - 0.0056025(A_2^{1.3334} - A_1^{1.3334}) \qquad (4.33)$$

where

N_1 = number of surviving trees per acre at age A_1

A_2 = some subsequent projection age

N_2 = expected number of surviving trees per acre at age A_2

An alternative approach to mortality prediction involves the prediction of individual tree mortality probabilities. When a stand table is available, prediction equations of this type can be applied to each dbh class to estimate expected mortality by dbh class. An example of such an equation is the following formula for predicting mortality of western white pine in northern Idaho (Hamilton, 1974).

$$P = 1/[1 + \exp (3.25309 - 0.00072647B + 0.0166809D)] \qquad (4.34)$$

where

P = mortality probability for the subsequent year

B = basal area per acre (square feet)

D = dbh (inches)

If this equation is solved with $B = 150$ square feet and $D = 6$ inches, the result is $P = .0375$. This means that in a stand with 150 square feet of basal area, 3.75 percent of the 6-inch-class trees can be expected to die within 1 year.

TABLE 4.3

Diameter Distribution Computations for a Shortleaf Pine Plantation at Age 20 with 900 Trees Planted on Site Index 55 Land

(1)	(2)	(3)	(4)	(5)	(6)	(7)	(8)	(9)	(10)
Dbh Class (in.)	Lower Limit (in.)	Upper Limit (in.)	Class Probability P_i	Class Frequency $N \times P_i$ (trees/acre)	Cumulative Frequency (trees/acre)	Class Midpoint (in.)	Average Height (ft)	Per-Tree Volume (ft³)	Class Volume (ft³/acre)
2	1.6087	2.5	.001482	1.06	1.06	2.054	21.8	0.000	0.00
3	2.5	3.5	.023805	17.12	18.18	3.0	30.2	0.244	4.17
4	3.5	4.5	.094676	68.07	86.25	4.0	35.9	0.903	61.46
5	4.5	5.5	.205391	147.68	233.93	5.0	39.9	1.824	269.45
6	5.5	6.5	.282363	203.02	436.95	6.0	42.8	3.008	610.68
7	6.5	7.5	.241632	173.73	610.68	7.0	45.0	4.455	773.92
8	7.5	8.5	.118177	84.97	695.65	8.0	46.8	6.176	524.77
9	8.5	9.5	.029212	21.00	716.65	9.0	48.2	8.156	171.27
10	9.5	10.5	.003138	2.35	719.00	10.0	49.3	10.390	24.42
11	10.5	11.5	.000123	0.00	—	—	—	—	—
Total				719.00					2440.14

113

*4.3.3 Individual Tree Growth Models

Recent improvements in high-speed computing equipment have made it possible for growth modelers to use the individual tree rather than the stand as the basic prediction unit. However, the fact that this is possible does not necessarily make it desirable, and considerable discussion has taken place concerning the relative merits of stand-level versus tree-level growth models. The basic distinction between the two types is that the predictor variables in stand-level models are stand statistics, while at least some of the predictor variables in any tree-level model are individual tree statistics. Munro (1974) suggested the following classification for growth models.

1. Stand-level models
2. Distance-independent tree-level models
3. Distance-dependent tree-level models

As pointed out above, stand-level models use stand statistic values (e.g., age, site index, basal area per acre, number of trees per acre) as inputs. Distance-independent tree-level models require at least some individual tree data, but they do not require any information concerning the spatial distribution of the trees involved in the growth projection. Distance-dependent tree-level models, on the other hand, also require individual tree data, but these data must include information on between-tree distances.

The previous sections of this chapter have presented a variety of stand-level models. It should be noted that some stand-level models (diameter distribution models) produce tree-level outputs (frequencies and average heights by dbh classes). However, they are still classified as stand-level models because the inputs are stand-level statistics.

Most distance-independent tree-level models use stand table data as inputs in addition to such stand-level information as age and site index. The stand table data involved are typically numbers of trees per acre and average heights by dbh classes. The equations comprising such a model are used to generate similar stand table data for some future point in time. Total projected volume and predicted volumes by diameter classes are then calculated from the future stand table. Some models of this type do not involve iterative calculations and require little more computer time than stand-level models. Typical examples are the New Zealand Monterey pine growth model developed by Clutter and Allison (1974), the growth model for thinned conifer plantations in East Africa developed by Alder (1979), and the Clutter and Jones (1980) growth model for old-field slash pine plantations. Other models of this type, typically those designed to handle mixed-species or uneven-aged conditions, do require iterative computations and are considerably more demanding of computer time than stand-level models. Noteworthy examples are the FREP (Forest Resources Evaluation

Program) model (U.S.D.A., 1979), which was developed for a variety of Lake States forest types, and the PROGNOSIS model (Stage, 1973), which is used for growth prediction in the mixed-species types of the Inland Empire region of eastern Washington, northern Idaho, and western Montana.

Distance-dependent tree-level models typically require a "tree list" as a major component of the input data. All trees for which growth is being projected are included, and the information provided for each tree typically includes dbh, height, sometimes crown ratio or crown diameter, and a pair of X-Y coordinates that specifies the tree's location within the area that constitutes the growth projection plot. Growth projection with such a model generally proceeds as follows.

1. A competition index value is computed for each tree (see Section 3.3). The competition index value is usually a function of the size and class of the tree involved and the sizes of, and distances to, neighboring competitor trees. Identification of neighboring competitors for calculation of the index value requires a separate search of the tree list for each tree involved.

2. Mortality probabilities are calculated as functions of the competition index values. These probabilities are defined in relation to a fixed-length growth period. A decision is then made concerning the survival of each tree. This decision is based on generation of a random number and interpretation of the outcome in relation to the previously computed mortality probability. Trees that die are removed from the tree list.

3. After the competitive status of each tree has been evaluated, the predicted periodic growth for each size measure of each tree is calculated and added to the corresponding current size value. The projection period involved is generally quite short (usually 1 year).

4. Steps 1, 2, and 3 are repeated iteratively until a projection of the desired length has been obtained.

5. Individual tree volumes are calculated from the final tree size measures and accumulated to obtain a plot volume. The plot volume is then usually expanded to a per-acre basis.

The fundamental assumption underlying the distance-dependent tree-level model approach involves the assertion that individual tree growth can be predicted more precisely if sizes and locations of neighboring competitors are known. In general, this assumption has not been empirically validated. Various studies (e.g., Beck, 1974; Daniels and Burkhart, 1975; Tennent, 1980) have shown that the use of various competition indexes contributed little or no improvement in growth prediction over that obtained using basal area per acre as the measure of competition.

It has been argued that distance-dependent tree-level growth models provide more detail on tree development and incorporate relationships expressing biological and ecological interactions at a more fundamental level than is possible with other model types. Some modelers seem to have drawn one or both of the following conclusions from this argument.

1. Stand-level yield estimates obtained by accumulating predicted individual tree yields will have greater statistical precision than comparable estimates generated by stand-level models.

2. Distance-dependent tree-level models can be used to reliably predict growth in stand types for which no empirical data are available.

However, other growth and yield specialists contend that no rigorous justification for either of the above conclusions is currently available, and the future utility of distance-dependent tree-level models seems to be a topic about which reasonable modelers may currently wish to disagree.

Experience to date suggests that distance-dependent tree-level growth models have proved to be useful tools for simulating various silvicultural practices. However, other current yield model applications such as inventory projections, stand valuation, and harvest scheduling generally utilize other model types that provide adequately detailed information at far less cost (Daniels et al., 1979; Clutter, 1980). Typical examples of distance-dependent tree-level growth models are the projection systems developed for Douglas-fir by Mitchell (1975), for loblolly pine by Daniels and Burkhart (1975), and for Monterey pine in New Zealand by Tennent (1980).

*4.3.4 Stand Table Projection

There are two general approaches available for estimating the current volume of a timber stand. If an appropriate yield equation or system of equations is available, measurements can be made in the stand to obtain values for the predictor variables (e.g., age, site index, basal area per acre, number of stems per acre), and the volume can then be estimated by solving the yield equation or equations. If no appropriate yield prediction system is available, the only alternative is to conduct a timber cruise using standard forest inventory procedures. The inventory approach can be considerably more expensive, especially if precise stand-level results are required. However, it requires few, if any, equations from analysis of other data (usually only individual tree volume equations).

A similar situation exists with respect to the estimation of future volume for a timber stand. If an appropriate yield model system for predicting future volumes is available, stand statistic values needed as inputs can be obtained and used to solve the prediction equation or equations involved. If no appropriate models exist for predicting the future yield, the usual recourse is use of one of the forest inventory procedures that estimate future stand growth from increment core measurements of past growth. These estimation procedures are generally referred to as *stand table projection methods*.

A detailed description of conventional stand table projection techniques will not be included here since the topic is more logically included in a coverage of forest inventory procedures. However, since most forest managers will, at some time or another, use yield estimates obtained in this way as an input to their decisions, some comments concerning the topic are appropriate. Although many variations on the theme exist, the general structure of stand table projection inventories can be summarized as follows.

1. A conventional cruise of the area is carried out to estimate the current numbers of trees, average heights, and/or average volumes per tree by dbh class. From these statistics, an estimate of total current volume is calculated. This conventional cruise usually entails measurement of dbh on a large number of sample trees.

2. A much smaller number of sample trees is selected and measurements of past periodic radial increment and total or merchantable height are obtained from these trees.

3. The stand table is "adjusted" to reflect the diameter growth expected to occur in some subsequent growth period. The adjustment procedure is based on the radial growth data collected in step 2.

4. A projected total volume is calculated using the new diameter distribution. If it is considered appropriate, some adjustments in the class frequencies to reflect mortality are made prior to the volume calculations.

Detailed discussions of the specific computational procedures involved have been in print for at least 45 years and have changed little over that period (e.g., Meyer, 1935; Meyer, 1936; Wahlenberg, 1941; Chapman and Meyer, 1949; Bruce and Schumacher, 1950; Davis, 1966; Husch et al., 1982; Avery, 1975).

Although stand table projection methods and equation prediction systems like those discussed in Sections 4.3.1 and 4.3.2 share the objective of predicting future yield, their philosophical approaches are quite different. With equation prediction systems, the prediction of growth and future yield is obtained by comparing the subject stand with other similar stands whose growth rates have been measured over time. (These measurements constituted the data base from which the yield equation or equations were developed.) Stand table projection methods, on the other hand, attempt to predict the future growth of a stand by measuring the past growth rates of trees in that same stand.

From measurement of increment cores it is possible to estimate the average diameter growth rate for trees that, say, 10 years ago were in the 6-inch dbh class. Is it then reasonable to assume that trees currently in the 6-inch dbh class will produce this same growth rate during the next 10 years? In an uneven-aged, northern hardwoods stand with a temporally stable size-class structure, this would be a relatively safe assumption. In a natural, even-aged stand of jack pine with a low growth rate, the assumption would still be tenable. In a rapidly growing plantation of southern pine or Douglas-fir, such an assumption could lead to highly inaccurate results. For example, in a loblolly pine plantation that is currently 20 years old with a site index of 60, diameter distribution yield tables by Lenhart and Clutter (1971) show that the 6-inch dbh trees are in the intermediate crown class with an average height well below that of their larger competitors. At age 10, according to these yield tables, 6-inch dbh trees were dominants or codominants and few trees were present with larger dbh values. Some users of stand table projection methods attempt to avoid this problem by assuming that the periodic growth rate of any tree over the next *n* years will equal its periodic growth rate during the immediately prior *n* years. With this approach, the 10-year growth rate of a 6-inch dbh tree would be estimated as the prior 10-year average growth of bored sample trees currently in the 6-inch class. One major difficulty with this approach is the question of which growth rate to assume as constant—diameter growth rate or basal area growth rate.[3]

Stand table projection is a valuable tool for growth estimation, and there will always be stands where no alternative procedure is available for the prediction of future yield. However, it is our belief that stand table projections are generally used inefficiently and are often applied incorrectly to give grossly inaccurate estimates of future growth and yield. The inefficiencies stem largely from two causes. The first is a faithful adherence to a computational procedure designed a half-century ago under a restriction that calculations had to be kept to an absolute minimum. Unless one is marooned on a desert island, such a restriction makes little sense today. A second major cause of inefficiency in stand table projection estimation is a general failure to formulate the problem in statistical sampling terms, as was done long ago with cruising procedures for estimating current volume. Few inventory specialists take such an approach to stand table projection.

To cast stand table projection in a statistical sampling context, view the stand table as a stratification of the tree population. Each dbh class constitutes a stratum and the estimated stratum size is given. The increment core data collected on sample trees can be used, for example, to develop a regression or ratio estimator of future basal area from present basal area, and the estimator could then be applied to the current basal area data for each stratum. Alternatively, if a constant growth assumption is used, a future volume estimate is

---

[3] The southern pine data we have examined does not support the assumption of constant diameter growth rate. The assumption of constant basal area growth rate for two successive 5-year periods is not contradicted by these data.

available for each increment core sample tree. Separate future volume/current volume ratio estimates can be developed for each stratum (dbh class) and multiplied by current volume to give separate estimates of future total volume by dbh class. Many other variations are also possible, all representing recognized statistical estimation procedures whose properties are well known. In addition, assumptions implicit in the conventional projection calculation, such as the rectangular distribution of diameters within a dbh class, are avoided.

Serious errors are often introduced into stand table projection estimates through incorrect selection of sample trees, application of invalid growth assumptions, and misestimation of mortality. The use of incorrect methods for selecting sample trees has been a frequent source of error. Since the stand table projection method adds growth on a per-tree basis, the selection method for sample trees should draw samples in proportion to trees present, not in proportion to forest type area. For example, some practitioners collect increment core data during a conventional line plot or strip cruise by selecting, at a fixed interval along the line or strip, the nearest tree as a sample tree for increment core data. Suppose this procedure is applied in a 100-acre tract where 50 acres contain pine plantations averaging 800 trees per acre and the other 50 acres support poorly stocked natural stands averaging 100 trees per acre. Approximately half of the sample trees used to estimate the growth relationship will come from plantations and half will come from natural stands. This relationship is then applied to estimate growth in a population consisting of 40,000 plantation trees and 5000 natural stand trees. Unless the plantation trees and the natural trees follow an identical growth relationship, the resulting estimate will be seriously biased. This problem is avoided by locating small, fixed-radius plots at intervals along the strip or line. For each plot, all trees occurring on the plot are sample trees and are bored for increment core measurement. Although the above example may seem somewhat extreme, it should be noted that the selection of single sample trees at fixed-travel intervals is a poor procedure even in reasonably homogeneous tracts since this procedure has a strong bias toward selection of relatively open-grown trees.

It is more difficult to provide useful advice on how to avoid errors that arise from the use of invalid growth assumptions and poor mortality estimates. Clearly, if constant diameter growth from past to future is assumed and constant basal area growth occurs, the final yield estimate will be seriously biased. Similarly, if no adjustment is made for mortality and heavy mortality subsequently occurs, future yield will be significantly overestimated. Since the collected data generally provide little or no information concerning the true growth relationship or the mortality rate, experience external to the tract involved must often be used. A good source of information is data from remeasured sample plots in stands similar to those whose yields are being projected. Such data obviously provide excellent information on mortality. Whenever the data span two or more growth periods, the validity of various growth hypotheses (e.g., constant diameter growth rate, constant basal area growth rate) can also be evaluated. Any practitioner with a frequent need for stand table projection methodology is well advised to accumulate an extensive remeasured-plot data base that can be used to validate stand table projection assumptions.

*4.4   DEVELOPMENT OF GROWTH AND YIELD MODELS

*4.4.1   Schumacher-Type Yield Models

Forest growth models involving the logarithm of some measure of stand production as the dependent variable and the reciprocal of age as a predictor variable were originally suggested in papers by MacKinney et al. (1937) and Schumacher (1939). MacKinney and Chaiken (1939) used a variation of this equation form to produce what was, to our knowledge, the first variable density yield prediction equation. Numerous studies subsequently used this same general equation form for predicting current volumes in a variety of forest populations (e.g., Bennett et al., 1959; Langdon, 1961; Nelson et al., 1961). In 1960, Schumacher and Coile published a detailed system for predicting the growth and yield of natural stands of the southern pines. The yield prediction equations contained therein used the same (logarithm of yield/reciprocal of age) model and were based on data from a large number of temporary plots scattered throughout the south. The growth aspects of the study were handicapped by a lack of remeasurement data and the use of a density measure that involved normality concepts. A similarly extensive set of growth and yield predictions for slash and loblolly pine plantations was developed by Coile and Schumacher (1964) as a proprietary document for certain forest industry sponsors. This publication was subsequently made available for general circulation. The strengths and weaknesses of the system were generally similar to those of the Schumacher and Coile natural stand results.

During the late 1940s, the Southeastern Forest Experiment Station began the installation of several extensive series of monumented growth plots. When remeasurement data became available from these studies, efforts were initiated to develop suitable analysis methods. As this work developed, it came to be based on two axioms.

1.   The basic Schumacher yield equation, which had been successfully applied in many southern pine studies, would serve as the model for predicting current yields.

2.   Any equation developed for prediction of growth should be compatible with the Schumacher yield function in the sense that integration of the growth equation should produce the yield function. [Work on compatible growth and yield models was being simultaneously conducted in the Lake States by Buckman (1962).]

The original results of the Southeastern Station efforts were published by Clutter (1963). Significant methodological improvements were developed later by Sullivan and Clutter (1972).

The particular form of the Schumacher yield function used as the starting point for subsequent derivations was

$$\ln (V) = \beta_0 + \beta_1 S + \beta_2 A^{-1} + \beta_3 \ln (B) \tag{4.35}$$

where

V = per-acre volume

S = site index

A = stand age

B = basal area per acre

Differentiation of this expression with respect to age gives the following equation for the relative rate of volume growth.

$$\frac{dV/dA}{V} = -\beta_2 A^{-2} + \beta_3 \left(\frac{dB/dA}{B} \right) \tag{4.36}$$

This equation shows that the relative rate of volume growth is a function of stand age and the relative rate of basal area growth. At the time of the original research, little experience was available concerning suitable equation forms for predicting basal area growth. However, graphs of basal area development published by Schumacher and Coile (1960) suggested the equation form

$$\ln (B) = \alpha_0 + \alpha_1 S + \alpha_2 A^{-1} + \alpha_3 \ln (B_{20}) A^{-1} + \alpha_4 A^{-1} S \tag{4.37}$$

where B_{20} equals basal area at age 20. Differentiation of this equation and algebraic rearrangement of the result give

$$\frac{dB}{dA} = A^{-1} B [\alpha_0 + \alpha_1 S - \ln (B)] \tag{4.38}$$

as the corresponding growth rate model. Equation (4.38) can be integrated to obtain the difference equation

$$\ln (B_2) = \left(\frac{A_1}{A_2} \right) \ln (B_1) + \alpha_0 \left(1 - \frac{A_1}{A_2} \right) + \alpha_1 S \left(1 - \frac{A_1}{A_2} \right) \tag{4.39}$$

where

A_1 = initial age

A_2 = projection age

B_1 = initial basal area

B_2 = the predicted basal area at age A_2

Equation forms (4.38) and (4.39) were successfully fitted to the original Southeastern Station data sets and have been subsequently used in many other basal area growth and projection analyses. Equation (4.39) is also a key to developing a direct volume projection equation. For prediction of a future volume, equation (4.35) can be written as

$$\ln(V_2) = \beta_0 + \beta_1 S + \beta_2 A_2^{-1} + \beta_3 \ln(B_2) \qquad (4.40)$$

which, by incorporating equation (4.39), can be written as

$$\ln(V_2) = \beta_0 + \beta_1 S + \beta_2 A_2^{-1} + \beta_3 (A_1/A_2) \ln(B_1)$$
$$+ \beta_3 \alpha_0 [1 - (A_1/A_2)] + \beta_3 \alpha_1 S [1 - (A_1/A_2)]$$

or

$$\ln(V_2) = \beta_0 + \beta_1 S + \beta_2 A_2^{-1} + \beta_3 (A_1/A_2) \ln(B_1)$$
$$+ \beta_4 [1 - (A_1/A_2)] + \beta_5 S [1 - (A_1/A_2)] \qquad (4.41)$$

where

$\beta_4 = \beta_3 \alpha_0$

$\beta_5 = \beta_3 \alpha_1$

Data from monumented plot remeasurements can be used to estimate the parameters of equation (4.41). In addition, the initial measurement of the same plots provides information on the β_0, β_1, β_2, and β_3 parameters, because of equation (4.35). Sullivan and Clutter (1972) presented analysis methods that use both initial measurement and remeasurement data to obtain the most efficient estimates of the parameters β_0, β_1, ... , β_5 and suggest that the basal area equation parameters then be estimated as

$$\hat{\alpha}_0 = \hat{\beta}_4/\hat{\beta}_3$$

$$\hat{\alpha}_1 = \hat{\beta}_5/\hat{\beta}_3$$

This approach provides a logically consistent set of equations for predicting:

1. Current volume
2. Future volume
3. Instantaneous volume growth rate
4. Future basal area
5. Instantaneous basal area growth rate

It should be noted that projection equations (4.39) and (4.41) possess some desirable logical properties. Consider equation (4.39).

1. As A_2 approaches A_1, ln (B_2) approaches ln (B_1). A projection model lacking this property is illogical.
2. As A_2 approaches ∞, ln (B_2) approaches $\alpha_0 + \alpha_1 S$. Thus, the model provides for an upper asymptote on future basal area and this asymptote is a function of site index.
3. Predicted future basal area values are not affected by the number of steps involved in the prediction. For example, suppose specified values for A_1, A_2, and B_1 are used to predict a future basal area B_2 and a second solution is then obtained to predict another future value B_3 from A_2, A_3, and B_2 where $A_3 > A_2 > A_1$. The predicted value obtained for B_3 will equal the value obtained in a single equation solution using A_1, A_3, and B_1 as inputs. Projection models that lack this property are inconsistent.

Many variations of the equation forms shown above are possible. However, a modification in any single equation usually implies changes in other parts of the system. For example, if equation (4.38) is modified to

$$\frac{dB}{dA} = A^{-1}B[\alpha_0 + \alpha_1 S - \alpha_2 \ln (B)] \tag{4.42}$$

the consistent form of equation (4.39) is

$$\ln (B_2) = (A_1/A_2)^{\alpha_2}\ln (B_1) + \frac{\alpha_0}{\alpha_2}[1 - (A_1/A_2)^{\alpha_2}]$$

$$+ \frac{\alpha_1}{\alpha_2}S[1 - (A_1/A_2)^{\alpha_2}] \tag{4.43}$$

and equation (4.41) must be written as

$$\ln (V_2) = \beta_0 + \beta_1 S + \beta_2 A_2^{-1} + \beta_3(A_1/A_2)^{\beta_6}\ln (B_1)$$

$$+ \beta_4[1 - (A_1/A_2)^{\beta_6}] + \beta_5 S[1 - (A_1/A_2)^{\beta_6}] \tag{4.44}$$

where

$$\beta_4 = \beta_3 \alpha_0 / \alpha_2$$
$$\beta_5 = \beta_3 \alpha_1 / \alpha_2$$
$$\beta_6 = \alpha_2$$

*4.4.2 Chapman-Richards Function Yield Models

The Chapman-Richards growth model (Richards, 1959; Chapman, 1961) was first used for forest growth modeling in studies reported by Turnbull (1963), Pienaar (1965), and Pienaar and Turnbull (1973). The model is derived from basic biological considerations and has proven to be very flexible in application. The standard formulation of the model conceptualizes the growth rate of an organism or a population as the resultant of an anabolic growth rate (constructive metabolism for an organism) and a catabolic growth rate (destructive metabolism for an organism). The anabolic rate is assumed to be proportional to the size of the organism or population, raised to a power, while the catabolic rate is assumed to be directly proportional to size. These relationships can be expressed symbolically as

$$\frac{dY}{dt} = \alpha Y^\beta - \gamma Y \tag{4.45}$$

where

$$Y = \text{size of the organism or population}$$

$$t = \text{time}$$

$$\alpha, \beta, \gamma = \text{constants } (\alpha > 0, \gamma > 0, 0 < \beta < 1)$$

Equation (4.45) belongs to a class of differential equations known as *Bernoulli equations*. When equation (4.45) is solved with the initial condition that $Y = 0$ when $t = t_0$, the resulting cumulative growth function (or production function) is

$$Y = \theta \{1 - \exp[-\phi(t - t_0)]\}^{[1/(1-\beta)]} \tag{4.46}$$

where

$$\theta = (\alpha/\gamma)^{[1/(1-\beta)]}$$

and

$$\phi = \gamma(1 - \beta)$$

The growth curve defined by equation (4.46) is sigmoid in shape, originates at the point $(t_0, 0)$, and has an upper asymptote equal to θ. If equation (4.45) is solved with the initial condition that $Y = Y_0$ when $t = t_0$, the following cumulative growth function is produced.

$$Y = \theta\{1 - \tau \exp\left[-\phi(t - t_0)\right]\}^{\{1/(1-\beta)\}} \qquad (4.47)$$

where θ and ϕ have their previous definitions and

$$\tau = 1 - (\gamma/\alpha)Y_0^{1-\beta} \qquad (4.48)$$

The parameters of either equation (4.46) or (4.47) can be estimated from (t, Y) data points using nonlinear least-squares techniques. Procedures for fitting a family of Chapman-Richards functions with one or more of the parameters changing across members of the family are discussed in Sections 2.4.2 and 2.4.3 of Chapter 2.

Pienaar and Turnbull (1973) used the Chapman-Richards model with data from remeasured slash pine plantations in South Africa to test and confirm the hypothesis that, on a given site, all stand density levels (in terms of trees per acre) converge to the same volumetric upper asymptote—the θ value in equations (4.46) and (4.47). More recent reseach by Pienaar (1979) provides techniques for generating slash pine plantation growth curves by predicting values for the parameters θ, ϕ, t_0, and β from site index and number of trees per acre at age 5. Substitution of these predicted values into equation (4.46) defines a specific growth curve. Another interesting model based on the Chapman-Richards function is the yield prediction model developed by Moser and Hall (1969) for uneven-aged mixed northern hardwood and oak-hickory stands in Wisconsin. Numerous authors have reported on the use of the Chapman-Richards function for development of site index curves. References to these studies have been provided in Chapter 2.

*4.4.3 Diameter-Distribution-Based Yield Models

It has been previously noted that any diameter distribution yield system operates by providing predicted values for the parameters of some probability distribution. Therefore, the task of developing a diameter distribution yield model is largely a matter of constructing regression equations that predict parameter values from stand statistics (age, number of trees per acre, and site index or average height of dominants and codominants). Since the Weibull is now the distribution most commonly used for diameter distribution work, our discussion is focused on developing prediction equations for the three parameters—a, b, and c—of the Weibull distribution.

The data required for model development include the following items measured on each of m sample plots from the population of interest.

1. Age
2. Total number of trees per acre
3. Site index (or, equivalently, average height of dominants and codominants)
4. Numbers of trees per acre by dbh classes
5. Height and dbh values for selected sample trees

A separate Weibull distribution is fitted to the dbh-class frequency data from each plot. A collection of FORTRAN computer programs for carrying out the necessary computations has been described by Bailey (1974). Programs are included for maximum likelihood estimation based on procedures developed by both Wingo (1972) and Harter and Moore (1965). When these fittings are completed, a data set of the form shown in Table 4.4 is available. This data set can then be used to develop regression equations of the form

$$a = f_1(A, N, S)$$

$$b = f_2(A, N, S)$$

$$c = f_3(A, N, S) \tag{4.49}$$

where

A = age

N = total number of trees per acre

S = site index

TABLE 4.4

Data Set for Developing Weibull Parameter Prediction Equations

Plot Number	Weibull Parameter Estimates			Stand Age	Number of Trees Per Acre	Site[a] Index
	a	b	c			
1	a_1	b_1	c_1	A_1	N_1	S_1
2	a_2	b_2	c_2	A_2	N_2	S_2
3	a_3	b_3	c_3	A_3	N_3	S_3
⋮	⋮	⋮	⋮	⋮	⋮	⋮
m	a_m	b_m	c_m	A_m	N_m	S_m

[a] Average height of dominants and codominants is often used instead of site index.

Some yield systems are based on predicting combinations of the parameters. The Smalley and Bailey (1974) equations previously given, for example, have the form

$$a = f_1(A, N, S)$$

$$a + b = f_2(A, N, S)$$

$$c = f_3(A, N, S) \tag{4.50}$$

so that b is actually obtained as

$$b = f_2(A, N, S) - f_1(A, N, S)$$

Percentile estimators are attractive alternatives to the maximum likelihood procedure just described. With percentile estimators, the voluminous computations involved in determining maximum likelihood estimates for each plot are unnecessary. The basic concept involved stems from the fact that, if three sample percentiles are known, each can be equated to its corresponding Weibull cumulative distribution function, and the three equations can be solved iteratively for estimates of a, b, and c. The form of these equations can be developed as follows. Let X_p represent the p-percentile value in the sample. (This is a value such that $100p$-percent of the sample values are less than X_p.) Then, from the definition of the Weibull cumulative distribution function,

$$p = 1 - \exp\{-[(X_p - a)/b]^c\}$$

The above expression can be solved for X_p to give

$$X_p = a + b[-\ln(1 - p)]^{(1/c)} \tag{4.51}$$

Dubey (1967) showed that the 24th and 93rd sample percentiles gave the most efficient parameter estimates for the two-parameter Weibull distribution. Abernethy (1981) developed a moment estimation procedure for the three-parameter Weibull that is based on the 24th, 63rd, and 93rd percentiles. Use of these percentiles with equation (4.51) gives the simultaneous equation set

$$X_{.24} = a + b[-\ln(.76)]^{(1/c)}$$

$$X_{.93} = a + b[-\ln(.07)]^{(1/c)}$$

$$X_{.63} = a + b$$

which can be rearranged to give

$$\frac{X_{.24} - X_{.63}}{X_{.93} - X_{.63}} = \frac{[-\ln (.76)]^{(1/c)} - 1}{[-\ln (.07)]^{(1/c)} - 1} \tag{4.52}$$

$$b = (X_{.24} - X_{.63})/\{[-\ln (.76)]^{1/c} - 1\} \tag{4.53}$$

and

$$a = X_{.63} - b \tag{4.54}$$

For any given set of values for $X_{.24}$, $X_{.63}$, and $X_{.93}$, equation (4.52) can be solved iteratively to obtain an estimate of c which is then used in equation (4.53) to produce the b parameter estimate. Once the b estimate is determined, equation (4.54) can be solved for the estimate of the origin parameter.

Several alternative approaches to diameter distribution prediction are available when percentile estimates are used. One possibility involves the application of equations (4.52), (4.53), and (4.54) on a plot-by-plot basis to develop individual plot estimates for a, b, and c. These estimates become part of a data set similar to that shown in Table 4.4 and this data set is then used to develop regression equations for predicting the a, b, and c Weibull parameters. A second alternative approach takes the plot-by-plot values for $X_{.24}$, $X_{.63}$, and $X_{.93}$ and uses these in conjunction with the age, site index, and total stems per acre data to develop regression equations of the following form (Abernethy, 1981).

$$X_{.24} = f_1(A, N, S)$$

$$X_{.63} = f_2(A, N, S)$$

$$X_{.93} = f_3(A, N, S) \tag{4.55}$$

A predicted diameter distribution for any specified combination of A, N, and S values is then obtained by solving equations (4.55) to obtain the three estimated percentile values and by inserting these percentile values in equations (4.52), (4.53), and (4.54) for calculation of the a, b, and c parameter estimates. Still a third variation involves development of a regression equation for direct prediction of the origin parameter plus the development of regressions for predicting the percentile values $X_{.24}$ and $X_{.93}$. With this approach, a predicted diameter distribution is obtained by directly estimating the origin parameter a and using the two predicted percentiles to solve first for the predicted c parameter with the equation

$$c = \frac{2.27108}{\ln (X_{.93} - a) - \ln (X_{.24} - a)} \tag{4.56}$$

and then for the predicted b parameter as

$$b = \frac{X_{.24} - a}{(.27444)^{(1/c)}} \qquad (4.57)$$

Equations (4.56) and (4.57) are obtained by substituting the two known (p, X_p) pairs into equation (4.51), treating a as known, and solving for b and c.

Once parameter estimates for the Weibull distribution are available, stem frequencies by dbh class can easily be obtained by repeated application of equation (4.16). However, translation of the stem frequency information into volume predictions requires the availability of a regression equation for predicting individual tree heights using age, site index (or average height of dominants and codominants), total number of stems per acre, and dbh as predictor variables. Such equations are developed from the sample tree measurements collected on the plots that provided the diameter distribution data. This sample tree data set typically takes the form shown in Table 4.5. In this type of data set,

h_{ij} = height of sample tree j on plot i

D_{ij} = dbh of sample tree j on plot i

A_i = age of plot i

N_i = total number of stems per acre for plot i

H_i = average height of dominants and codominants for plot i

S_i = site index for plot i

n_i = number of measured sample trees for plot i

m = number of plots

The equation form used by Bennett and Clutter (1968; also see Burkhart, 1971) in their original diameter distribution paper was

$$\ln (h) = \beta_0 + \beta_1 S + \beta_2 N + \beta_3 A^{-1} + \beta_4 D^{-1} \qquad (4.58)$$

For any particular stand, this reduces to a height/diameter relationship of the form

$$\ln (h) = \alpha + \beta D^{-1} \qquad (4.59)$$

Subsequent work by Lenhart and Clutter (1971) used the following equation form for predicting individual tree height.

TABLE 4.5

Typical Sample Tree Data Set for Developing Individual Tree Height Prediction Equations

Plot Number	Sample Tree Number	Tree Height	Tree dbh	Stand Age	Number of Trees Per Acre	Average Height of Dominants and Codominants	Site Index
1	1	$h_{1,1}$	$D_{1,1}$	A_1	N_1	H_1	S_1
1	2	$h_{1,2}$	$D_{1,2}$	A_1	N_1	H_1	S_1
...	...	...	...	...	...	...	...
1	n_1	h_{1,n_1}	D_{1,n_1}	A_1	N_1	H_1	S_1
2	1	$h_{2,1}$	$D_{2,1}$	A_2	N_2	H_2	S_2
2	2	$h_{2,2}$	$D_{2,2}$	A_2	N_2	H_2	S_2
2	...	...	...	...	...	...	...
2	n_2	h_{2,n_2}	D_{2,n_2}	A_2	N_2	H_2	S_2
...	...	...	...	...	...	...	...
m	1	$h_{m,1}$	$D_{m,1}$	A_m	N_m	H_m	S_m
m	2	$h_{m,2}$	$D_{m,2}$	A_m	N_m	H_m	S_m
...	...	...	...	...	...	...	...
m	n_m	h_{m,n_m}	D_{m,n_m}	A_m	N_m	H_m	S_m

$$\ln(h/H) = \beta_0 + \beta_1(D^{-1} - D_{max}^{-1}) + \beta_2 A^{-1}(D^{-1} - D_{max}^{-1})$$
$$+ \beta_3(D^{-1} - D_{max}^{-1})\ln(N) \tag{4.60}$$

where D_{max} is usually defined as either the midpoint value or the upper limit of the largest occupied dbh class. For any given stand, equation (4.60) also reduces to the form

$$\ln(h) = \alpha + \beta D^{-1}$$

but, in this case, the value for α is directly tied to the average height of dominants and codominants defined by the site index equation. This forces the predicted heights for the larger dbh classes to be close to the specified average height of dominants and codominants. Variants of this equation have been widely used in diameter distribution yield prediction systems.

A somewhat different approach was suggested by Smith (1978) who used the model

$$h/H = \beta_0 + \beta_1 A^{-1}H + \beta_2 \ln[F(D) + 1]$$
$$+ \beta_3 A^{-1}H \ln[F(D) + 1] \tag{4.61}$$

where $F(D)$ is the cumulative distribution function value associated with the dbh value D. In terms of sample data, $F(D)$ is simply the sample percentile value associated with the dbh value D. For a predicted distribution, $F(D)$ is the Weibull cumulative distribution function value associated with the dbh value D. For any particular stand, equation (4.61) reduces to the form

$$h = H\{\alpha + \beta \ln[F(D) + 1]\} \tag{4.62}$$

where α and β are both functions of H and A. The predicted height associated with the minimum dbh value in the population is thus

$$h_{min} = \alpha H \tag{4.63}$$

and the predicted height associated with the maximum dbh value is

$$h_{max} = H(\alpha + 0.69315\beta) \tag{4.64}$$

Applications of equation (4.61) in other populations might require some revision of the model form, but use of the quantity $\ln[F(D) + 1]$ as a predictor variable appears to be a very powerful technique since it provides an expression of relative dbh that can be easily obtained whenever predicted Weibull parameters are available.

*4.4.4 Mortality Functions

The development of mortality (or survival) prediction equations generally requires data from the remeasurement of monumented plots. Randomly located temporary plots in stands of varying ages can provide some information on survival trends, but most mortality analyses are based on remeasurement data that include the following variables.

A_1 = initial age

N_1 = number of trees per acre at age A_1

A_2 = remeasurement age

N_2 = number of trees per acre at age A_2

Measurements of site index are also usually obtained, but many analyses have failed to show any effect of site index on tree mortality.

Remeasurement data of the type just described are generally used to fit some kind of a difference equation model that predicts N_2 as a function of A_1, A_2, and N_1. This model should possess the following logical properties.

1. If A_2 equals A_1, N_2 should equal N_1.
2. For even-aged stands, if A_2 is greater than A_1, N_2 should be less than N_1.
3. For even-aged stands, as A_2 becomes very large, N_2 should approach 0.
4. If the model is used to predict N_2 at age A_2 and A_2 and N_2 are then used to predict N_3 at age A_3 ($A_3 > A_2 > A_1$), the result obtained should be equal to that given by a single projection from A_1 to A_3.

Specification of a difference equation model that possesses these properties and properly expresses the population relationship is often a difficult task.

In many cases, the most productive approach for developing a suitable difference equation model involves an initial exploration of mortality rate models. A mortality rate model that shows promising properties can then be integrated to obtain the corresponding difference equation model. For example, the simplest assumption concerning the proportional instantaneous mortality rate would be the specification that this quantity is a constant. This can be expressed symbolically as

$$\frac{dN/dA}{N} = K \tag{4.65}$$

where

N = number of trees per acre present at age A

dN/dA = instantaneous mortality rate operating at age A

K = a constant

Integration of equation (4.65) with the initial condition that $N = N_1$ when $A = A_1$ gives the difference equation model

$$N_2 = N_1 e^{K(A_2 - A_1)} \tag{4.66}$$

which would be an appropriate model for use in populations where the proportional mortality rate is constant for all ages, site indexes, and stand densities. If, however, the proportional mortality rate were related to age and site index in the following way

$$\frac{dN/dA}{N} = \beta_0 + \beta_1 A^{-1} + \beta_2 S \tag{4.67}$$

integration shows the appropriate difference equation model would be

$$N_2 = N_1 (A_2/A_1)^{\beta_1} \exp\left[(\beta_0 + \beta_2 S)(A_2 - A_1)\right] \tag{4.68}$$

Two survival models previously shown, equations (4.26) and (4.33), have the functional forms

$$N_2 = [N_1^{\beta_1} + \beta_2(A_2^{\beta_3} - A_1^{\beta_3})]^{(1/\beta_1)} \tag{4.69}$$

and

$$\ln(N_2) = \ln(N_1) + \beta_1(A_2^{\beta_2} - A_1^{\beta_2}) \tag{4.70}$$

Equation (4.69) was obtained by integrating the mortality rate function

$$\frac{dN/dA}{N} = \alpha A^\delta N^\gamma \tag{4.71}$$

The relationships linking the parameters in the two models are

$$\beta_1 = -\gamma$$
$$\beta_2 = -\alpha\gamma/(\delta + 1)$$
$$\beta_3 = \delta + 1$$

The mortality rate model implied by equation (4.70) is

$$\frac{dN/dA}{N} = \alpha A^\gamma \tag{4.72}$$

where

$$\alpha = \beta_1\beta_2 \quad \text{and} \quad \gamma = \beta_2 - 1$$

Individual tree growth models require mortality models that differ considerably from the stand-level models discussed above (Monserud, 1976). In individual tree models, predictions must be made concerning the probability of survival for each tree involved in the growth projection. The approach developed by Hamilton (1974) has been applied by a number of authors including Hamilton and Edwards (1976), Daniels and Burkhart (1975), and Hann (1980). This method involves the logistic model

$$P = \{1 + \exp(\beta_0 + \beta_1 X_1 + \cdots + \beta_k X_k)\}^{-1} \tag{4.73}$$

where

P = probability of mortality in a specific time interval

X_i = ith predictor variable ($i = 1, 2, \ldots, k$)

Since observed data in individual tree studies are dichotomous (1 = live at end of growth period; 0 = dead), equation (4.73) is fitted by special regression techniques (Hamilton, 1974; Hamilton and Wendt, 1975). Equation (4.34) is an example of this model, with X_1 equal to basal area per acre and X_2 equal to tree dbh at the beginning of the growth period.

REFERENCES

Abernethy, N. C. 1981. Predicted and projected diameter distributions of thinned old-field slash pine plantations. Masters thesis, School of Forest Res., Univ. of Georgia.

Alder, D. 1979. A distance-independent tree model for exotic conifer plantations in East Africa. *For. Sci.* **25**:59–71.

Avery, T. E. 1975. *Natural resources measurements*. McGraw-Hill, New York.

Bailey, R. L., and T. R. Dell. 1973. Quantifying diameter distributions with the Weibull function. *For. Sci.* **19**:97–104.

Bailey, R. L. 1974. Computer program for quantifying diameter distributions with the Weibull function. *For. Sci.* **20**:229.

Beck, D. E. 1974. Predicting growth of individual trees in thinned stands of yellow-poplar. In *Growth models for tree and stand simulation*. Royal Coll. For., Res. Notes No. 30, Stockholm.

Bennett, F. A., C. E. McGee, and J. L. Clutter. 1959. Yield of old-field slash pine plantations. *U.S.D.A. For. Serv., S.E. For. Exp. Stn. Paper No. 107.*

Bennett, F. A., and J. L. Clutter. 1968. Multiple-product yield estimates for unthinned slash pine plantations—pulpwood, sawtimber, gum. *U.S.D.A. For. Serv., Res. Paper SE-35.*

Bennett, F. A. 1970a. Yields and stand structural patterns for old-field plantations of slash pine. *U.S.D.A. For. Serv., Res. Paper SE-60.*

Bennett, F. A. 1970b. Variable-density yield tables for managed stands of natural slash pine. *U.S.D.A. For. Serv., Res. Note SE-141.*

Bickford, C. A., F. S. Baker, and F. G. Wilson. 1957. Stocking, normality, and measurement of stand density. *J. For.* **55**:99–104.

Bruce, D., and F. X. Schumacher. 1950. *Forest mensuration.* 3rd ed. McGraw-Hill, New York.

Buckman, R. E. 1962. Growth and yield of red pine in Minnesota. *U.S.D.A. Tech. Bull. 1272.*

Burkhart, H. E. 1971. Slash pine plantation yield estimates based on diameter distributions: an evaluation. *For. Sci.* **17**:452–453.

Burkhart, H. E., R. C. Parker, and R. G. Oderwald. 1972. Yields for natural stands of loblolly pine. *Div. of For. and Wildlife Res., Va. Polytechnic Inst. and State Univ., FWS-2-72.*

Burkhart, H. E., R. C. Parker, M. R. Strub, and R. G. Oderwald. 1972. Yields of old-field loblolly pine plantations. *Div. of For. and Wildlife Res., Va. Polytechnic Inst. and State Univ., FWS-3-72.*

Burkhart, H. E., and M. R. Strub. 1974. A model for simulation of planted loblolly pine stands. In *Growth models for tree and stand simulation.* Royal Coll. For., Res. Notes No. 30, Stockholm.

Chambers, C. J. 1980. Empirical growth and yield tables for the Douglas-fir zone. *State of Washington, Dept. of Nat. Res., Rpt. No. 41.*

Chapman, D. G. 1961. Statistical problems in population dynamics. In *Proc. Fourth Berkeley Symp. Math Stat. and Prob.* Univ. Calif. Press, Berkeley.

Chapman, H. H., and W. H. Meyer. 1949. *Forest mensuration.* McGraw-Hill, New York.

Clutter, J. L. 1963. Compatible growth and yield models for loblolly pine. *For. Sci.* **9**:354–371.

Clutter, J. L., and B. J. Allison. 1974. A growth and yield model for *Pinus radiata* in New Zealand. In *Growth models for tree and stand simulation.* Royal Coll. For., Res. Notes No. 30, Stockholm.

Clutter, J. L., and D. M. Belcher. 1978. Yield of site-prepared slash pine plantations in the lower Coastal Plain of Georgia and Florida. In *Growth models for long term forecasting of timber yields.* Div. of For. and Wildlife Res., Va. Polytechnic Inst. and State Univ., FWS-1-78.

Clutter, J. L. 1980. Forest management opportunities for the future. In *Forecasting forest stand dynamics.* Sch. of For., Lakehead Univ., Thunder Bay.

Clutter, J. L., and E. P. Jones. 1980. Prediction of growth after thinning in old-field slash pine plantations. *U.S.D.A. For. Serv., Res. Paper SE-217.*

Coile, T. S., and F. X. Schumacher. 1964. *Soil-site relations, stand structure, and yields of slash and loblolly pine plantations in the southern United States.* T. S. Coile Inc., Durham, N.C.

Cole, D. M. 1971. A cubic-foot stand volume equation for lodgepole pine in Montana and Idaho. *U.S.D.A. For. Serv., Res. Note INT-150.*

Daniels, R. F., and H. E. Burkhart. 1975. Simulation of individual tree growth and stand development in managed loblolly pine plantations. *Div. of For. and Wildlife Res., Va. Polytechnic Inst. and State Univ., FWS-5-75.*

Daniels, R. F., H. E. Burkhart, and M. R. Strub. 1979. Yield estimates for loblolly pine plantations. *J. For.* **77**:581–583, 586.

Davis, K. P. 1966. *Forest management: regulation and valuation.* 2nd ed. McGraw-Hill, New York.

Dell, T. R., D. P. Feduccia, T. E. Campbell, W. F. Mann, and B. H. Polmer. 1979. Yields of unthinned slash pine plantations on cutover sites in the west gulf region. *U.S.D.A. For. Serv., Res. Paper SO-147.*

Dubey, S. D. 1967. Some percentile estimators for Weibull parameters. *Technometrics* **9**:119–129.

Feduccia, D. P., T. R. Dell, W. F. Mann, T. E. Campbell, and B. H. Polmer. 1979. Yields of unthinned loblolly pine plantations on cutover sites in the west gulf region. *U.S.D.A. For. Serv., Res. Paper SO-148.*

Gingrich, S. F. 1978. Growth and yield. In *Uneven-aged silviculture and management in the United States.* U.S.D.A. For. Serv., Gen. Tech. Rpt. No. 24.

Hamilton, D. A. 1974. Event probabilities estimated by regression. *U.S.D.A. For. Serv., Res. Paper INT-152.*

Hamilton, D. A., and D. L. R. Wendt. 1975. SCREEN: a computer program to identify predictors of dichotomous dependent variables. *U.S.D.A. For. Serv., Gen. Tech. Rpt. INT-22.*

Hamilton, D. A., and B. M. Edwards. 1976. Modeling the probability of individual tree mortality. *U.S.D.A. For. Serv., Res. Paper INT-185.*

Hann, D. W. 1980. Development and evaluation of an even- and uneven-aged ponderosa pine/Arizona fescue stand simulator. *U.S.D.A. For. Serv., Res. Paper INT-267.*

Harter, H. L., and A. H. Moore. 1965. Maximum likelihood estimation of parameters of the gamma and Weibull populations from complete and from censored samples. *Technometrics* **7**:639–643.

Husch, B., C. I. Miller, and T. W. Beers. 1982. *Forest mensuration.* 3rd ed. Wiley, New York.

Langdon, O. G. 1961. Yield of unmanaged slash pine stands in south Florida. *U.S.D.A. For. Serv., Res. Paper SE-123.*

Leak, W. B., P. H. Allen, J. P. Barrett, F. K. Beyer, D. L. Mader, J. C. Mawson, and R. K. Wilson. 1970. Yields of eastern white pine in New England related to age, site, and stocking. *U.S.D.A. For. Serv., Res. Paper NE-176.*

Lenhart, J. D., and J. L. Clutter. 1971. Cubic foot yield tables for old field loblolly pine plantations in the Georgia Piedmont. *Ga. For. Res. Council, Report 22 Series 3.*

Lenhart, J. D. 1972a. Predicting survival of unthinned, old field loblolly pine plantations. *J. For.* **70**:754–755.

Lenhart, J. D. 1972b. Cubic volume yields for unthinned old-field loblolly pine plantations in the interior west gulf coastal plain. *Stephen F. Austin State Univ., Texas Forestry Paper 14.*

MacKinney, A. L., F. X. Schumacher, and L. E. Chaiken. 1937. Construction of yield tables for nonnormal loblolly pine stands. *Jour. Agr. Res.* **54**:531–545.

MacKinney, A. L., and L. E. Chaiken. 1939. Volume, yield and growth of loblolly pine in the mid-Atlantic region. *U.S.D.A. For. Serv., Appalachian For. Exp. Stn. Tech. Note No. 33.*

McGee, C. E., and L. Della-Bianca. 1967. Diameter distributions in natural yellow-poplar stands. *U.S.D.A. For. Serv., Res. Paper SE-25.*

Meyer, H. A. 1935. A simplified increment determination on the basis of stand tables. *J. For.* **33**:799–806.

Meyer, H. A. 1936. Increment determination on the basis of stand tables. *J. For.* **34**:948–950.

Mitchell, K. J. 1975. Dynamics and simulated yield of Douglas-fir. *For. Sci. Monograph No. 17.*

Monserud, R. A. 1976. Simulation of forest tree mortality. *For. Sci.* **22**:438–444.

Moser, J. W., and O. F. Hall. 1969. Deriving growth and yield functions for uneven-aged forest stands. *For. Sci.* **15**:183–188.

Munro, D. D. 1974. Forest growth models—a prognosis. In *Growth models for tree and stand simulation.* Royal Coll. For., Res. Notes No. 30, Stockholm.

Nelson, T. C., J. L. Clutter, and L. E. Chaiken. 1961. Yield of Virginia pine. *U.S.D.A. For. Serv., S. E. For. Exp. Stn. Paper No. 124.*

Nelson, T. C., and F. A. Bennett. 1965. A critical look at the normality concept. *J. For.* **63**:107–109.

Oliver, W. W. 1979. Fifteen-year growth patterns after thinning a ponderosa-Jeffrey pine plantation in northeastern California. *U.S.D.A. For. Serv., Res. Paper PSW-141.*

Perala, D. A. 1971. Growth and yield of black spruce on organic soils in Minnesota. *U.S.D.A. For. Serv., Res. Paper NC-56.*

Pienaar, L. V. 1965. Quantitative theory of forest growth. Ph.D. dissertation, Univ. of Washington.

Pienaar, L. V., and K. J. Turnbull. 1973. The Chapman-Richards generalization of Von Bertalanffy's growth model for basal area growth and yield in even-aged stands. *For. Sci.* **19**:2–22.

Pienaar, L. V. 1979. An approximation of basal area growth after thinning based on growth in unthinned plantations. *For. Sci.* **25**:223–232.

Pienaar, L. V., and B. D. Shiver. 1981. Survival functions for site prepared slash pine plantations in the flatwoods of Georgia and northern Florida. *So. J. App. For.* **5**(2):59–62.

Richards, F. J. 1959. A flexible growth function for empirical use. *J. Exp. Bot.* **10**:290–300.

Rose, D. W., and A. R. Ek. 1972. Construction of a local nonlinear growth and yield model for red pine in northwestern Wisconsin. *Univ. of Wisconsin For. Res. Notes No. 164.*

Schlaegel, B. E. 1971. Growth and yield of quaking aspen in northcentral Minnesota. *U.S.D.A. For. Serv., Res. Paper NC-58.*

Schnur, G. L. 1937. Yield, stand and volume tables for even-aged upland oak forests. *U.S.D.A. Tech. Bull. 560.*

Schreuder, H. T., W. L. Hafley, and F. A. Bennett. 1979. Yield prediction for unthinned natural slash pine stands. *For. Sci.* **25**:25–30.

Schumacher, F. X. 1939. A new growth curve and its application to timber-yield studies. *J. For.* **37**:819–820.

Schumacher, F. X., and T. S. Coile. 1960. *Growth and yield of natural stands of the southern pines.* T. S. Coile Inc., Durham, N.C.

Smalley, G. W., and D. R. Bower. 1968. Volume tables and point-sampling factors for shortleaf pines in plantations on abandoned fields in Tennessee, Alabama and Georgia highlands. *U.S.D.A. For. Serv., Res. Paper SO-39.*

Smalley, G. W., and D. R. Bower. 1971. Site index curves for loblolly and shortleaf pine plantations on abandoned fields in Tennessee, Alabama and Georgia highlands. *U.S.D.A. For. Serv., Res. Note SO-126.*

Smalley, G. W., and R. L. Bailey. 1974. Yield tables and stand structure for shortleaf pine plantations in Tennessee, Alabama, and Georgia highlands. *U.S.D.A. For. Serv., Res. Paper SO-97.*

Smith, J. L. 1978. Volume yields of site prepared loblolly pine plantations in the lower coastal plain of the Carolinas, Georgia, and north Florida. Masters thesis, School of Forest Res., Univ. of Georgia.

Stage, A. R. 1973. Prognosis model for stand development. *U.S.D.A. For. Serv., Res. Paper INT-137.*

Sullivan, A. D., and J. L. Clutter. 1972. A simultaneous growth and yield model for loblolly pine. *For. Sci.* **18**:76–86.

Tennent, R. B. 1980. A simulation model for *Pinus radiata* in New Zealand. Ph.D. dissertation, School of Forest Res., Univ. of Georgia.

Turnbull, K. J. 1963. Population dynamics in mixed forest stands. Ph.D. dissertation, Univ. of Washington.

U.S.D.A. 1979. A generalized forest growth projection system applied to the Lake States Region. *U.S.D.A. For. Serv., Gen. Tech. Rpt. NC-49.*

Vimmerstedt, J. P. 1962. Southern Appalachian white pine plantations: site, volume and yield. *U.S.D.A. For. Serv., S.E. For. Exp. Stn. Paper No. 149.*

Wahlenberg, W. G. 1941. Methods of forecasting timber growth in irregular stands. *U.S.D.A. Tech. Bull. 796.*

Wingo, D. R. 1972. Maximum likelihood estimation of the parameters of the Weibull distribution by modified quasilinearization. *IEEE Trans. Rel.* **R-21**.

PART 2

FINANCIAL ASPECTS OF TIMBER MANAGEMENT

5

Forest Finance

Individuals make investments in an attempt to achieve an optimum pattern of consumption over time. Since present consumption is preferable to future consumption, investors will only forgo present enjoyment if the prospective future enjoyment has greater utility. If investments are to be made wisely, the owner or owners of the investment capital must specify the present utility and the objectives of future consumption. In public investment this kind of specification is a complex and difficult task since the owners are clearly the people, and each voter has one vote in the determination of objectives. Given the diversity of our people, it is not surprising that attempts to specify public investment objectives often involve strife and conflict.

The objectives of the corporation prove easier to specify. The ownership of corporations resides with the claimants to residual income—the holders of the common stock. The shareholders bear the risk and specify the objectives. One share of stock allows one vote in the governance of the corporation. Although corporations have many goals and objectives, maximization of shareholder wealth dominates the goal structure. This normative goal provides a clear investment policy and defines the objective of the corporation.

Writers in financial theory have shown that the goal of maximization of shareholder wealth can best be accomplished by maximizing the market price of the outstanding common stock. Corporate forest products firms should, therefore, manage their forestry investments with this wealth maximization goal clearly in mind. Of course, decisions regarding capital investment in forestry activities do not directly affect share price. Decisions made by the marginal investor determine stock prices. However, if investors perceive the firm's investment decisions as being "good," then increased demand for the stock will produce an increase in its price. It should be recognized that the market is the ultimate judge concerning the optimality of capital investment decisions, and the current price of a share of stock is a function of expected future dividends.

5.1 THE TIME VALUE OF MONEY

Money has alternative uses. Financial institutions exist which will pay for the use of capital funds. Any competitive thrift institution will accept a dollar today and return a larger amount, say $1 + X$ dollars, in the future. Thus an investment of $1 today returns more than $1 one year hence. The converse must also be true. One dollar to be received in the future is worth less than $1 today. This is true because current ownership provides the opportunity for immediate investment.

5.1.1 Simple and Compound Interest

Suppose an amount V_0 is deposited in an institution that pays i percent compounded annually. At the end of 1 year, the depositor would have the original investment V_0, plus the interest iV_0. The total amount that could be withdrawn is $V_0 + iV_0$ or $V_0 (1 + i)$. If the interest iV_0 were withdrawn, then the original amount V_0 would remain for another period. Thus an amount iV_0 could be withdrawn each period in perpetuity. This is an illustration of simple interest. By withdrawing interest as it is earned, the basic amount on which the interest accrues (V_0) remains constant.

In the case of compound interest, the interest earned is not withdrawn but is itself invested. As before, it is assumed that V_0 is deposited in an institution that pays i percent annual interest. At the end of the first year, interest in the amount of iV_0 is paid and becomes part of the deposited capital. The amount then on deposit is the initial amount V_0 plus the earned interest iV_0, which totals $V_0 + iV_0$ or $V_0 (1 + i)$. This amount then earns at the rate i. At the end of the second year, the amount available is $V_0 (1 + i) + i[V_0 (1 + i)]$, which can be written as $V_0 (1 + i)(1 + i) = V_0 (1 + i)^2$. At the end of the third period, the amount on deposit is $V_0 (1 + i)^2 + i[V_0 (1 + i)^2] = V_0 (1 + i)^3$. The general

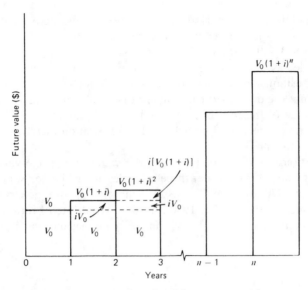

Figure 5.1 Asset growth with compound interest.

relationship is

$$V_n = V_0 (1 + i)^n \tag{5.1}$$

where

V_n = future value of a single amount V_0 deposited at time 0 or now

V_0 = initial amount

i = appropriate interest rate per period[1]

n = number of periods involved

Asset growth through compound interest is illustrated in Figure 5.1.

To illustrate this relationship, suppose $100 is invested in a savings and loan association that pays 6 percent compounded annually. The amount that could be withdrawn at the end of the 10th year is

$$V_n = 100 \, (1.06)^{10}$$

$$= 100 \, (1.7908)$$

$$= \$179.08$$

---

[1] We assume, for now, that the compounding occurs annually. The topic of more frequent compounding will be addressed in Section 5.1.7.

As the length of the holding period increases, future value increases dramatically. For example, with the 6 percent interest rate used above, $100 invested today will be worth $33,930 at the end of 100 years.

For example, assume $50 per acre is invested in fertilizing a loblolly pine plantation at establishment. If a 30-year rotation age is used, how much additional value must be derived at rotation age to earn 8 percent on the investment? The future value of the fertilizer costs is $V_n = \$50(1.08)^{30} = \$503.13$, and the 8 percent earning rate would be achieved if fertilization increases the value of the harvest by this amount.

In the relationship $V_n = V_0 (1 + i)^n$, the value of any one variable can be determined if values for the other three variables are available. Suppose an asset is purchased in 1970 for $400. The asset incurs no expense, generates no intermediate incomes, and is sold in 1980 for $800. What rate of return was earned by the investment? In this case, V_n, V_0, and n are known and i can be determined. Since

$$V_n = V_0 (1 + i)^n$$

then

$$i = (V_n/V_0)^{(1/n)} - 1 \qquad (5.2)$$

and, for this example,

$$i = (800/400)^{0.1} - 1 = 0.0718 \qquad \text{or} \qquad 7.18 \text{ percent}$$

5.1.2 Present Value

Forest resource managers must make decisions today despite the fact that their information concerning future cash inflows comes from expectations rather than facts. Decisions to invest in a tract of land and timber or in site preparation and planting of a particular site must be made now. The cash inflows associated with either of these investments may occur in the fairly distant future. Therefore, the key question is: How much is a promise of future income worth today? This involves the concept of present value. If $1 invested today will yield more than $1 in the future, it follows that $1 today is worth more than the promise of $1 n years hence. The relationship involved is obtained by rearranging equation (5.1) as

$$V_0 = V_n/(1 + i)^n = V_n(1 + i)^{-n} \qquad (5.3)$$

If i is positive, V_0 will be less than V_n. Equation (5.3) shows that present value is a function of (1) the amount of cash to be received n years hence, (2) the length of time until the receipt of the cash inflow, and (3) the interest rate. In a future value context, i is usually referred to as the interest rate, but in present value calculations i is often called the discount rate. It is important to note that equations (5.1), (5.2), and (5.3) involve only two payments—the initial amount V_0 and the terminal amount V_n. The quantity $1/(1 + i)^n$ is referred to as the *present value of a single sum* and has been extensively tabled for various combinations of i and n. However, modern calculators have made the use of present value tables a rarity since it is usually easier to calculate $1/(1 + i)^n$ than to look up the value in tables.

To illustrate the calculation of the present value of a single sum, consider an investment in a tract of land and timber that is expected to yield $10,000 when liquidated 10 years from now. If there are no cash flows prior to liquidation, the present value of this future sum with a discount rate of 8 percent is

$$V_0 = \$10,000/1.08^{10} = \$4,631.93$$

Forestry investments seldom involve a single outflow followed by a single inflow. The typical pattern consists of an initial outflow followed by a series of inflows and outflows. Investments in timber growing often show (1) an initial outflow for land purchase, site preparation, and planting; (2) a series of outflows representing ad valorem taxes and management expenses; and (3) inflows from thinnings, major harvests, and assumed liquidation of the land and residual growing stock at some future date. The general equation for the present value of such a series of cash flows is

$$V_0 = \sum_{t=0}^{n} C_t/(1 + i)^t \qquad (5.4)$$

where

V_0 = present value of the cash flows

C_t = cash flow to be received or invested at time t (this value is positive for cash receipts and negative for investments)

n = number of periods

i = appropriate discount rate

Formula (5.4) is often used to appraise the value of an asset. If the cash flows generated by ownership of an asset (not including the initial purchase of the asset) are evaluated with equation 5.4, the resulting value of V_0 is one possible estimate of the "appraised value" of the asset. This represents the so-called *income approach* to valuation,[2] which defines the value of an asset as the present value of the cash flows generated by ownership of the asset. The logic of this type of computation is obvious and the arithmetic involved is relatively simple. The real difficulty, of course, lies in estimating the cash flows that will, in the future, emanate from the ownership of any particular asset. This problem is obviously most serious when the ownership period is long, as is the case with many forestry investments.

The concept of present value involves the discount rate as a conversion factor between current dollars and future dollars. For example, consider the purchase of a guaranteed (risk-free) note that will pay $100 ten years from now. What is the present value associated with ownership of such a note? It should be clear that this present value, X, must satisfy the relationship $\$0 < X < \$100$. It would be irrational to say that $X = \$100$, since this would implicitly deny the existence of financial institutions that pay positive interest rates to investors. Suppose a particular investor states that he would now pay $40 for the note just described. This statement indicates that the operative discount rate for this particular investor is 9.6 percent since $\$40.00 = \$100.00/1.096^{10}$. Proper application of this discount rate to future cash flows expected by this investor transforms the future cash flows to present values.

To illustrate, suppose an investor with a 10 percent discount rate is considering the purchase of a tract of land and timber. The following data describe the details of the potential investment.

Thin 2 years from now:
Remove 10 cords/acre at $18/cord   = $180
Liquidate land and timber 5 years
hence:
   30 cords/acre at $20/cord   = $600
   Sell land for $200/acre   = $200
Annual management costs and
ad valorem taxes are $4.00/acre

The expected cash flows, ignoring income taxes, are shown in Table 5.1. The present value of these cash flows is

$$V_0 = \frac{-4}{1.1} + \frac{176}{1.1^2} - \frac{4}{1.1^3} - \frac{4}{1.1^4} + \frac{796}{1.1^5}$$

$$= \$630.32$$

---

[2] Other recognized approaches to valuation are the *cost approach* and the *fair-market-value approach*. An excellent discussion of all three methods and their relative merits and disadvantages is given by Davis (1966).

TABLE 5.1

Expected per-Acre Cash Flows for a Hypothetical Forestry Investment

Year	Amount
1	$ − 4.00
2	176.00
3	− 4.00
4	− 4.00
5	796.00

The variable V_0 is the maximum amount the investor can pay for the tract and still earn the rate of return specified in the discount rate. If the asset could be purchased for $630.32, the investment would earn exactly 10 percent. A purchase price less than $630.32 would produce a yield greater than 10 percent, while a purchase price greater than $630.32 would result in an earnings rate less than 10 percent.

Another interpretation of the cash flow present value arises from the statement that, if the calculated present value were paid for the asset with all investments financed by borrowing at the specified discount rate, the cash inflows would be just adequate to repay the borrowed capital and accrued interest. This relationship is illustrated in Table 5.2 for the land and timber investment just discussed.

TABLE 5.2

Cash Flow for a Hypothetical Forestry Investment Financed with Funds Borrowed at 10 percent

Year	Item	Income	Item	Expense	Loan Balance
0	Borrow	$630.32	Buy tract	$630.32	$630.32
1	Borrow	4.00	Pay tax	4.00	634.32
	Borrow	63.03	Pay interest	63.03	697.35
2	Net income	176.00	Pay interest	69.74	697.35
			Reduce loan	106.26	591.09
3	Borrow	59.11	Pay interest	59.11	650.20
	Borrow	4.00	Pay tax	4.00	654.20
4	Borrow	65.42	Pay interest	65.42	719.62
	Borrow	4.00	Pay tax	4.00	723.62
5	Net income	796.00	Pay interest	72.36	723.62
			Repay loan balance	723.62	0.00

5.1.3 Annuities

The present value of any cash flow pattern can be computed with equation (5.4).
However, some commonly encountered cash flow sequences have particular
structures that simplify the evaluation calculations. One such case is a cash flow
sequence involving a finite number of periods and cash flows of equal amounts
in all the periods. The first cash flow occurs at the end of period 1 and the last
cash flow occurs at the end of period n. Any cash flow sequence with this structure
is called an *annuity*. The present value of such a cash flow sequence is

$$V_0 = \frac{A}{1 + i} + \frac{A}{(1 + i)^2} + \frac{A}{(1 + i)^3} + \cdots + \frac{A}{(1 + i)^n} \qquad (5.5)$$

where

A = per-period cash flow amount

The series on the right-hand side of equation (5.5) is a *geometric series*. (A series
is a geometric series whenever each term after the first is a constant multiple of
the immediately preceding term.) A standard equation is available for calculating
the sum of any geometric series.[3] For the series in equation (5.5)

$$a_1 = A (1 + i)^{-1}$$

and

$$r = (1 + i)^{-1}$$

so that the sum is given by

$$V_0 = \frac{A (1 + i)^{-1} [1 - (1 + i)^{-n}]}{1 - (1 + i)^{-1}}$$

---

[3] The principal results concerning geometric series can be summarized as follows: Let $a_1, a_2, \ldots,$
a_n denote the terms of the series. The basic property of a geometric series is given by

$$a_i = ra_{i-1} \qquad i = 2, 3, \ldots, n$$

where r is referred to as the common ratio. If S denotes the sum of the terms in a geometric series,
it is easily shown that

$$S = \frac{a_1 (1 - r^n)}{1 - r}$$

which reduces to

$$V_0 = A \left[\frac{(1 + i)^n - 1}{i (1 + i)^n} \right] \qquad (5.6)$$

The quantity within the square brackets in equation (5.6) is commonly referred to as the *present value of an annuity of $1.00*. Tables have been prepared showing the values of this quantity for various combinations of i and n.

To illustrate the use of equation (5.6), consider an investor who leases a tract of forestland for 5 years with an annual payment of $20 per acre. The present value of the lease payments with a discount rate of 10 percent is

$$V_0 = \$20 \left[\frac{1.1^5 - 1}{0.1 (1.1)^5} \right]$$

$$= \$75.82$$

It is important to remember that equation (5.6) is basically a special case of equation (5.4). If the present value for the problem just considered is evaluated with equation (5.4)

$$V_0 = \frac{\$20}{1.1} + \frac{\$20}{1.1^2} + \frac{\$20}{1.1^3} + \frac{\$20}{1.1^4} + \frac{\$20}{1.1^5}$$

$$= \$75.82$$

Equation (5.6) also states the basic relationships involved in a loan repayment situation. The lender immediately gives the borrower an amount V_0 and accepts, in return, the promise of an annuity involving n payments of A dollars each. The present value of this annuity is equal to V_0. A formula for the annual payment amount required to repay any given loan can be obtained by solving equation (5.6) for the variable A. This gives

$$A = V_0 \left[\frac{i (1 + i)^n}{(1 + i)^n - 1} \right] \qquad (5.7)$$

where

V_0 = amount of the loan

n = number of years required for full repayment of the loan

i = discount rate

A = annual payment required

Equation (5.7) is often called the *installment payment formula*.

The application of equation (5.7) can be illustrated by considering a $10,000 loan made at an interest rate of 12 percent. The loan is to be repaid in 10 equal annual installments. The required annual payment is

$$A = \$10,000 \left[\frac{0.12 (1.12)^{10}}{1.12^{10} - 1} \right]$$

$$= \$1769.84$$

The repayment process is shown in Table 5.3 Since the calculations shown are rounded to the nearest cent, some rounding error is present in the results. However, the computations show that, within the limits of rounding error, the series of payments does repay the principal and pay appropriate interest charges.

Equation (5.6) provides the necessary formulation for computing the present value of any annuity. However, in some situations, the quantity of interest is the future value of the annuity. This is the single amount V_n received n years from now that would have equivalent value to receipt of an annuity of n payments of A dollars each. The appropriate formulation is easily obtained by using the present value-future value equivalence shown in equation (5.1)

$$V_n = V_0 (1 + i)^n$$

TABLE 5.3

Repayment of a $10,000 Loan with 10 Equal Annual Payments

Year	Payment Amount	Interest Paid	Principal Repaid	Principal Outstanding at Year End
0				$10,000.00
1	$ 1,769.84	$1,200.00	$ 569.84	9,430.16
2	1,769.84	1,131.62	638.22	8,791.94
3	1,769.84	1,055.03	714.81	8,077.13
4	1,769.84	969.26	800.58	7,276.55
5	1,769.84	873.19	896.65	6,379.90
6	1,769.84	765.59	1,004.25	5,375.65
7	1,769.84	645.08	1,124.76	4,250.89
8	1,769.84	510.11	1,259.73	2,991.16
9	1,769.84	358.94	1,410.90	1,580.26
10	1,769.84	189.63	1,580.21	—
Totals	$17,698.40	$7,698.45	$9,999.95	

and noting that, for this case,

$$V_0 = A \left[\frac{(1 + i)^n - 1}{i (1 + i)^n} \right]$$

Multiplication by $(1 + i)^n$ gives

$$(1 + i)^n V_0 = A \left[\frac{(1 + i)^n - 1}{i} \right]$$

so that

$$V_n = A \left[\frac{(1 + i)^n - 1}{i} \right] \tag{5.8}$$

It is important to remember that equation (5.8) applies to situations where the first annuity payment is made 1 year hence. There are n equal payments, and these payments are made $1, 2, \ldots, n$ years from now.

To illustrate the use of equation (5.8), consider an investor who deposits $2000 per year for 5 years in a thrift institution that pays interest at a rate of 8 percent per year compounded annually. Immediately after the fifth deposit is made, the investor's account should contain

$$V_n = \$2000 \left[\frac{1.08^5 - 1}{0.08} \right]$$

$$= \$11,733.20$$

Of course, this same result can also be obtained by carrying out a separate future value computation for each deposit and summing the results. With this approach

$$V_n = \$2000 (1.08)^4 + \$2000 (1.08)^3 + \$2000 (1.08)^2$$

$$+ \$2000 (1.08) + \$2000$$

$$= \$2720.98 + \$2519.42 + \$2332.80$$

$$+ \$2160.00 + \$2000.00$$

$$= \$11,733.20$$

In some annuity future value situations, the problem is to determine what annuity amount must be deposited annually to give a specified future value amount. This requires a revision of equation (5.8), whereby A is expressed as a function of V_n, n, and i. The appropriate equation is

$$A = V_n \left[\frac{i}{(1 + i)^n - 1} \right] \tag{5.9}$$

This expression is often called the *sinking fund formula*. Its use can be illustrated by considering a firm that wishes to build a new forest headquarters 6 years from now. Construction costs are estimated to be $100,000. Funds to finance the construction will be set aside during each of the next 6 years and invested at an interest rate of 8 percent. Equal amounts are to be invested each year. The amount that must be invested annually is

$$A = \$100,000 \left[\frac{0.08}{1.08^6 - 1} \right]$$

$$= \$13,631.54$$

5.1.4 Perpetuities

Forestry investments are usually long-term investments. Indeed, corporations and government agencies such as the U.S. Forest Service have unlimited planning horizons so that most forest-based industries and public land management agencies anticipate managing their forests forever. To evaluate an asset that produces cash flows over an indefinitely long time frame, it is necessary to have a procedure for calculating the present value of an infinite series of cash flows. Equation (5.6) gives the present value of a finite series of equal payments as

$$V_0 = \frac{A \left[(1 + i)^n - 1 \right]}{i (1 + i)^n}$$

which can be rewritten as

$$V_0 = \frac{A (1 + i)^n}{i (1 + i)^n} - \frac{A}{i (1 + i)^n} = \frac{A}{i} - \frac{A}{i (1 + i)^n} \tag{5.10}$$

The limit of this expression as n approaches infinity is

$$V_0 = \frac{A}{i} \tag{5.11}$$

Thus, the present value of an infinite series of equal annual amounts A, the first of which is to be received 1 year hence, is simply A/i. The relationship for the finite series (equation 5.10)

$$V_0 = \frac{A}{i} - \frac{A/i}{(1 + i)^n}$$

is revealing. This shows that the present value of n annual payments is the present value of an infinite payment series less the present value of the payments in periods $n + 1$ to infinity. As an example of the use of equation (5.11), consider an investment that will produce a return, in perpetuity, of $100 per year. For an investor with a discount rate of 10 percent, the present value of this investment is

$$V_0 = \$100/0.10$$

$$= \$1000$$

Many people find it difficult to accept the concept that some finite amount of current money can be as valuable as a stream of payments that continues forever. The validity of the concept can, however, be easily demonstrated by noting that, if an investor now possesses $1000 and if a thrift institution exists that pays 10 percent interest, the investor can deposit the $1000 and begin receiving a perpetual income of $100 per year.

Although the difference between a finite-length annuity and a perpetuity is conceptually very great, the difference in their present values is negligible for some comparisons. The present values of some annuities and perpetuities are shown in Table 5.4. For an interest rate of 8 percent, the present value of $100 per year for 50 years is $1223.35, while the present value of a perpetuity of $100 per year at 8 percent is $1250. Thus, the present value of all perpetuity payments after the 50th year is only $26.65, which is only 2.1 percent of the total perpetuity present value.

TABLE 5.4

Present Values of Some Annuities and Perpetuities at Interest Rates of 4, 8, and 12 Percent

	Present Value of $100 per Year for				Present Value of $100 per Year in Perpetuity
Interest Rate	10 Years	25 Years	50 Years	100 Years	
0.04	$811.09	$1562.21	$2148.22	$2450.50	$2500.00
0.08	671.01	1067.48	1223.35	1249.43	1250.00
0.12	565.02	784.31	830.45	833.32	833.33

5.1.5   Present Value of Nonannual Periodic Cash Flows

Forest investments often generate periodic cash flows with period lengths longer than 1 year. The period could be the rotation length or the harvesting interval in an all-aged stand. In this situation, the present value of the cash flow series is

$$V_0 = \frac{A}{(1 + i)^m} + \frac{A}{(1 + i)^{2m}} + \cdots + \frac{A}{(1 + i)^{mn}}$$

where

n = number of terms in the series

m = length of the period between cash flows

This is again a geometric series with $a_1 = A (1 + i)^{-m}$ and $r = (1 + i)^{-m}$. The formula for the sum of a geometric series has been previously given as

$$S = a_1 \frac{1 - r^n}{1 - r}$$

so that, for this particular series,

$$V_0 = A (1 + i)^{-m} \frac{[1 - (1 + i)^{-mn}]}{[1 - (1 + i)^{-m}]}$$

which is algebraically equivalent to

$$V_0 = \frac{A [(1 + i)^{mn} - 1]}{(1 + i)^{mn} [(1 + i)^m - 1]} \tag{5.12}$$

It should be noted that the annuity present value formula [equation (5.6)] is a special case of equation (5.12), with the period length m set to equal 1.

Consider a property that promises to return 10 incomes of $50 each. The incomes will be received every 5 years, with the first occurring 5 years hence. If the discount rate is 10 percent, the present value of the asset is

$$V_0 = \frac{\$50 (1.1^{50} - 1)}{(1.1)^{50} (1.1^5 - 1)}$$

$$= \$81.20$$

With nonannual periodic cash flows, the early cash flows often contribute most of the total present value. In this example, the first two payments account for 62 percent of the total present value.

The present value of an infinite series of periodic payments can be obtained by noting that equation (5.12) can be rewritten as

$$V_0 = \frac{A}{[(1 + i)^m - 1]} - \frac{A}{(1 + i)^{mn} [(1 + i)^m - 1]}$$

and taking the limit as n approaches infinity. The result is

$$V_0 = \frac{A}{[(1 + i)^m - 1]} \tag{5.13}$$

If m equals 1, this result reduces to equation (5.11), which is the formula for the present value of a perpetuity received annually.

*5.1.6 Present Value of Cash Flows Involving a Constant Growth Rate

Considerable attention has been devoted to the analysis of cash flows involving terms of equal value. In many investment situations, it is reasonable to believe that the cash flows generated by the investment will increase through time at some constant growth rate.[4] Consider an asset that generates a current annual cash flow of C_0 dollars. This annual cash flow is expected to grow at a constant rate g per year for the next n years. The expected cash flow in period t is therefore $C_0 (1 + g)^t$. The present value of the asset can be estimated as

$$V_0 = \sum_{t=1}^{n} \frac{C_0 (1 + g)^t}{(1 + i)^t}$$

This is a geometric series with $a_1 = C_0 (1 + g)/(1 + i)$ and $r = (1 + g)/(1 + i)$. Since the sum of any geometric series is given by

$$S = a_1 \frac{1 - r^n}{1 - r}$$

---

[4] We assume here that this growth is an increase in constant dollar value and is not simply a result of inflationary changes in currency values. Appropriate analysis techniques for dealing with the effects of inflation are discussed in Section 5.4

the result in this particular case is

$$V_0 = C_0 \left[(1 + g)/(1 + i) \right] \frac{1 - \left[(1 + g)/(1 + i) \right]^n}{1 - \left[(1 + g)/(1 + i) \right]}$$

which reduces to

$$V_0 = C_0 \left(\frac{1 + g}{i - g} \right) \frac{\left[(1 + i)^n - (1 + g)^n \right]}{(1 + i)^n} \tag{5.14}$$

To illustrate the use of equation (5.14), consider a forest landowner who has agreed to lease his land for 60 years to a forest products firm. Base price for the lease is $25 per acre per year with an annual increase of 3 percent per year. At the end of the first year of the lease, the landowner will receive $25 (1.03) per acre. At the end of the second year, he will receive $25 $(1.03)^2$, and so forth. If the landowner's interest rate is 8 percent, the present value of all lease payments is

$$V_0 = \$25 \left(\frac{1.03}{0.05} \right) \frac{(1.08^{60} - 1.03^{60})}{1.08^{60}}$$

$$= \$485.03 \text{ per acre}$$

It is sometimes necessary to calculate the present value of a perpetual cash flow involving a constant growth rate. The appropriate formula is obtained by noting that equation (5.14) can be written

$$V_0 = C_0 \left(\frac{1 + g}{i - g} \right) \left[1 - \left(\frac{1 + g}{1 + i} \right)^n \right]$$

and taking the limit of this expression as n approaches infinity. If $g \geq i$, the limit does not exist, but if $g < i$, the limit is

$$V_0 = C_0 \left(\frac{1 + g}{i - g} \right) \tag{5.15}$$

If, in the preceding example, the land were leased in perpetuity, the present value of all lease payments would be

$$V_0 = \$25 \left(\frac{1.03}{0.05} \right)$$

$$= \$515 \text{ per acre}$$

Equation (5.15) is widely used in corporate finance to appraise the value of a share of common stock. If the common stock of firm X pays a current annual dividend of $2.00, and if this dividend is expected to increase at a constant compound rate of 5 percent, the maximum amount an investor can pay per share and still earn 8 percent on the investment is

$$V_0 = \frac{2\,(1.05)}{(0.08 - 0.05)} = \$70.00$$

*5.1.7 Compounding More Than Once a Year

Financial growth is a function of the growth rate and the number of growth periods involved. It is usually assumed that growth takes place at the end of each year, and growth rates or interest rates are usually quoted as annual rates. However, growth or compounding can and frequently does occur more often than once a year. Suppose Bank A pays 6 percent compounded annually and Bank B pays 6 percent compounded semiannually. Rational investors would choose to deposit their funds in Bank B since a basic and very noncontroversial tenet of finance advises that more dollars are preferable to fewer dollars. The investor who deposits $100 in Bank A could withdraw $106.00 at the end of 1 year. The investor who invests in Bank B could withdraw $106.09. An investment in Bank B would earn a half year's interest or $3 at the end of 6 months. For the second growth period (months 7 through 12), interest would be earned on $103.00 rather than $100.00. The value of the account at the end of the year would be $103.00 × 1.03 = $106.09. Thus, Bank B has actually paid interest at an "effective annual rate" of 6.09 percent. The general formula for computing the effective annual rate (*EAR*) is

$$EAR = \left(1 + \frac{i}{m}\right)^{m} - 1 \tag{5.16}$$

where

i = nominal (stated) rate

i/m = periodic rate

m = number of compounding periods per year

Equation (5.16) shows that the effective annual rate equivalent to a nominal rate of 6 percent with semiannual compounding is

$$EAR = \left(1 + \frac{0.06}{2}\right)^{2} - 1 = 0.0609 \qquad \text{or 6.09 percent}$$

The effective annual rates for various compounding periods and a nominal rate of 6 percent are shown in Table 5.5. The bottom line of Table 5.5 involves what is known as *continuous interest*. Continuous interest occurs when m approaches infinity and the periodic rate i/m approaches zero. Therefore, for continuous compounding, the effective annual rate is given by

$$EAR = \lim_{m \to \infty} \left(1 + \frac{i}{m} \right)^{m} - 1 = e^{i} - 1$$

When interest is compounded more frequently than once per year, the appropriate formulas for calculating present and future values are

$$V_0 = V_n \Big/ \left(1 + \frac{i}{m} \right)^{mn} \tag{5.17}$$

and

$$V_n = V_0 \left(1 + \frac{i}{m} \right)^{mn} \tag{5.18}$$

where n is the number of years involved. With continuous compounding, the equivalent relationships are

$$V_0 = V_n \, e^{-in} \tag{5.19}$$

and

$$V_n = V_0 \, e^{in} \tag{5.20}$$

TABLE 5.5

Effective Annual Rate (EAR) for Various Compounding Periods with a 6 Percent Nominal Rate

Nominal Rate	Periodic Rate	Number of Compounding Periods per Year	Effective Annual Rate
6.0%	3.0%	2	6.09%
6.0	1.5	4	6.14
6.0	0.5	12	6.17
6.0	0.115	52	6.180
6.0	0.016	365	6.183
6.0		∞	6.184

5.2 CRITERIA FOR FINANCIAL INVESTMENTS

Capital investment usually involves an outlay of funds today in return for an expectation of larger inflows in the future. Financial decision makers are frequently confronted with the problem of choosing the best investment from a series of proposed alternatives. How should this choice be made? What is meant by the "best" investment? To determine a "best" investment, there must be a specification of some criterion for ranking the proposed alternatives. Several of these criteria are currently in use. Any satisfactory financial criterion should be firmly based on two fundamental principles. These are (1) the "bigger the better principle" and (2) the "bird in the hand principle." Other things being equal, larger cash flows are preferred over smaller cash flows. Also, early cash flows are preferable to later cash flows. Any financial criterion selected should give weight to these two factors: the magnitude of the cash flows and the timing of the cash flows. Criteria that fully reflect the magnitude and timing of the cash flows are referred to as *discounted cash flow criteria*. The next three subsections discuss the most commonly used discounted cash flow criteria.

5.2.1 Net Present Value[5]

The net present value criterion is a logical application of the present value formulas previously presented. The net present value (*NPV*) associated with any cash flow sequence can always be calculated as[6]

$$NPV = \sum_{t=0}^{n} \frac{C_t}{(1 + i)^t} \tag{5.21}$$

where

C_t = net cash flow in period t

n = number of years involved

i = discount rate

For any proposed investment, the *NPV* for the expected cash flows can be calculated. If the *NPV* is positive, the investment would earn a profit after repaying the capital and paying interest costs incurred. If the *NPV* is negative, the returns from the investment will not be sufficient to repay the capital invested

---

[5] Other equivalent names are *present net worth* and *net discounted revenue*.
[6] For many special-case cash flows, simpler formulas for calculating *NPV* are available. A number of these have been previously discussed.

and pay the interest charges (or opportunity costs) incurred at the stated interest rate i. If a number of investments are available, the *NPV* values are used to rank the alternatives with the highest priorities assigned to the investments with the highest *NPV* values.[7]

One of the most difficult problems associated with use of the net present value criterion is selection of an appropriate value for the discount rate. The *NPV* value obtained by solution of equation (5.21) is quite sensitive to changes in the discount rate, especially for cash flow sequences that extend far into the future. As a result, relatively small changes in the discount rate can significantly alter project rankings and profitability conclusions. Although no general consensus exists concerning exact procedures for selecting the discount rate value, there does seem to be general agreement that three considerations should be taken into account.

1. The overall financial position of the firm.
2. The risk characteristics of the project being evaluated.
3. The impact of the project on the firm's financial position.

The impact of overall financial position is primarily quantified by the firm's weighted average cost of capital. For a noncorporate firm, this would simply be the interest rate at which additional funds can be borrowed. For a corporation, the value would be a weighted average cost to the firm of debt funding (borrowing money) and equity funding (obtaining money through the sale of additional stock). In almost all situations, debt funding is considerably less expensive than equity funding. Appropriate procedures for calculating the weighted average cost of capital are described in most textbooks on corporate finance (e.g., Van Horne, 1977; Brealey and Myers, 1981; Weston and Brigham, 1981). Many firms determine a weighted average cost of capital and then apply the value obtained in all financial analyses where a discount rate value is required. This amounts to ignoring two of the three considerations mentioned above: riskiness and impact on financial position. However, such an approach is justified if all projects being evaluated have similar risk and financial impact characteristics.

Risk is usually incorporated in a net present value analysis by increasing the discount rate in proportion to the riskiness of the project. This approach has intuitive appeal since it assigns a greater present value to a certain cash flow than to a risky cash flow of the same amount and with the same time of occurrence. Further discussion of risk-adjusted interest rates and an introduction to other techniques for quantifying the impact of risk are presented in Section 6.3.

The third consideration listed above relates to the changes in the firm's fi-

---

[7] Some special situations requiring modification of this simple ranking procedure are discussed in Section 5.3.

nancial position that would stem from implementation of the project being evaluated. Historically, this aspect of investment analysis has received little attention, but its importance has been increasingly recognized in recent years. The prime concern here is the impact of the project on the firm's ability to obtain debt financing. For example, consider Projects A and B that are assumed to be equally risky and produce identical cash flow sequences. Suppose that Project A involves the purchase or creation of assets that can be used as security to obtain debt funding, while Project B does not involve any such assets. This means that Project A has more value to the firm than Project B and this fact should be recognized by decreasing the discount rate used to evaluate a project in proportion to the project's contribution to the debt capacity of the firm. This consideration is particularly important in the investment analyses made by integrated forest products companies since investments in land and timber significantly enhance a firm's debt capacity position, while other potential investments contribute very little to debt capacity. Specific procedures for evaluating these financial impacts have been discussed by Miller and Modigliani (1966) and Brealey and Myers (1981).

5.2.2 Internal Rate of Return

The internal rate of return is defined as that discount rate which makes the net present value (*NPV*) of a project equal to 0. In mathematical terms, the internal rate of return is that value of i, say i^*, such that

$$\sum_{t=0}^{n} C_t/(1 + i^*)^t = 0 \qquad (5.22)$$

Consider an investment involving the purchase of a tract of land and timber for $1000. One year from now, timber sales will generate $200 in income. Two years hence, the land and timber will be sold for $950. What rate of return will the investment earn? For this investment, equation (5.22) takes the form

$$-1000 + \frac{200}{1 + i^*} + \frac{950}{(1 + i^*)^2} = 0$$

Determination of the rate of return is accomplished by finding the values of i^* that satisfy this equation. This is most easily achieved by making the substitution $X = 1/(1 + i^*)$, so that the equation becomes

$$950X^2 + 200X - 1000 = 0$$

This equation is easily solved with the quadratic formula and the roots are found to be $X = 0.9261$ and $X = -1.1366$. The corresponding values of i^* are 0.0798

(7.98%) and -1.8798 (-187.98%). Since it is obvious that the rate of return for this investment must be positive, the negative value can be dismissed as a spurious solution[8] and it can be concluded that the correct rate of return for this investment is 7.98 percent.

The example just considered constitutes a very simple rate of return computation. In contrast, consider an investment where $10,000 is spent at time 0, $5000 is spent at the end of year 1, and annual incomes of $2500 are received at the ends of years 2 through 10. Calculation of the rate of return for this cash flow pattern requires that the roots of the following equation be determined.

$$-10,000 + \frac{-5000}{1 + i^*} + \frac{2500}{(1 + i^*)^2} + \frac{2500}{(1 + i^*)^3} + \frac{2500}{(1 + i^*)^4}$$

$$+ \cdots + \frac{2500}{(1 + i^*)^{10}} = 0$$

Following the substitution $X = 1/(1 + i^*)$, the equation to be solved is a 10th-order polynomial equation in X. At this point, the following mathematical principles become pertinent.

1. In general, no closed-form solution procedures exist for polynomial equations of order greater than 4. This means that solutions to the above equation can only be obtained by trial-and-error methods.

2. An nth-order polynomial equation has n roots. Depending on the properties of the particular equation, some, all, or none of these roots are real, with the remainder being complex.

For an analyst seeking one (and only one) rate of return, these considerations are hardly comforting.

A partial resolution of these difficulties is possible. Any cash flow pattern can be categorized as uniquely belonging to one of two classes.

1. Conventional cash flow pattern—there is one and only one sign change in the cash flow sequence.

2. Nonconventional cash flow pattern—there is more than one sign change in the cash flow sequence.

---

[8] Even in cases where it is possible for the rate of return to be negative, solutions where i^* is less than -1.0 are usually ignored since this would imply that the losses for the project involved exceed the total investment.

An example of each type is shown in Table 5.6. With any conventional cash flow pattern, there will be one, and only one, real, positive solution for X [where $X = (1 + i^*)^{-1}$]. Hence, there will be a unique solution for i^*, and this solution will be greater than -1.0.

With nonconventional cash flow patterns, the situation is confused. Any given nonconventional cash flow pattern may have none, one, or several rates of return. As a case in point, consider the nonconventional cash flow sequence shown in Table 5.6. For this sequence, 0 percent is clearly a rate of return since the sum of the undiscounted inflows equals the sum of the undiscounted outflows. However, 100 percent is also a rate of return since

$$-\$1000 + \frac{\$3000}{(1 + 1)} - \frac{\$2000}{(1 + 1)^2} = 0$$

A graph showing the present value of this cash flow sequence as a function of the discount rate is shown in Figure 5.2. The graph confirms the existence of 0 percent and 100 percent as rates of return and also shows that net present value is at a maximum when the discount rate is approximately 0.3. (Differential calculus methods can be used to show that NPV is at a maximum when $i = 1/3$.)

In general, iterative procedures must be used to solve for rates of return. The calculation of internal rates of return is tedious if done manually. However, computer programs that solve for rates of return are widely available. Several models of hand-held calculators will automatically calculate the rate of return for a limited number of unequal cash flows. When the cash flows are equal, the annuity present value formula can be used to calculate rate of return.

Rate of return problems involving perpetuities can often be solved without recourse to trial-and-error methods. If an initial investment of $1000 returns a

TABLE 5.6

Example of Conventional and Nonconventional Cash Flow Patterns

Conventional Cash Flow Pattern		Nonconventional Cash Flow Pattern	
Year	Amount	Year	Amount
0	$ – 3000	0	$ – 1000
1	– 1000	1	3000
2	2000	2	– 2000
3	2000		
4	2000		
5	2000		

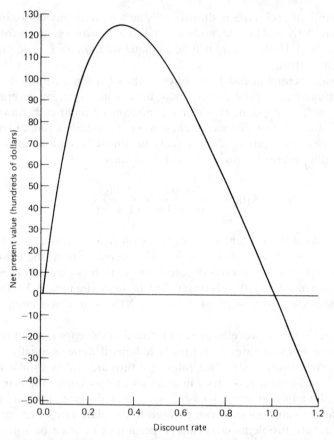

Figure 5.2 Present value of an example cash flow sequence as a function of the discount rate.

perpetual annual income of $75, the *NPV* is clearly given by

$$NPV = -\$1000 + \frac{\$75}{1 + i} + \frac{\$75}{(1 + i)^2} + \frac{\$75}{(1 + i)^3} + \cdots$$

$$= -\$1000 + \frac{\$75}{i}$$

Since the rate of return is that value of i (i^*) which makes the *NPV* equal to zero,

$$i^* = \frac{\$75}{\$1000}$$

$$= 0.075 \qquad \text{or } 7.5 \text{ percent}$$

Similarly, suppose an initial investment of $500 produces a perpetual periodic return of $1000 every 25 years. In this case,

$$NPV = -\$500 + \frac{\$1000}{(1 + i)^{25}} + \frac{\$1000}{(1 + i)^{50}} + \cdots$$

$$= -\$500 + \frac{\$1000}{(1 + i)^{25} - 1}$$

By making $NPV = 0$ and simplifying, we obtain

$$(1 + i^*)^{25} = \frac{\$1000}{\$500} + 1$$

which is easily solved to obtain the solution $i^* = 0.0449$ or 4.49 percent.

The use of the internal rate of return as an investment criterion involves the following steps.

1. Calculate the internal rate of return.

2. Compare the internal rate of return with the investor's required rate of return.

3. If the internal rate of return exceeds the required rate of return, the project should be accepted.

The required rate of return is usually determined by the investor's marginal after-tax cost of funds. The internal rate of return is the expected yield of these funds if they are invested in the project under consideration. The decision rule is based on the simple logic that funds should not be invested unless the expected yield exceeds the cost of acquiring the funds. If this criterion is used to rank alternative investments, the highest priorities would usually be assigned to the investments with the largest internal rate of return values.

5.2.3 The Benefit-Cost Ratio

Many government agencies are required by law to use the benefit-cost ratio when evaluating investment projects. In corporate finance the benefit-cost ratio, or *BCR*, if often referred to as the profitability index, or *PI*. Considerable controversy exists concerning the proper definition of the benefit-cost ratio. Some argue[9] that the proper formulation of the benefit-cost ratio is

$$BCR = \frac{\sum_{t=0}^{n} \dfrac{B_t}{(1 + i)^t}}{\sum_{t=0}^{n} \dfrac{C_t}{(1 + i)^t}} \tag{5.23}$$

where

B_t = benefits in period t

C_t = costs in period t

i = discount rate

n = number of periods involved

In this formulation the benefit and cost cash flows are discounted separately. In the preferred formulation,[10]

$$BCR = \left[\sum_{t=1}^{n} F_t/(1 + i)^t \right]/C_0 \tag{5.24}$$

where

F_t = net cash flow in period t

C_0 = initial outlay

i = discount rate

n = number of periods involved

In this formulation the denominator is the initial outlay. If a decision is made to invest in the project, the outlays in subsequent time periods are usually deductions from income rather than investments. Equation (5.24) properly recognizes this distinction.

An alleged advantage of the *BCR* arises from the fact that it is a dimension-free quantity. (Index numbers and correlation coefficients are other examples

---

[9] See Quirin, 1967, p. 35.
[10] See Van Horne, 1977, pp. 81 to 88.

of dimension-free values.) Net present value is measured in dollars and internal rate of return is a percent, but the BCR has no units attached. Some argue that this property increases the usefulness of the BCR for projects that differ greatly in size. However, it is unlikely that the maximization of *BCRs* for a corporation would maximize the wealth of the shareholders.

The steps involved in using the benefit-cost ratio as an investment criterion are as follows.

1. Calculate the benefit-cost ratio using an appropriate discount rate.
2. If the benefit-cost ratio is greater than 1, fund the project.

A benefit-cost ratio of 1 implies that the present value of the benefits equals the present value of the costs; therefore, net present value is zero. Projects with *BCRs* greater than 1 have positive net present values and internal rates of return in excess of the discount rate.

5.2.4 Payback Period

In spite of the logical considerations supporting discounted cash flow criteria, a number of firms use payback period as an investment criterion. *Payback period* is defined as the number of years required to recapture the initial investment. For example, consider the cash flow sequence shown in Table 5.7. Inspection of the cumulative cash flow values shows that the payback period is 3.5 years. The original investment is recovered in this period of time. If a project generates equal annual cash flows, then

$$\text{Payback period} = \text{Initial outlay/Annual inflow}$$

It is important to note that payback period satisfies neither of the previously stated requirements for an acceptable investment criterion. For example, con-

TABLE 5.7

Determination of Payback Period for an Example Cash Flow Sequence

Year	Cash Flow	Cumulative Cash Flow
0	$-9000	$-9000
1	2000	-7000
2	3000	-4000
3	3000	-1000
4	2000	1000
5	2000	3000

sider the cash flow sequences for Projects A and B in Table 5.8. Although the payback period for both projects is 2 years, any rational investor would clearly prefer Project B. The payback period computation ignores all cash flows after payback is achieved and, therefore, does not give proper weight to the magnitude of the cash flows. A comparison of the Project C and Project D cash flows is also interesting. The "bird in the hand" principle dictates that Project C is preferable to Project D. Yet the payback criterion indicates that the two projects are equally desirable.

The widespread use of payback period as an investment criterion indicates that decision makers gain some insight into the risk and liquidity of a project from this statistic. Cash poor firms may need to know how quickly funds can be recycled. Although it is alleged that a short payback period indicates low risk, this is not necessarily true since variability in expected cash flows is the real cause of risk. Therefore, payback period accounts for risk only to the extent that early cash flows can be forecast more accurately than later cash flows. In view of the limitations previously discussed, payback period is more appropriately used as a constraint on project selection than as an investment criterion.

5.3   CHOICE OF THE INVESTMENT CRITERION

Any investment criterion based on discounted cash flow procedures will give proper accept-reject signals. Consider any set of investment projects. If the projects are subdivided into acceptable and unacceptable groups with each of the three discounted cash flow criteria, the groupings for all three methods will be the same. Projects with BCRs greater than 1 will have positive net present value and internal rates of return greater than the discount rate. However, even though the accept-reject signals are the same for all three criteria, the ranking of projects is affected by the criterion choice. In the analysis of mutually exclusive

TABLE 5.8

Cash Flows for Four Hypothetical Investment Projects

	Cash Flows			
Year	Project A	Project B	Project C	Project D
0	$-100	$-100	$-100	$-100
1	50	50	60	40
2	50	50	40	60
3	10	25	50	50
4	5	20	50	50
5	5	10		

projects, projects must not only be categorized as accepted or rejected; the best projects must also be identified.

Project ranking can be particularly difficult when the projects differ greatly in size. Since the internal rate of return is stated as a percentage of cost the internal rates for projects with very different investments are, in a sense, not really comparable. When projects vary greatly in size, the internal rate of return analysis should be done on an incremental basis. An example of such an analysis is shown in Table 5.9 for two mutually exclusive projects. These projects could, for example, represent two levels of automation in a harvesting system in which the more expensive system results in greater annual cost savings. A simple comparison of the A and B internal rates of return would lead to selection of Project A. However, the choice of Project A may not be optimum for the firm. The incremental analysis shows that the incremental investment is $700,000. This incremental investment produces annual cash savings of $125,000 for 10 years. The rate of return on the incremental investment is 12.22%. If the cost of capital were less than 12.22%, the optimum strategy would be to select the more expensive harvesting system since the return on the incremental investment exceeds the cost of capital.

Table 5.9 also shows that an incremental approach must be used to reach the

TABLE 5.9

Incremental Internal Rate of Return Analysis for Two Mutually Exclusive Projects

	Cash Flows		
Year	Project A	Project B	Incremental (B − A)
0	$ − 300,000	$ − 1,000,000	$ − 700,000
1	75,000	200,000	125,000
2	75,000	200,000	125,000
3	75,000	200,000	125,000
4	75,000	200,000	125,000
5	75,000	200,000	125,000
6	75,000	200,000	125,000
7	75,000	200,000	125,000
8	75,000	200,000	125,000
9	75,000	200,000	125,000
10	75,000	200,000	125,000
Internal rate of return (%)	21.41	15.10	12.22
NPV at 10%	$160,842	$228,913	$68,071
BCR at 10%	1.54	1.23	1.10

correct decision with the benefit-cost ratio (*BCR*) as the decision criterion. The *BCR* for Project A exceeds that of Project B but, since the *BCR* for the incremental investment is greater than one, Project B is the preferred investment. If net present value is used as the decision criterion, an incremental analysis is unnecessary and the proper decision can be obtained by simply comparing the net present values for the two projects. (The net present value for the incremental investment is simply the difference between the Project A and Project B net present values and, therefore, provides no additional information.) Although correct decisions can be made with any of the criteria, net present value is easier to calculate and always results in correct decisions if the goal of the organization is wealth maximization.

Considerable disagreement has existed over the years concerning the relative merits of internal rate of return as opposed to net present value as an appropriate criterion for ranking investment opportunities. Which of the two is preferable depends on the reinvestment environment involved. If intermediate returns from a selected investment will be reinvested at the internal rate of return, then use of the internal rate of return criterion will produce optimum decisions. On the other hand, if intermediate returns will be reinvested at the discount rate, then use of the net present value criterion will produce the best decisions. ("Best" in this context means maximizing the cash on hand at the termination of the investment period.)

As an illustration of these concepts, consider the two project cash flow patterns shown in Table 5.10. If internal rate of return is used as the investment criterion, Project P would be preferred over Project Q. However, if net present value is used as the investment criterion with a 7 percent discount rate, Project Q would be selected as the more desirable. The key consideration in comparing the two projects involves the reinvestment rate for the intermediate cash flows in Project P. Table 5.11 shows calculation of the terminal values for the two projects when

TABLE 5.10

Cash Flow Analysis for Two Mutually Exclusive Projects

	Cash Flows		
Year	Project P	Project Q	Incremental (P − Q)
0	$ − 5000	$ − 5000	$ 0
1	2500	0	2500
2	2500	0	2500
3	2500	8640	− 6140
Internal rate of return (%)	23.38	20.00	14.50
NPV at 7%	$1560.79	$2052.81	

TABLE 5.11

Calculation of Terminal Values with Reinvestment Rates of 23.38 Percent and 7 Percent

Year	Cash Flow	Terminal Values	
		At 23.38%	At 7%
Project P			
0	$ – 5000	$ – 9391	$ – 6125
1	2500	3806	2862
2	2500	3085	2675
3	2500	2500	2500
Total		$ 0	$1912
Project Q			
0	$ – 5000	$ – 9391	$ – 6125
1	0	0	0
2	0	0	0
3	8640	8640	8640
Total		$ – 751	$2515

intermediate cash flows are reinvested at rates of 23.38 percent (the internal rate of return for Project P) and 7 percent. With a reinvestment rate of 23.38 percent, the terminal value for Project P is greater than that for Project Q, and Project P would clearly be preferable in this case. However, if the terminal values are calculated with a reinvestment rate of 7 percent, the terminal values for Projects P and Q are $1912 and $2515, respectively, so that Q is preferable.

Table 5.12 shows terminal values for Projects P and Q with a variety of reinvestment rates. Examination of these values shows that Project Q has the

TABLE 5.12

Terminal Values for Projects P and Q with Different Reinvestment Rates

Reinvestment Rate	Terminal Values	
	Project P	Project Q
0%	$2500	$3640
5	2093	2852
10	1620	1985
14.5	1134	1134
15	1077	1036
20	460	0
25	– 234	– 1126

larger terminal value for reinvestment rates less than 14.5 percent. If the reinvestment rate is greater than 14.5 percent, Project P has the greater terminal value. At 14.5 percent, both projects have equal terminal values. It is of interest to note that this "indifference rate of return" is the internal rate of return for the incremental cash flow between the two projects (see Table 5.10).

A convenient method of analysis is to construct present value profiles for the competing proposals. Present value profiles are constructed by graphing the net present values for each project as a function of the discount rate. The net present values for these two projects are displayed in Table 5.13 and the corresponding graph is shown in Figure 5.3. This graph clearly shows that the relative desirability of the two projects is dependent on the reinvestment rate.

The terminal value concept can be used to calculate an adjusted net present value or an adjusted internal rate of return when different reinvestment rates are assumed throughout the planning horizon. Consider Project P in Table 5.10 with annual cash flows of $2500 in years 1 through 3. Suppose it is expected that the cash flow in year 1 can be reinvested at 10 percent and the cash flow in year 2 can be reinvested at 15 percent. The terminal value (TV) for this project is

$$TV = \$2500 \ (1.1)(1.15) + \$2500 \ (1.15) + \$2500 = \$8537.50$$

The adjusted rate of return can be found as the value for i^* such that

$$0 = \frac{\$8537.50}{(1 + i^*)^3} - \$5000$$

TABLE 5.13

Net Present Value for Project P and Q with Varying Discount Rates

Discount Rate	Net Present Value	
	Project P	Project Q
0%	$2500	$3640
5	1808	2464
10	1217	1491
14.5	756	756
15	708	681
20	266	0
25	− 120	− 576

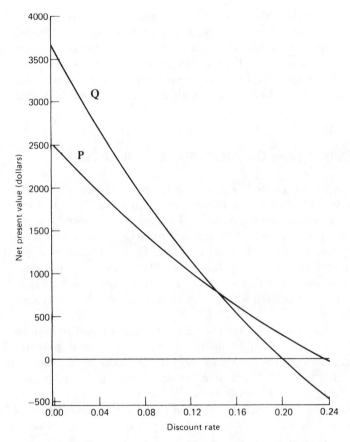

Figure 5.3 Present value profiles for two mutually exclusive investments.

In this case, $i^* = 19.52\%$. An adjusted net present value may be calculated in a similar manner. The adjusted net present value is defined as

$$\text{Adjusted net present value} = \frac{\text{Terminal value}}{(1 + i)^n} - \text{Cost}$$

where i is the discount rate. For this example, with a discount rate of 12%, the adjusted net present value is $\$8537.50/(1.12)^3 - \$5000 = \$1076.82$.

In summary, it is generally agreed that use of the net present value criterion will result in the optimum portfolio of projects given the goal of wealth maximization and the presence of perfect capital markets. If there are market imperfections such as capital rationing then constrained maximization of net present value is appropriate. Mathematical programming models are useful in selecting a portfolio of investments subject to constraints, such as a budget ceiling on capital investment. In theory, if a firm adopts a project with a net present value of $1000, the value of the firm should increase $1000. Net present value is the generally preferred investment criterion because it is unambiguous, relatively easy to calculate, and compatible with the goal of wealth maximization of the owners.

5.4 ADJUSTING FOR ANTICIPATED INFLATION

The decade of the 1970s was characterized by sustained high rates of inflation. Inflation rates for several countries are shown in Table 5.14. Of those considered, only West Germany managed to hold the rate of inflation to a tolerable level in the period mentioned. With rates of inflation in excess of 8 percent, long-term investments are difficult to evaluate. Forest investments are, by nature, long-term investments that are not liquid. Many forest-resource decision makers have erred in the evaluation of investment projects because they failed to include the effects of anticipated inflation in their analyses. A typical scenario can be outlined as follows.

Suppose a firm is appraising the value of a tract of land and timber. The stand involved is a 5-year-old pine plantation. The firm plans to harvest the stand at age 30 years and sell the bare land. Ad valorem taxes and management expenses are estimated to be $1.75 per acre per year. Current stumpage rates are $25.00 per cord. On the basis of comparable sales, the current bare land value is estimated to be $300 per acre. Yield at harvest is estimated to be 45 cords per acre, and the firm's cost of capital is 15 percent. The appraised value of the tract is

$$V_0 = (45 \times \$25 + \$300)/(1.15)^{25} - \$1.75 \left(\frac{1.15^{25} - 1}{0.15 \, (1.15)^{25}} \right)$$

$$= \$43.29 - \$11.31$$

$$= \$31.98 \text{ per acre}$$

Of course, this appraised value borders on absurdity. The reason lies in the fact that the cash flows are estimated on the basis of constant dollars, but the discount rate includes the impact of anticipated inflation. If a firm sells bonds to raise capital, the investors who purchase the bonds adjust the price they bid for the bonds to include expected inflation. If the firm borrows funds from a lending institution such as a bank, the interest rate includes an adjustment for the anticipated effects of inflation. Irving Fisher (1930) first developed the theory, stating that the nominal rate of interest is the product of the "pure" interest

TABLE 5.14

Consumer Price Inflation for Selected Countries (percent change per year)

	Canada	United States	Japan	West Germany
1960–1970	2.6	2.7	5.6	2.5
1971–1973	5.0	4.6	7.5	5.9
1974–1975	10.8	10.1	18.1	6.5
1976–1980	9.0	9.1	6.3	4.1

Source: Review, Federal Reserve Bank of St. Louis, July 1978, p. 12, and *Review,* Federal Reserve Bank of St. Louis, June/July 1981, p. 23.

rate and the anticipated inflation rate. Historically, the pure interest rate has remained around 3 to 4 percent. If the inflation rate is 10 percent and the pure rate is 4 percent, the nominal interest rate will be $(1 + 0.04)(1 + 0.1) = 1.144$, or 14.4 percent. In general,

$$(1 + k) = (1 + i)(1 + g) \tag{5.25}$$

where

k = nominal rate

i = "pure" interest rate

g = expected inflation rate

It follows that $k = i + g + ig$. Since ig is usually small, it is often ignored, and k is estimated as simply $i + g$. In the preceding example, if the inflows are estimated in uninflated dollars and the pure interest rate is 3 percent,

$$V_0 = (45 \times \$25 + 300)/(1.03)^{25} - 1.75 \left(\frac{1.03^{25} - 1}{0.03(1.03)^{25}} \right)$$

$$= 680.50 - 30.47$$

$$= \$650.12 \text{ per acre}$$

An alternative approach is to express the cash flows in terms of inflated dollars. If the cash flows are calculated in inflated dollars, the discount rate should include an adjustment for anticipated inflation. If all costs and returns inflate at a constant rate, then no adjustment is necessary. In this situation,

$$NPV = \sum_{t=0}^{n} \frac{C_t(1 + g)^t}{(1 + i)^t (1 + g)^t}$$

The inflation factors cancel in each term and

$$NPV = \sum_{t=0}^{n} C_t/(1 + i)^t$$

where C_t is the cash flow in constant dollars and i is the pure or inflation-free discount rate.

The most general approach to this problem is to recognize that all cost and income components are affected similarly by overall inflation (since inflation is basically a redefinition of the currency), but that each component has its own "real value" (i.e., constant dollar) escalation rate. To reflect these concepts, the following variables are defined.

C_{tj} = jth cash flow item occurring in year t

r_j = real value growth rate for cash flow item j

i = inflation-free interest rate

g = expected inflation rate

m = number of different cash flow items

n = number of years

Net present value can be calculated as

$$NPV = \sum_{t=0}^{n} \frac{\sum_{j=1}^{m} C_{tj} (1 + r_j)^t (1 + g)^t}{(1 + i)^t (1 + g)^t} \tag{5.26}$$

The computations can be carried out in this form so that inflated values actually appear in the computations. However, the factor $(1 + g)^t$ can be canceled in the numerator and denominator of equation (5.26) so that the equation

$$NPV = \sum_{t=0}^{n} \frac{\sum_{j=1}^{m} C_{tj} (1 + r_j)^t}{(1 + i)^t} \tag{5.27}$$

gives results identical to those obtained with equation (5.26).

The appraisal of forest properties using inflated cash flows has not found wide acceptance. This is partly because inflated values seem unduly high. For example, if the current stumpage price for pine pulpwood is \$25 per cord and if stumpage prices increase at a rate of 12 percent per year for 25 years, the projected stumpage price 25 years hence is \$25 $(1.12)^{25}$ = \$425.00 per cord. Few forest decision makers are comfortable in the presence of stumpage prices of this magnitude. Yet, as shown earlier, the general level of prices has risen at almost 10 percent annually for the past decade. The key question is how long will double-digit inflation persist. During this past period of high inflation, firms have incorrectly rejected forest investment opportunities by failing to incorporate the effects of inflation in their analyses (Gregersen, 1975). Discounting constant-dollar cash flows by an inflation-adjusted cost of capital has resulted in unrealistically low appraised values and an underinvestment in forest properties and silvicultural practices.

REFERENCES

Boulding, K. 1955. *Economic analysis*. 3rd ed. Harper & Brothers, New York.

Brealey, R., and S. Myers. 1981. *Principles of corporate finance*. McGraw-Hill, New York.

Davis, K. P. 1966. *Forest management: regulation and valuation*. McGraw-Hill, New York.

Faustman, M. 1849. Berechnung des Werthes, welchen Waldboden, sowie noch nicht haubara Holzbestände für die Waldwirthschaft besitzen. *Allg. Forst U. Jagd Ztg.* **15**:441–455. (An English translation of this paper is contained in Gane, 1968.)

Fisher, I. 1930. *The theory of interest*. Macmillan, New York.

Flick, W. A. 1975. A note on inflation and forest investments. *For. Sci.* **22**:30–32.

Fortson, J. C., and R. C. Field. 1979. Capital budgeting techniques for forestry: a review. *So. J. App. For.* **3**(4):141–143.

Foster, B. B. 1979. Adjusting discount rates for risk. *J. For.* **77**:287–288.

Gane, M. 1968. Martin Faustman and the evolution of discounted cash flow. *Oxford Institute Paper 42*.

Gregersen, H. M. 1975. Effect of inflation on evaluation of forestry investments. *J. For.* **73**:570–572.

Hirshleifer, J. 1970. *Investment, interest and capital*. Prentice-Hall, Englewood Cliffs, N.J.

Marty, R. 1969. The composite internal rate of return. *For. Sci.* **16**:276–279.

Miller, M. H., and F. Modigliani. 1966. Some estimates of the cost of capital in the electrical utility industry: 1954–1957. *Amer. Econ. Rev.* **56**:333–391.

Quirin, G. D. 1967. *The capital expenditure decision*. Irwin, Homewood, Ill.

Samuelson, P. A. 1976. Economics of forestry in an evolving society. *Economic Inquiry* **XIV**:466–492.

Schallau, C. H., and M. E. Wirth. 1980. Reinvestment rate and the analysis of forestry enterprises. *J. For.* **78**:740–742.

Van Horne, J. C. 1977. *Financial management and policy*. 4th ed. Prentice-Hall, Englewood Cliffs, N.J.

Weston, J. F., and E. F. Brigham. 1981. *Managerial finance*. Dryden, Hinsdale, Ill.

6

Taxes and Risk in the Evaluation of Forest Investments

A significant portion of the incomes generated by firms and households is not available for consumption or reinvestment but instead flows to various governmental units in the form of taxes. Incomes generated from forest properties are used to pay income, property, yield, and severance taxes. The amounts of these taxes have great significance for forest investors since only the residual after-tax cash flows are available for use by the investor. Publicly held forest properties are generally exempt from taxation, but tax considerations are involved in nearly every business decision made by individuals and profit-oriented firms.

The discussion on taxes in this section is very general and specifically restricted to the United States. United States tax laws are complex and subject to frequent modification. Tax considerations are of such importance that most firms and individuals managing substantial forest properties require assistance in tax planning and return preparation from appropriately qualified specialists.

6.1 FEDERAL INCOME TAXES

The Sixteenth Amendment to the United States Constitution was adopted in 1913. This amendment provided for a federal income tax. Initially, the amount of the tax was an inconsequential item for most taxpayers but, over the years, federal income tax rates have increased substantially and the maximum marginal tax rate on personal income has, at times, been as high as 90 percent. The federal government has also learned that the income tax is a useful tool for implementing certain aspects of national policy. Minor changes in the tax structure are frequently introduced to stimulate or dampen the rate of economic growth. In addition, activities deemed by the government to be socially desirable can be encouraged by the passage of tax legislation that makes investment in these activities economically attractive.

Although the tax laws as passed by Congress and the regulations, rulings, and court decisions interpreting those laws are constantly evolving, the basic structure of the income tax laws has been relatively stable. Generally speaking, the computation of the income tax obligation for any individual or corporation follows the formula

$$T = TR[f(I) - g(E)] - C \qquad (6.1)$$

where

T = amount of tax

$f(I)$ = function of the incomes received

$g(E)$ = function of the expenditures incurred

TR = tax rate, which is a function of $[f(I) - g(E)]$

C = tax credits

The quantity $[f(I) - g(E)]$ is referred to as *taxable income* and the items included in $g(E)$ are *tax deductions*. It is important to understand the distinction between a tax deduction and a tax credit. Deductions are subtracted from income prior to multiplication by the tax rate. Tax credits are subtracted, in their entirety, from the computed tax.

6.1.1 Incomes

For federal income tax purposes, any income is classified into one of two categories. The first of these, *capital gains*, includes profits from the sale of capital assets, where capital assets are defined as assets that are not bought or sold in the ordinary course of a person's or firm's trade or business. Any taxable income that does not qualify as capital gains income is considered to be *ordinary income*. Capital gains and ordinary income are taxed differently for both corporations and individuals.

From the taxpayer's standpoint, capital gains income is more valuable than

TABLE 6.1

Federal Income Tax Rates for Corporations—1982

Taxable Income (*TI*)	Amount of Tax
1. Ordinary Income	
0– $25,000	0.16 (*TI*)
$25,000– $50,000	$4000 + 0.19 (*TI* − $25,000)
$50,000– $75,000	$8750 + 0.30 (*TI* − $50,000)
$75,000–$100,000	$16,250 + 0.40 (*TI* − $75,000)
$100,000 +	$26,250 + 0.46 (*TI* − $100,000)
2. Capital Gains Income	
	Tax = 0.28 (Taxable gain)

ordinary income because it is, in effect, taxed at a lower rate.[1] For individuals, 60 percent of net long-term capital gains is exempt from taxation. The remaining 40 percent is taxed at the individual's marginal ordinary income tax rate. Therefore, since the maximum ordinary income tax rate for individuals is now (as of January 1, 1982) 50 percent, the maximum effective tax rate on individual capital gains income is 20 percent. The 60 percent capital gains exclusion does not apply to corporate taxpayers. Corporations derive advantages from capital gains income through a process known as the *alternative tax calculation*. When the alternative tax calculation is used, the corporation's tax obligation is computed in two ways.

1. All income is treated as ordinary income and taxed at the appropriate ordinary income rate. (The 1982 corporate tax rates for ordinary income are shown in Table 6.1).

2. Separate taxable income figures are obtained for capital gains and ordinary income. A tax rate of 28 percent is applied to taxable capital gains, and the appropriate ordinary income tax rate is applied to taxable ordinary income. The total tax is the sum of the two components.

The final tax obligation (before deduction of tax credits) is the lesser of the two amounts.

A superficial examination of the alternative tax calculation might suggest the conclusion that corporate taxpayers with capital gains income will always benefit

---

[1] It should be noted that this more favorable tax treatment is available only to capital gains produced by the sale or exchange of capital assets that have been owned for more than 1 year. Such incomes are termed *long-term capital gains*. *Short-term capital gains* are taxed at the same rate as ordinary income.

from use of method 2. Such a conclusion would be incorrect since there are at least two situations in which method 1 would produce a lower tax obligation. The first of these is fairly obvious and involves corporate taxpayers with less than $50,000 of total taxable income (capital gains plus ordinary income). In this situation the marginal ordinary income tax rate is less than the capital gains tax rate.

The second situation in which method 1 might be preferred arises when a corporate taxpayer's potential deductions against ordinary income exceed the ordinary income and results from the fact that a taxable income figure cannot be less than 0 (i.e., it is impossible to have a negative tax). As the simplest example of such a situation, consider a corporate taxpayer with taxable capital gains of $1 million, no ordinary income, and $500,000 of potential deductions against ordinary income. (These potential deductions against ordinary income cannot be used as deductions against capital gains income.) Under method 1 of the alternative tax calculation, the total ordinary income is $500,000 and the tax obligation is $210,250 (from Table 6.1). Under method 2, the $1 million capital gain is taxed at 28 percent to give a required tax payment of $280,000. Method 1 gives a lower tax obligation in this case, but neither method is able to take full advantage of the taxpayer's potential tax benefits. With method 1, the taxpayer receives no benefit from capital gains tax treatment while, with method 2, no reduction in taxes results from the potential deductions against ordinary income. If the taxpayer's income consisted of $600,000 in ordinary income and $400,000 of capital gains, the method 2 calculation of tax would give

$$\text{Tax} = \$26,250 + 0.28(\$400,000)$$
$$= \$138,250$$

In this case, the taxpayer has taken full advantage of the capital gains tax rate and the potential deductions against ordinary income. The considerations developed in the above discussion of the alternative tax calculation are particularly pertinent to the forest products industry where it is quite possible for the major portion of a firm's income to be in the form of capital gains.

6.1.2 Deductions

For both individuals and corporations, all legitimate business expenditures may be used as income tax deductions.[2] Any given expenditure is applied as a deduction by either "expensing" the amount involved or "capitalizing" it. When

---

[2] A number of nonbusiness expenditures can be used as deductions by individuals. Such deductions are called *itemized deductions* Examples are nonbusiness-related interest costs, state sales tax expense, and, in some cases, a portion of medical costs.

a cost is expensed, it is deducted, in its entirety, during the tax year in which the cost is incurred. When a cost is capitalized, it is not entirely deducted from income during the tax year involved. As a general rule, expenditures that do not directly contribute to the firm's productivity in future tax years may be expensed. Expenditures that do contribute directly to future productivity must, in general, be capitalized. Cost items that are typically expensed include salaries and wages, property taxes, supplies, raw materials, and utility expenses. Expenditures that must be capitalized generally represent the purchase prices or construction costs of income-producing assets. Thus, the cost of such items as motor vehicles, manufacturing equipment, buildings, and land must be capitalized.

There are three general methods for deducting capitalized expenditures. The first applies to the cost of any "nonwasting" asset and simply involves subtracting the cost of the asset (the asset's "cost basis" or "basis") from the amount realized by the sale of the asset. The taxable gain (or loss) is therefore the amount realized from the sale less the asset's basis. This is the only method available for deducting costs incurred for the purchase of land. When land is bought, the purchase expense is not recognized for tax purposes until the land is sold.

The cost of any "wasting" asset (i.e., any asset that wears out or becomes obsolete during its period of use) is deducted through a process known as *depreciation*. When the cost of an asset is depreciated, a portion of the cost basis is deducted in each of several years. The total of all deductions taken cannot exceed the cost basis of the asset. Prior to 1981, the cost basis of an asset was deducted over the "useful life" of the asset. The amount deductible in any given year was determined by the straight-line method or an accelerated method. The straight-line method produced equal deductions during each year of the asset's useful life. For example, for an asset with a 10-year expected useful life, 10 percent of the original cost basis would be deducted each year for 10 years. In comparison to the straight-line method, accelerated methods generated larger depreciation deductions during the early years of an asset's useful life and smaller deductions in the later years. The two most popular methods of accelerated depreciation are known as the *sum of the year's digits* and the *declining-balance method*.

The Economic Recovery Tax Act of 1981 has replaced the previous depreciation calculation methods with a totally new depreciation system known as the *accelerated cost recovery system* or *ACRS*. In the previously used methods, selection by the taxpayer of a useful life for each asset (subject to IRS approval) determined the pattern of deductions claimed. The ACRS approach does not involve the concept of useful life. Instead the nature of an asset now places it in one of four general cost recovery classes: the 3-year class, 5-year class, 10-year class, or 15-year class. For each class, prescribed percentages are applied to the original cost basis to determine the allowable depreciation in each year of the cost recovery period involved. The applicable percentages by class for property placed in service after December 31, 1980 and before January 1, 1985 are shown in Table 6.2. For a 5-year asset placed in service on January 1, 1983 and costing $10,000, the allowable depreciation by years would be

1983	$1,500
1984	2,200
1985	2,100
1986	2,100
1987	2,100
Total	$ 10,000

The following are some examples of the kinds of property that fall into each cost recovery class.

1. *Three-year property*: Automobiles, light trucks, research and development equipment, and other personal property[3] that previously had an expected useful life of 4 years or less.

2. *Five-year property*: Heavy-duty trucks, most production-line machinery, most office furniture, office machines and office equipment, ships, aircraft, single-purpose agricultural and horticultural structures (e.g., chicken houses and greenhouses), and other personal property that previously had an expected useful life of more than 4 years.

3. *Ten-year property*: Railroad tank cars, manufactured residential homes, and depreciable real property[3] that previously had an expected useful life of 12.5 years or less.

4. *Fifteen-year property*: Depreciable real property that previously had an expected life of more than 12.5 years.

It is possible for the taxpayer to select a longer "optional" recovery period in place of the standard period for the class of property involved. However, this selection must be made for all property in a particular class that is placed in service during a given year. With an optional recovery period, depreciation is calculated using the straight-line method.

In comparison to previous depreciation methods, the accelerated cost recovery system provides for a much more rapid tax writeoff of capital investment, which,

---

[3] The earth's crust and objects firmly attached to it constitute real property. Other items that can be owned are personal property. The basic distinction is that personal property can be moved about and real property cannot.

TABLE 6.2

Depreciation Percentages by Cost Recovery Class for Property Placed in Service after December 31, 1980 and before January 1, 1985.

	Applicable Percentage by Class			
Recovery Year	3 Year	5 Year	10 Year	15 Year
1	25	15	8	5
2	38	22	14	10
3	37	21	12	9
4		21	10	8
5		21	10	7
6			10	7
7			9	6
8			9	6
9			9	6
10			9	6
11				6
12				6
13				6
14				6
15				6

in turn, should stimulate new capital formation and lead to increased productivity. In addition, the use of shorter cost recovery periods will reduce certain inequities that exist in depreciation systems during periods of high inflation.

The third method used for deducting capitalized expenditures is *cost depletion* or simply *depletion*. Cost depletion is used to deduct timber acquisition costs and capitalized timber growing costs. To compute the annual depletion deduction, timber owners must have three items of information: (1) the dollar amount of their investment in timber (the basis), (2) the number of timber volume units in their holdings, and (3) the number of timber volume units cut from their holdings during the tax year. The depletion rate per unit volume is calculated by dividing the number of timber volume units owned into the dollar amount of the timber investment. Depletion for the taxable year is then calculated as the product of the depletion rate per unit and the number of units cut. The dollar amount of the basis is reduced by the depletion deduction that is taken during the taxable year.

To illustrate the procedure, consider the case of a tree farmer Mr. Jones. Mr. Jones purchased a tract of land and timber in 1963 for $30,000. At the time of purchase the tract contained 500 Mbf (thousand board feet) valued at $30 per Mbf. The depletion basis was, therefore, $15,000. In 1979, Mr. Jones sold 500 Mbf at $100 per Mbf. By the time of the sale, the volume of timber on the tract had increased to 1000 Mbf. The depletion rate per unit volume was therefore $15,000/1000 Mbf = $15 per Mbf. The depletion deduction was calculated as $15 per Mbf times 500 Mbf = $7500 to give a taxable gain of $50,000 − $7500 = $42,500. As of January 1, 1980, the adjusted basis for depletion became $15,000 − $7500 = $7500, and the timber account contained 500 Mbf. The depletion rate after the sale still amounted to $15 per Mbf. In subsequent years, any capitalized timber-growing costs would be added to the basis and the volume would be increased to reflect growth. In timber growing, expenditures that must be capitalized include site preparaton costs, cost of seedlings or seed, planting costs, and construction of permanent roads and fire lines. The timber owner can elect to expense or capitalize such expenditures as annual ad valorem or property tax; interest costs associated with financing the timber; costs of thinning, pruning, and improvement cutting; costs of protection against fire, insects, and disease; and cost of prescribed burning. The profit-oriented firm will usually expense these items since this will, in effect, delay the payment of taxes.

Many people mistakenly believe that cost depletion provides preferential tax treatment for timber owners. There is no preferential or special-interest aspect involved in cost depletion. The tax laws universally allow for the tax-free recovery of invested capital when any asset is sold, with tax being paid only on the difference between the selling price and the seller's cost. Cost depletion is simply the process by which the tax-free recovery of timber investments is accomplished.[4]

Now that the distinction between expensed and capitalized deductions has been made and procedures for capitalizing expenses have been discussed, it is pertinent to point out an important property of deductible expenditures. When an expenditure can be deducted for income tax purposes, the ultimate after-tax cost of the expenditure will generally be less (and often considerably less) than the actual cash outlay. For example, suppose a large corporation gives one of its executives a $10,000 bonus. For tax purposes, this bonus would be treated as an ordinary expense (i.e., as a deduction against ordinary income). Payment of the bonus will therefore reduce the corporation's taxable ordinary income by $10,000 and, as a result, the total tax paid by the corporation will be reduced by $4600 (assuming the corporation has a marginal tax rate of 46 percent). With the tax saving, the after-tax cost of the $10,000 bonus is only $5400. The general relationship is

$$ATC = BTC(1 - TR) \qquad (6.2)$$

---

[4] Many people confuse cost depletion with percentage depletion, which provides special tax credits for owners of oil wells, coal mines, and certain other similar facilities.

where

ATC = after-tax cost

BTC = before-tax cost

TR = effective tax rate

It is important to remember that this relationship only applies in situations where the expenditure can be used as a deduction. If a firm does not make a profit, it will pay no taxes and some of the expenditures incurred will not generate any tax reduction. The after-tax cost of these expenditures will be equal to the before-tax cost.

6.1.3 Tax Credits

A wide variety of unrelated situations generate opportunities for tax credits. Unlike deductions, which are subtracted from income prior to multiplication by the tax rate, credits are subtracted, in their entirety, from the tax obligation. Most tax credit opportunities apply to only a few taxpayers and are of little overall importance. One tax credit, however, that does have great general significance is the investment tax credit which was first introduced in 1962. The investment tax credit allows an individual or corporation to claim a percentage of the dollar amount expended for new, long-term capital investment as a credit against income tax.

Prior to passage of the Economic Recovery Tax Act of 1981, the allowable investment credit percentage depended on the useful life of the asset. (For example, with an asset having a 7-year useful life, the taxpayer could claim a tax credit equal to 10 percent of the asset's cost. The equivalent figure for an asset with a 3-year useful life was $3\frac{1}{3}$ percent.) Since provisions of the accelerated cost recovery system, which is part of the Economic Recovery Tax Act, removed the concept of useful life from depreciation calculation, modifications in investment credit procedures were also provided to achieve consistency. For depreciable property placed in service after 1980, the investment credit is based on the recovery period used in determining depreciation deductions. A 10 percent credit rate is used for all four classes of property (3-year, 5-year, 10-year, and 15-year classes). With 5-year, 10-year, and 15-year property, 100 percent of the cost qualifies for inclusion in computation of the investment credit. Thus, if a firm in 1983 purchases a $20,000 asset classified as 5-year property, the firm would be entitled to an investment tax credit of $2000 (0.10 × $20,000) on its 1983 tax return. However, with 3-year property, only 60 percent of the cost can be used for computation of the credit. Thus, the investment tax credit created by purchase of a 3-year asset costing $15,000 would be $900 [0.10(0.60 × $15,000)].

Investment tax credits stimulate investment by increasing the after-tax yield of investment projects. Public Law 96-451, enacted in October 1980, provides a 10 percent investment tax credit on reforestation expenses for qualified taxpayers. The specifics of this legislation will be discussed in Section 6.1.5.

6.1.4 Tax Treatment of Timber Incomes

Capital gains income has been previously defined as income arising from the sale of capital assets. Capital assets are assets that are not bought and sold in the ordinary course of the taxpayer's trade or business. Thus, if a forester bought 100 shares of stock for $5000 and sold them 2 years later for $7000, the profit of $2000 would be taxed as a long-term capital gain. However, if identical transactions had been made by a stockbroker, the $2000 would be taxed as ordinary income. Since 1944, U.S. tax regulations have included special provisions concerning the applicability of capital gains treatment for timber incomes. These provisions make it possible for a taxpayer who owns and disposes of timber to receive capital gains treatment on the income received, even though the taxpayer is in the business of growing and selling timber. Congress adopted these provisions to encourage capital investment in timber growing, and there is no doubt that the provisions have had the intended effect (Fortson and Hargreaves, 1974).[5] The impact of capital gains tax treatment for timber incomes is sufficiently significant to justify some discussion of the history of the pertinent legislation.

Prior to 1944, there was only one situation in which income from a timber sale could be taxed as capital gains (Briggs and Condrell, 1978). This situation occurred if, and only if,

1. The seller was not in the business of growing and selling timber.
2. The timber income was obtained from a so-called "lump-sum" sale in which the timber was sold outright at a fixed total price.

If owners cut timber for processing in their own manufacturing facilities, they were required to pay taxes at ordinary income tax rates on any gains resulting from this practice. Moreover, if owners of timber marked their stands for selective harvesting and sold the marked timber at an agreed on price per unit volume, the income received was taxed as ordinary income. These obvious inequities were corrected in 1944 with the enactment of Section 117K as a part

---

[5] It is not uncommon for Congress to modify the tax laws to encourage "socially desirable" investments. For example, interest from municipal bonds has, for some time, been exempt from federal income taxation because Congress feels it is in the public interest for municipalities to be able to raise funds at relatively low cost. More recently, Congress responded to the energy shortage by making special tax credits available for investments that improve energy efficiency.

of the Internal Revenue Code of 1939. In addition to dealing with the inequities that affected small landowners who made occasional timber sales, Section 117K also made it possible for individuals and firms in the business of growing timber to receive capital gains tax treatment for their timber incomes. Although President Roosevelt vetoed the initial version of the bill, it was subsequently signed into law.

In 1954, Section 117K was re-enacted as Section 631 of the Internal Revenue Code of 1954. Section 631(a) permits taxpayers who cut timber for sale or use in their own trade or business to claim a gain or loss equal to the difference between the fair market value of the timber and the adjusted basis for depletion. *Fair market value* is defined as the price that a willing buyer would pay a willing seller when neither one is under a compulsion to buy or sell and both are reasonably informed of all pertinent facts. Most vertically integrated forest products firms use the provisions of Section 631(a) in determining their income tax obligation. For tax computation purposes, the process essentially assumes that a hypothetical sale has taken place with the amount of the sale being equal to the fair market value of the timber. The difference between the fair market value and the adjusted basis for depletion is taxed as a capital gains income to the woodlands sector of the firm, whereas the fair market value of the timber is treated as an ordinary expense for the manufacturing sector of the firm.

The provisions of Section 631(b) make it possible for all timber owners to receive capital gains treatment for income from the sale of timber that they have owned for at least 12 months if the timber is disposed of under a contract that provides for a "retained economic interest" on the part of the seller. The capital gain is the amount received from the sale less the adjusted basis for depletion. Section 631(b) is applicable to situations in which timber cutting rights are transferred to another party (i.e., stumpage sales). The wording of the timber sale contract determines whether the seller has a retained economic interest. If the contract specifies a total fixed price for the timber (a lump-sum sale), the seller does not have a retained economic interest. However, if the contract provides for a stated price per unit volume with the total income to the seller being dependent on the volume actually harvested, then the seller has a retained economic interest and is unquestionably entitled to capital gains tax treatment for the incomes received.

Timber owners who sell stumpage without retaining an economic interest are entitled to capital gains treatment only if the growing and selling of timber is outside the course of their normal trade or business. Determining whether the growing and selling of timber is "primarily for sale to customers in the ordinary course of business" is often a difficult matter. The most important consideration seems to be whether the sales occur frequently over a considerable period of time or are isolated and casual. Sections 631(a) and 631(b) qualify timber income for capital gains treatment regardless of the frequency of timber sales; therefore, less risk is involved if the owner elects to qualify for capital gains treatment under one of these provisions of the code.

*6.1.5   Tax Incentive Provisions of Public Law 96-451

On October 14, 1980, Public Law 96-451 became law. An amendment to this law, often referred to as the Packwood Amendment, provides incentives for reforestation. The key provisions are: (1) a 10% investment tax credit and (2) a 7-year amortization schedule for the first $10,000 of capitalized reforestation expenses each year. The amortization period begins at the midpoint of the tax year in which the expenses are incurred and ends at the midpoint of the seventh year thereafter. As a result, amortization deductions will be included on the returns for 8 different years.

The effective date of this act was December 31, 1979, and the law is applicable to the 50 states and the District of Columbia. The 7-year amortization schedule allows landowners to deduct 1/14 of their regeneration expenditures in the year in which the investment is made (year 1). During each of the next 6 years (years 2 to 7), 1/7 of the expense can be deducted, with the remaining 1/14 deducted in year 8. Therefore, landowners spending $10,000 in site preparation and planting are eligible to receive a $1000 tax credit (10 percent times $10,000) in the year of the investment. In addition, investors could deduct $714 (1/14 times $10,000) in the year of the investment and $1429 (1/7 times $10,000) in years 2 to 7. In year 8, the remaining $714 would be deducted.

6.2   PROPERTY, YIELD, AND SEVERANCE TAXES

In addition to income taxes, forest owners must pay property taxes. In recent years, many states have modified the property tax laws to provide forest landowners some measure of relief from property tax rates that had increased, in some places to the point of becoming confiscatory. In some states (e.g., Georgia, Kentucky, and South Carolina), both forestland and standing timber are subject to property taxes. This is in marked contrast to agricultural enterprises where only the land is taxed. However, forestland is usually taxed differently from agricultural land.

The annual property tax (or "ad valorem" tax) is calculated as the product of the appraised value, the assessment ratio, and the tax rate (or "millage" rate). In Georgia, for example, the current assessment ratio is 40 percent of full market value. Thus, if an acre of land and timber has a market value of $750, its assessed value is 0.4 times $750, which is $300. With a tax rate of 15 mills (1.5 cents of tax per dollar of assessed value), the annual property tax would be $4.50 per acre.

Many states now require that all property be assessed at full market value. Full market value appraisal promotes uniform appraisals throughout a state and reduces inequities resulting from different methods of appraisal in various tax districts. Since the market is the ultimate determiner of value, full market value appraisal is objective. Property has traditionally been valued on the so-called "highest and best use" basis rather than on an actual use basis. Thus, forestlands located near interstate highways or urban developments are often taxed on their value as sites for commercial development or subdivisions. Once the land is taxed at a commercial or residential rate, the owner is virtually forced, economically, to remove the land from timber production and develop it. Florida is one of the states that has recognized this problem and has adopted an appraisal system based on present use rather than highest and best use. In Florida, forestland is valued by discounting the expected future cash flows generated by the sale of timber. The impact of site quality on timber yield is considered, and sites with high-growth potential have higher appraised values.

The assessment of annual property taxes on standing timber creates difficulties for both the taxpayer and the taxing authority. In theory, the assessed value should increase as the per-acre timber value increases and it should decrease whenever timber is harvested. However, in practice, few taxing authorities attempt to fully implement such a system because of the complex bookkeeping involved. If assessed values on standing timber do increase as the stand grows older, landowners will be tempted to shorten their rotations and this may impair forest productivity. These considerations have led a number of states to replace their annual property tax on standing timber with a tax on the value of harvested timber. Such a tax is referred to as a *yield tax*. A yield tax is a substitute for property taxes on standing timber, but the existence of a yield tax does not generally exempt the land from annual ad valorem taxation. Yield taxes are usually calculated as a percentage of stumpage value for the timber harvested. Hargreaves (1980) reports that 16 states now have some form of a yield tax.

Severance taxes are similar in some respects to yield taxes but are imposed to generate revenues in addition to that produced by a yield tax or an ad valorem tax on standing timber. In some cases, the revenue generated from the severance tax is earmarked for state forestry programs. Severance taxes are usually paid by the timber harvester with the rate set as a specific amount per unit volume. In Alabama, for example, the severance tax for pine sawtimber is 30 cents per 1000 board feet, Doyle log scale. In 1980, seven states had severance taxes (Condrell, 1980).

*6.3 METHODS FOR EVALUATING RISK IN FOREST INVESTMENTS

An investment made today in site preparation and planting will not produce economic returns until, perhaps, 25 to 50 years (or longer) in the future, and any analysis of this investment requires the prediction of harvest yields and stumpage prices in the future. Only wizards can make such predictions with certainty. Ordinary mortals will always find such predictions difficult and, if they are wise mortals, they will realize that the predictions they make concerning future cash flows are subject to error. The inability to estimate future cash flows with certainty is the basic cause of risk in an investment. A government security is termed *risk free* because the future cash flows are known with almost absolute certainty. If a 3-month U.S. Treasury bill is purchased today, the owner is certain that he will receive the face value of the bill at maturity. Of course, inflationary risks are always present. Although the face value of the bill is known, the purchasing power of this specific future amount is not known.

Risk occurs whenever there is a statistical distribution of the possible cash flow outcomes. Generally, the greater the dispersion of the cash flow estimates, the greater the risk.[6] What will the average price of southern pine pulpwood be in 10 years? Most nonwizards would truthfully reply, "I don't know." However, decisions must be made today on the basis of uncertain future costs and returns. Even though the future stumpage price is unknown, it may be possible to specify a distribution of future prices. Suppose the set of stumpage prices and associated probabilities shown in Table 6.3 is felt to be applicable. Such estimates are, of course, subjective. They are usually based on a knowledge of past trends and are augmented by intuitive feelings about the future. For such a distribution, the expected outcome is calculated as

$$E[O] = \sum_{j=1}^{n} O_j P_j \qquad (6.3)$$

where

n = number of possible outcomes

O_j = value of the jth outcome

P_j = probability of the jth outcome.

In the example distribution shown in Table 6.3, the O_j values used in such a computation are the class midpoint values. Thus, for this example,

$$
\begin{aligned}
E[O] &= \$23(.05) + \$28(.10) + \$33(.40) \\
&\quad + \$38(.25) + \$43(.15) + \$48(.05) \\
&= \$35.50
\end{aligned}
$$

---

[6] In statistical decision theory, a distinction is made between the terms *risk* and *uncertainty*. Risk situations are defined as those in which the probabilities of the outcomes are known. Uncertainty situations are defined as those in which probabilities cannot be determined for the outcomes. No such distinction between risk and uncertainty will be involved here.

TABLE 6.3

Probability Distribution of Future Stumpage Prices

Stumpage Price per Cord 10 Years Hence	Probability
$21–$25	.05
$26–$30	.10
$31–$35	.40
$36–$40	.25
$41–$45	.15
$46–$50	.05

Since risk is associated with variability in the future cash flows, the standard deviation is a useful statistic for quantifying risk. The standard deviation (SD) is the square root of the variance, which, for a discrete probability distribution, is defined as

$$VAR(O) = E[O - E(O)]^2 \qquad (6.4)$$

and is calculated as

$$VAR(O) = \sum_{j=1}^{n} [O_j - E(O)]^2 P(O_j) \qquad (6.5)$$

For the example considered here,

$$VAR(O) = .05(\$23.00 - \$35.50)^2 + .10(\$28.00 - \$35.50)^2$$
$$+ \cdots + .05(\$48.00 - \$35.50)^2$$
$$= \$33.75$$

and

$$SD = \sqrt{\$33.75}$$
$$= \$5.81$$

Any certain cash flow has only one possible outcome and the probability associated with that outcome is 1. The variance of a certain cash flow is 0. The greater the dispersion of the cash flows, the greater the risk and its measure, the standard deviation.

*6.3.1　The Risk-Adjusted Discount Rate

The method most commonly used to adjust for risk involves manipulation of the discount rate. The risk-adjusted discount rate is defined as $r = k + P$, where k is the risk-free rate and P is a premium for risk. This approach is based on the premise that risky cash flows are worth less today than certain cash flows and must therefore be discounted at a higher rate. There are two problems associated with the use of the risk-adjusted discount rate. First, use of a risk-adjusted discount rate assumes risk is compounding over time. Second, no specific guidelines are available on how to determine the appropriate adjustment factor.

*6.3.2　Certainty-Equivalent Coefficients

A theoretically preferred method of adjusting for risk is the use of certainty-equivalent coefficients. Certainty-equivalent coefficients transform risky cash flows into equivalent certain amounts. The certainty-equivalent coefficient for period t is defined as α_t, where $0 \leq \alpha_t \leq 1$. A certainty coefficient of 1 implies that the cash flow is risk free. A certainty-equivalent coefficient of 0 implies the cash flow is so risky that it has no value. Certainty-equivalent coefficients have the property that

$$C_t^* = \alpha_t C_t$$

where C_t is the risky cash flow and C_t^* is the equivalent risk-free amount. With this approach, net present value is calculated as

$$NPV = \sum_{t=0}^{n} \alpha_t C_t / (1 + k)^t \tag{6.6}$$

where

C_t = risky cash flow in period t

α_t = certainty-equivalent coefficient for period t

k = risk-free discount rate

As usual, the project should be funded if net present value is positive. Since the $\alpha_t C_t$ values are riskless amounts, they should be discounted at the risk-free rate. An appropriate value for the risk-free rate is the yield of U.S. government obligations having the same maturity date as the project being considered.

It should be noted that the use of a risk-adjusted discount rate is a special case of the certainty-equivalent coefficient method. If

$$\alpha_t = \frac{(1 + k)^t}{(1 + r)^t}$$

where r is the risk-adjusted rate, then equation (6.6) reduces to

$$NPV = \sum_{t=0}^{n} C_t/(1 + r)^t$$

which is simply the net present value calculated with a risk-adjusted discount rate. When $\alpha_t = (1 + k)^t/(1 + r)^t$, the values $\alpha_1, \alpha_2, \ldots, \alpha_n$ constitute a geometric series with a common ratio equal to $(1 + k)/(1 + r)$. Thus, when the α_t values used with the certainty-equivalent coefficient method constitute a geometric series with a common ratio (CR) value greater than 0 and less than or equal to 1, the NPV value obtained will be identical to the NPV value calculated with a risk-adjusted discount rate as

$$NPV = \sum_{t=0}^{n} C_t/(1 + r)^t \tag{6.7}$$

where

$$r = \frac{1 + k}{CR} - 1 \tag{6.8}$$

If the α_t values do not constitute a geometric series where $0 < CR \leq 1$, then there is no risk-adjusted discount rate that could be applied to give the same NPV value as that obtained with the certainty-equivalent coefficient method. This emphasizes the fact that the certainty-equivalent coefficient method is much more flexible than the risk-adjusted discount rate approach. The great difficulty with the use of certainty-equivalent coefficients is, of course, the problem of finding a nonarbitrary and defensible procedure for assigning specific values to the coefficients.

*6.3.3   Use of Subjective Probability Distributions

A third way to cope with risk involves the use of subjective probability distributions. This technique directly recognizes that the basic cause of risk is variability in the expected cash flows. Suppose a pine plantation, presently 10 years old, is available for lease. The plantation can be thinned 10 years hence and produce 8 cords per acre. A clear-felling 20 years hence, when the stems are 30 years old, will produce 55 cords per acre. The landowner will lease the land and timber for 20 years at $75 per acre per year. There are no stipulations about regeneration at the end of the rotation and the landowner will pay all property taxes. Assume the yield projections are valid and ignore the risk of loss due to

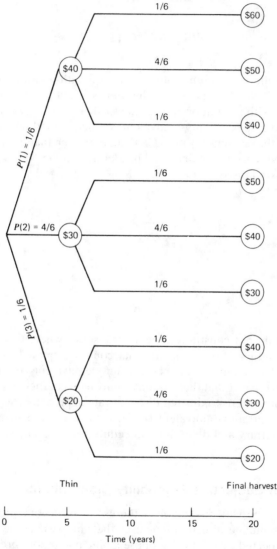

Figure 6.1 Distribution of stumpage prices for the hypothetical example.

fire, insects, and disease. The sole cause of risk is then uncertainty concerning future stumpage prices. Although future stumpage prices are unknown, reasonable estimates may be made of optimistic, most likely, and pessimistic values. Estimates of per-cord stumpage prices at the time of thinning are as follows: most likely $30, optimistic $40, and pessimistic $20. Subjective probability estimates of 4/6, 1/6, and 1/6 are assigned to these estimates.

Stumpage prices at the time of final harvesting are felt to depend on the stumpage rates that prevailed at the time of thinning. As shown in Figure 6.1, the final harvest stumpage price is contingent on the stumpage price at thinning. Thus, there is felt to be a 4/6 probability of the final harvest stumpage price being $50 if the thinning stumpage price at thinning is $40, but a $50 stumpage rate at final harvest is felt to be impossible if the stumpage rate at thinning is $20.

With these assumptions, there are nine possible sets of cash flows. The cash flow for path 1, which involves a $40 stumpage price at thinning and a $60 stumpage price at final harvest, has the following components.

1. An income of $320 ten years hence (harvest of 8 cords per acre at $40 per cord).

2. An income of $3300 twenty years hence (harvest of 55 cords per acre at $60 per cord).

3. Lease payments of $75 per year during each of the next 20 years.

If the risk-free rate is 8 percent, and if income taxes are ignored, the net present value for path 1 is computed as

$$NPV = \$320/1.08^{10} + \$3300/1.08^{20} - \$75\frac{(1.08^{20} - 1)}{0.08(1.08)^{20}}$$

$$= \$119.87$$

Similar calculations have been carried out for each of the nine price alternatives. The results are shown in Table 6.4. The probability that net present value is positive is 5/36, since only paths 1 and 2 result in positive expected net present values. The probabilities for each path are obtained by multiplication of the two probabilities involved. The probability of a $30 stumpage price at thinning is 4/6. The probability that stumpage prices will be $50 at final harvest, given that the stumpage price at thinning was $30, is 1/6. Therefore, the joint probability of a $30 thinning stumpage price and a $50 final harvest stumpage price is 4/6 × 1/6 = 4/36.

TABLE 6.4

Net Present Values and Associated Probabilities for Nine Stumpage Price Alternatives

Alternative	Probability	Net Present Value
1	1/36	$119.87
2	4/36	1.87
3	1/36	− 116.13
4	4/36	− 35.18
5	16/36	− 153.18
6	4/36	− 271.19
7	1/36	− 190.24
8	4/36	− 308.25
9	1/36	− 426.25
	1.0	

The expected net present value is calculated as

$$E[NPV] = \sum_{k=1}^{9} P_k O_k$$

$$= (1/36)(\$119.87) + (4/36)(\$1.87)$$

$$+ \cdots + (1/36)(-\$426.25)$$

$$= -\$153.18$$

The variance of the expected net present value is obtained as

$$VAR(NPV) = \sum_{k=1}^{n} [O_k - E(O)]^2 P_k$$

$$= (1/36)[\$119.87 - (-\$153.18)]^2$$

$$+ \cdots + (1/36)[-\$426.25 - (-\$153.18)]^2$$

$$= \$12,656.11$$

The corresponding standard deviation is $112.50. With this technique, the decision maker can obtain estimates of the two primary determinants of value—expected return and risk.

Much work remains to be done on the development of financial analysis procedures that correctly express and evaluate risk considerations. Most human beings have a natural tendency to ignore or assume away difficult concepts such as risk. However, the fact that a concept is difficult is not sufficient grounds to ignore it. The ultimate test is: "Does the use of these procedures result in better decisions?" If this query can be positively answered, then procedures to account for risk merit consideration.

REFERENCES

Anonymous. Undated. *The new reforestation tax incentives.* 2nd ed. Forest Industries Committee on Timber Valuation and Taxation, Washington.

Anonymous. 1981. *Concise explanation of the economic recovery tax act of 1981.* Prentice-Hall, Englewood Cliffs, N.J.

Anonymous. 1981. *The economic recovery tax act of 1981.* Price Waterhouse, New York.

Briggs, C. W., and W. K. Condrell. 1978. *Tax treatment of timber.* 6th ed. Forest Industries Committee on Timber Valuation and Taxation, Washington.

Condrell, W. K. 1965. The three ways to capital gains treatment on timber. *Forest Farmer* **XXIV**(9):10–12, 20–23.

Condrell, W. K. 1980. *Timber tax journal* **16**(1). Forest Industries Committee on Timber Valuation and Taxation, Washington.

Fortson, J. C., and L. A. Hargreaves. 1974. Capital gains taxation and the industrial forests of the South. *J. For.* **72**:345–348.

Hargreaves, L. A. 1980. Developments in property taxation. In *Forest farmers manual edition,* Forest Farmers Assoc., Atlanta.

Sommerfeld, R. M., H. M. Anderson, and H. R. Brock. 1979. *An introduction to taxation, 1980 edition.* Harcourt Brace Jovanovich, New York.

PART 3

TIMBER MANAGEMENT PLANNING

7

Timber Management— Some Introductory Comments

In this and subsequent chapters, basic decision-making problems that arise in the practice of timber management are considered and methods for solving these problems are presented. These solution methods rely heavily on the mensurational material presented in Chapters 1 through 4 and on the economic techniques described in Chapters 5 and 6. The conceptual approach used is applicable to decision problems involving any forest resource or combination of resources, but the discussion here is restricted to timber production situations.

7.1 THE NATURE OF TIMBER MANAGEMENT ACTIVITIES

Although a literal rendering of the term *timber management* would construe the meaning as "the management of timber," a correct definition for common usage of the term would be the *management of forestland for the production of commercial timber products*. It is in this latter sense that the term will be employed throughout this book. The scope of the term is quite broad, and it could well be proposed that timber management activities involve most of the material taught in any undergraduate forestry curriculum. Acceptance of this proposition implies that any textbook pretending to cover all aspects of timber management would truly be encyclopedic in content and size. We have no illusions concerning the content of this book and recognize that many aspects of timber management have escaped our attention. We do, however, believe that the topics included constitute a logically recognizable subject matter area.

The process of timber management can be usefully subdivided into three components.

1.   *Decision making:* Problem identification, design of alternative solutions, and selection of the best alternative.
2.   *Implementation:* The carrying out of activities required to complete the selected program.
3.   *Control:* The process of making sure that the implemented activities were indeed carried out and the verification that the results of these activities are those expected.

The material to be presented in this and subsequent chapters deals almost exclusively with the first component: decision making. This body of subject matter is dealt with as completely and clearly as possible. Readers interested in the other two components are referred to the wealth of material currently in print covering such topics as silviculture, forest protection, forest engineering, photogrammetry, administration, and so forth.

7.2   THE FUNDAMENTALS OF DECISION MAKING

The decision-making process is usefully viewed as involving four distinct steps.

1.   Problem recognition.
2.   Specification of strategies.
3.   Specification of a decision criterion.
4.   Selection of the optimum strategy.

Of these four, the problem recognition step is, in a sense, the most important since problems that go unrecognized will almost certainly remain unsolved. However, good advice on how to recognize important problems is difficult to provide. It is perhaps useful to note that the terms "overmanagement" and "undermanagement" are, to a certain extent, synonymous with recognition of too many or too few problems. As previously noted, unrecognized problems usually remain unsolved; conversely, resources devoted to solving unimportant problems or "nonproblems" are not available for assignment to important problems. This latter consideration is inelegantly but effectively summarized in the popular admonition, "If it ain't broke, don't fix it."

Once a decision situation has been identified, the decision makers move to step 2 and specify the various alternatives available to them. Each of these alternatives is referred to as a *strategy*. *Decision making* is essentially a matter of selecting one of the available strategies. It is pointless to consider strategies that cannot possibly be implemented. On the other hand, when feasible strategies are omitted from consideration, the final decision will be adversely affected if one or more of the omitted strategies is superior to the best strategy of those considered.

A *decision criterion* is a quantifiable characteristic that can be evaluated for each strategy and whose values express the desirability of the outcomes produced by the various strategies. Selection of an appropriate decision criterion is possible only if the decision maker has clearly identified the objectives of management and has properly perceived the relationships among the various potential criteria and the objectives. In profit-oriented organizations, the decision criteria used are almost always measures of economic desirability such as discounted present value, rate of return, or cost. In decision situations involving goods, services, or amenities that are not valued in some type of economic market, an appropriate decision criterion may not be readily available. This is a common problem in multiresource forest management situations in which water, recreation, wildlife, and range considerations are involved instead of, or in addition to, timber production.

After the decision criterion has been specified, values of the criterion are calculated for all the strategies under consideration. The strategies can then be ranked in order of desirability according to the decision criterion values. With some criteria, large values indicate high desirability (e.g., discounted present value, rate of return), while small values indicate high desirability for other criteria (e.g., cost). Knowledgeable decision makers do not always select the strategy with the most desirable decision-criterion value. For example, consider two strategies, A and B, where A has a slightly more desirable decision-criterion value than B. However, calculation of the value for A has involved the use of some questionable data items, whereas considerable confidence can be placed in the inputs used to compute the decision-criterion value for strategy B. In such a situation, it would not be irrational for the decision maker to prefer strategy B over strategy A. (The argument could well be made that the decision maker has adopted a new criterion in choosing B over A. However, it might be difficult or impossible for the decision maker to formally quantify this new criterion.)

Here we have considered only the simplest decision-making procedure. A considerable body of literature exists concerning methods applicable to more complex situations. Good introductory discussions of the techniques involved have been prepared by Miller and Starr (1969), Moskowitz and Wright (1979), and Eppen and Gould (1979). Some applications of more advanced procedures in forest management have been discussed by Thompson (1968).

7.3   THE APPLICATION OF DECISION-MAKING TECHNIQUES IN TIMBER MANAGEMENT

The basic decision-making method described in the previous section provides the conceptual framework for any timber management decision situation. In most cases, the mensurational techniques presented in Chapters 1 through 4 and the financial analysis procedures of Chapters 5 and 6 will also be involved. For example, consider a decision situation in which a timber manager is in possession of 100 acres of cutover land. The manager is considering three alternatives.

1.   Site prepare and plant loblolly pine, clearcut the stand for pulpwood at age 25, and sell the land.
2.   Site prepare and plant loblolly pine, thin for pulpwood at age 17, clearcut for pulpwood and sawlogs at age 35, and sell the land.
3.   Direct seed loblolly pine without site preparation, clearcut for pulpwood at age 25, and sell the land.

These alternatives constitute the manager's set of strategies. (Realistically, a much larger set of strategies should be used. However, for simplicity, we restrict ourselves to these three strategies.) A term often used for a strategy of the type considered here is a *management regime*. A management regime can be defined as a specified sequence of timber management activities.

To choose among the strategies, the timber manager must predict the harvest yields that would be generated by each strategy. Estimates of costs and selling prices are then used to generate a predicted cash flow pattern for each of the three alternatives. Selection of the optimal strategy then amounts to deciding which of the three cash flow patterns is most desirable. This could be done using discounted present value as the decision criterion or it could be accomplished using rate of return as the decision criterion. The two criteria would not necessarily produce the same decision. As previously pointed out in Chapter 5, discounted present value is generally thought to be the more appropriate criterion for timber management decisions. The details of analyses similar to this example constitute the subject matter of the next three chapters.

REFERENCES

Duerr, W. A., D. E. Teeguarden, N. B. Christiansen, and S. Guttenberg. 1979. *Forest resource management.* Saunders, Philadelphia.

Eppen, G. D., and F. J. Gould, 1979. *Decision making without algorithms.* Prentice-Hall, Englewood Cliffs, N. J.

Miller, D. W., and M. K. Starr. 1969. *Executive decisions and operations research.* Prentice-Hall, Englewood Cliffs, N.J.

Moskowitz, H., and G. P. Wright. 1979. *Operations research techniques for management.* Prentice-Hall, Englewood Cliffs, N.J.

Thompson, E. F. 1968. The theory of decision under uncertainty and possible applications in forest management. *For. Sci.* **14**:156–163.

8

Stand-Level Management Planning

All timber management planning situations can be divided into two distinct categories.

1. Those situations in which planning can be done independently for each stand.
2. Those situations in which the planning must be coordinated for all stands in the forest being considered.

The first situation will be referred to as *stand-level management planning*, while the second will be identified as *forest-level management planning*. Some of the literature in timber management seems to assume that foresters should always practice forest-level management planning. We believe such an assumption is contrary to both the logic of the situation and the empirical facts concerning actual management.

In stand-level management, each individual stand is treated in the way that will best achieve the goal of the forest owner. Thus, if the owner's goal is profit maximization, each stand would probably be managed to maximize the present value of future cash flows produced by the stand. If all stands in the forest can be managed in this way, the economic benefits to the owner will be greater than those possible under any other plan that can be devised. However, some forests cannot be operated with stand-level management because the resulting overall forest plan is not feasible, regardless of its apparent economic desirability. For example, if the forest involved has been acquired or established to provide raw material for certain processing facilities, significant year-to-year variations in harvest volumes will simply be unacceptable. Similarly, a forest landowner without processing facilities but whose total income is derived from timber harvest may also be unable to operate with a forest plan in which revenues produced by the forest fluctuate wildly from year to year. It should also be noted that large compact forests, which support their own work force, require operational stability. In such a situation, a small harvest in one year leads to a shortage of harvesting labor for any expansion of the cut in the next year. For any of the cases mentioned above, stand-level management planning will seldom be acceptable, since this procedure typically produces overall forest plans with large fluctuations in annual harvests and revenues. Thus, in situations where stable patterns of harvest, income, regeneration acreage, and so on, are important, forest-based management planning methods must be used. The details of forest-based management planning are presented in Chapters 9 and 10, while the remainder of this chapter is concerned with stand-level management. Before further consideration is given to the details of stand-level management, two important points regarding stand-level and forest-level planning should be noted.

1. Forest-level planning is required when some kind of "smoothing" of forest operations is necessary.[1] The vast majority of private forest holdings, at least in the United States, can be managed quite effectively without any such smoothing. It may be that a professional fascination with the term *sustained yield* has produced a misunderstanding of this point. We would argue very strongly that the southern pine forests of the southeastern United States constitute an immensely valuable asset and this asset must produce a reasonably stable sustained yield of forest products. However, any contention that this must or should be accomplished by stabilizing annual yields on every individual forest holding seems to us quite irrational.

2. Any kind of smoothing costs money. Every forest has an economically optimum management plan that is simply a consolidation of the optimum

---

[1] Occasionally, unusual circumstances affecting the forest owner require revision of the stand optimization strategy to a solution involving greater fluctuations in harvests and revenues than are produced by the stand optimization strategy. Such situations are relatively uncommon and most realistic forest-planning situations involve the imposition of constraints designed to stabilize harvests and cash flows. However, the forest-level planning procedures described in Chapter 10 can be used to deal with either situation.

stand-level plans for all stands in the forest. Any change in this consolidated plan to smooth annual yields or revenues means that some stands
will no longer be managed according to their most economically effective
strategies, and the total economic benefits to the forest owner will decrease
accordingly. Smoothing must often be done, particularly in industrial forestry and public land situations, but smoothing just for the sake of smoothing is an expensive hobby.

8.1 THE GROWTH OF EVEN-AGED TIMBER STANDS—
VOLUMETRIC CONSIDERATIONS

Even-aged stands have a definite beginning and end in time. Stand establishment
or regeneration marks the beginning of such a stand and, with the final harvest,
the stand ceases to exist. At any time during its life, the stand has a known or
determinable age, and the total length of the growth period from stand establishment to final harvest is referred to as the *rotation*. Plantations fit this description exactly, while some naturally regenerated stands, which become established over a period of a few years, lack an exact beginning but are still
usefully conceptualized as being even-aged.

The graph of volume per acre over age for any even-aged stand is a typical
sigmoid growth curve. During the early years of stand development, volume
production proceeds slowly. As the stand ages, the growth rate increases to a
maximum and then declines. If the stand is left long enough without harvest,
the net growth rate will eventually fall to zero and then become negative when
mortality exceeds accretion growth. Figure 8.1 shows a typical but hypothetical
stand volume development curve. This particular curve is defined by the function

$$Y_t = 100(1 - e^{-0.05t})^{2.0} \qquad (8.1)$$

where

t = stand age in years

Y_t = merchantable volume at age t in cunits per acre

The curve is only shown for ages 10 through 40 years since it is assumed that
little or no merchantable volume is present before age 10 and that rotations
longer than 40 years are of no interest. This particular volume/age relationship
is assumed to apply for plantations of a particular species growing on land of a
given site index with a specified combination of initial planting density and site
preparation treatment.

Table 8.1 has been constructed from the yield relationship defined by equation
(8.1). The values shown in column (1) of the table are obtained by solving

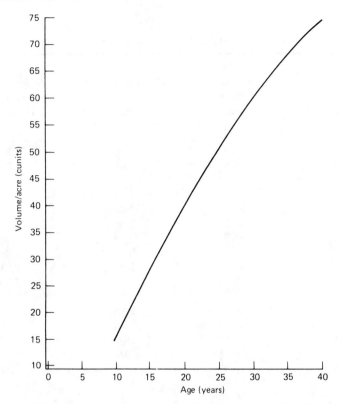

Figure 8.1 Stand volume development curve for a typical even-aged stand.

equation (8.1) for ages 10 through 40 years. Column (2) contains current annual increment figures, which are simply differences between successive pairs of yield values. The values shown in column (3) are average annual growth rates corresponding to the various stand ages. These are obtained by dividing the yield values by their corresponding ages and are referred to as *mean annual increment* values. The mean annual increment value of 2.00 cunits associated with an age of 20 years means that, between inception and age 20, the stand has grown at an average rate of 2.00 cunits per acre per year.

The yield, current annual increment, and mean annual increment values from Table 8.1 have been plotted in Figure 8.2. Several notable and significant facts appear in this graph. The current annual increment (*CAI*) curve reaches a maximum relatively early in the life of the stand and then declines. Its maximum value occurs at the age where the slope of the yield curve is steepest. The mean annual increment (*MAI*) curve reaches its maximum at a later age and intersects the current annual increment curve at this maximum value. This relationship

TABLE 8.1

Volume Development for a Typical but Hypothetical Even-Aged Stand

Age (years)	(1) Per-Acre Yield (cunits)	(2) Current Annual Increment (cunits/acre/year)	(3) Mean Annual Increment (cunits/acre/year)
10	15.48	2.42	1.55
11	17.90	2.46	1.63
12	20.36	2.49	1.70
13	22.84	2.50	1.76
14	25.34	2.50	1.81
15	27.84	2.48	1.86
16	30.32	2.46	1.90
17	32.79	2.43	1.93
18	35.22	2.39	1.96
19	37.61	2.35	1.98
20	39.96	2.30	2.00
21	42.26	2.25	2.01
22	44.51	2.19	2.02
23	46.70	2.13	2.03
24	48.83	2.07	2.03
25	50.91	2.01	2.04 (2.0363)
26	52.92	1.96	2.04 (2.0354)
27	54.87	1.89	2.03
28	56.76	1.83	2.03
29	58.59	1.76	2.02
30	60.35	1.70	2.01
31	62.06	1.64	2.00
32	63.70	1.58	1.99
33	65.28	1.52	1.98
34	66.80	1.46	1.96
35	68.26	1.41	1.95
36	69.67	1.35	1.94
37	71.02	1.30	1.92
38	72.32	1.25	1.90
39	73.57	1.20	1.89
40	74.76	—	1.87

should be apparent since, if *CAI* is greater than *MAI*, *MAI* must be increasing while, if *CAI* is less than *MAI*, *MAI* must be decreasing.

The age at which mean annual increment reaches a maximum is referred to as the *age of maximum mean annual increment*. This statistic has considerable management significance. Table 8.1 shows that the maximum *MAI* value of

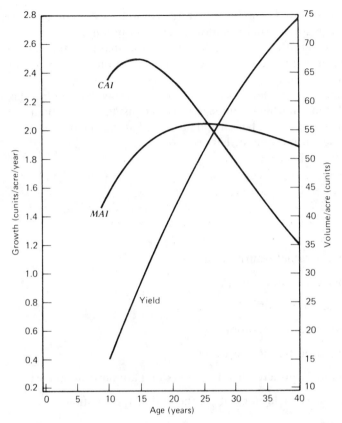

Figure 8.2   Some aspects of growth in a typical even-aged stand.

2.0363 cunits per acre per year occurs at age 25. If successive rotations of the stand type considered here were grown using a rotation age of 25 years, the average production would be 2.0363 cunits per acre per year. Use of any other rotation age in the continuing series of plantations would result in a lower average annual production rate. Thus, for a forest owner whose objective is maximum volume production, the rotation age used should be the rotation of maximum mean annual increment.

8.2   THE GROWTH OF EVEN-AGED TIMBER STANDS— ECONOMIC CONSIDERATIONS

Few timber managers are able to achieve the objectives of the forest owner while restricting their attention to volumetric considerations since the objectives of most owners are economic in nature. Another way to phrase the matter is to note that it is an unusual situation where an optimum strategy can be selected without knowing the costs and incomes associated with the various strategies. Therefore, it is important to devote some attention to the economic aspects of stand development.

As an initial example, consider a simple case involving before-tax returns for a planted stand in which stumpage price is constant (rather than increasing with age). If such a stand is planted and harvested at the end of t years, the net return to the owner at the time of harvest would be

$$N_t = SY_t - R(1 + i)^t - T[(1 + i)^t - 1]/i \qquad (8.2)$$

where

N_t = per-acre net return at harvest

S = per-cunit stumpage price

t = rotation length

R = per-acre regeneration cost

i = inflation-free interest rate

T = annual per-acre ad valorem tax and administration cost

Y_t = per-acre yield in cunits at the end of the rotation

To illustrate this relationship, it will be assumed that Y_t is defined by equation (8.1) and that

$$S = \$35.00$$
$$R = \$100.00$$
$$i = 0.04$$
$$T = \$1.50$$

Solutions of equation (8.2) with the above values for rotation ages of 10 through 40 years are shown in Table 8.2. For each rotation age, column (1) shows the per-acre yield in cunits (Y_t) and column (2) shows the per-acre net return at harvest (N_t). The present value of the per-acre net return at harvest is shown in column (3) and is calculated as $N_t/(1 + i)^t$. Column (4) of Table 8.2 contains

TABLE 8.2

Economic Development for a Typical but Hypothetical Even-Aged Stand

Age (years)	(1) Per-Acre Yield (cunits)	(2) Net Return at Harvest (dollars/acre)	(3) Present Value of Net Return (dollars/acre)	(4) Bare Land Value (dollars/acre)
10	15.48	$ 375.77	$253.85	$782.45
11	17.90	452.33	293.82	838.49
12	20.36	529.96	331.01	881.75
13	22.84	607.95	365.12	914.11
14	25.34	686.29	396.32	937.98
15	27.84	764.27	424.37	954.21
16	30.32	841.17	449.10	963.55
17	32.79	917.31	470.92	967.73
18	35.22	991.65	489.51	966.69
19	37.61	1064.16	505.09	961.43
20	39.96	1134.82	517.92	952.73
21	42.26	1203.27	528.04	940.96
22	44.51	1269.49	535.67	926.69
23	46.70	1333.10	540.87	910.14
24	48.83	1394.10	543.87	891.76
25	50.91	1452.80	544.97	872.11
26	52.92	1508.49	544.09	851.06
27	54.87	1561.49	541.55	829.09
28	56.76	1611.78	537.49	806.41
29	58.59	1659.34	532.07	783.20
30	60.35	1703.78	525.31	759.47
31	62.06	1745.79	517.56	735.65
32	63.70	1784.64	508.73	711.56
33	65.28	1820.65	499.03	687.46
34	66.80	1853.78	488.57	663.41
35	68.26	1884.01	477.44	639.50
36	69.67	1911.66	465.81	615.88
37	71.02	1936.34	453.68	592.50
38	72.32	1958.36	441.19	569.49
39	73.57	1977.70	428.41	546.87
40	74.76	1993.96	415.32	524.59

quantities identified as bare land values. This concept is easily grasped by considering a continuing series of rotations of the type used in calculating Table 8.2. The bare land value associated with a given rotation age is the present value of the net returns from all the rotations in the continuing series. For rotation age

t, the bare land value is denoted as BLV_t and is calculated as[2]

$$BLV_t = \frac{N_t}{(1 + i)^t - 1} = \frac{SY_t - R(1 + i)^t - T[(1 + i)^t - 1]/i}{(1 + i)^t - 1} \quad (8.3)$$

Conceptually, this is simply the present value of all cash flows produced by an infinite series of rotations using a rotation age of t years. Hence, if a rotation age of 20 years is used in such a continuing venture, the anticipated cash flows have a present value of $952.73. For comparison, if a rotation age of 30 years is used, the present value of all future cash flows is $759.47.

It is very important to note that the basic formula for bare land value can be written in several forms, all of which are algebraically equivalent. The most common forms for the simple plant and clearcut situation just described are

$$BLV_t = -R + \frac{SY_t - R}{(1 + i)^t - 1} - \frac{T}{i} \quad (8.4)$$

and

$$BLV_t = \frac{SY_t - R(1 + i)^t}{(1 + i)^t - 1} - \frac{T}{i} \quad (8.5)$$

When the same input values are used, equations (8.3), (8.4), and (8.5) produce identical BLV_t values.

It is often necessary to calculate bare land values for management regimes that are much more complex than the case considered above. Such regimes may involve expenses at various points in time for fertilization, precommercial thinning, competing vegetation control, and so forth. In addition, intermediate cuts may produce incomes in addition to those received at rotation age. For any such regime, the total costs and incomes can always be summarized in a table of the following form.

---

[2] In the forest economics literature, the present value of the cash flows generated by a continuing series of rotations is generally referred to as the *soil expectation value* or the *land expectation value*, while the term *bare land value* is used to denote an estimate of land value obtained from analysis of comparable market sales. However, it is our impression that most forest managers use the three terms interchangably; therefore, our usage in this text considers soil expectation value, land expectation value, and bare land value to be equivalent in meaning.

Year	Income	Cost
0	I_0	C_0
1	I_1	C_1
2	I_2	C_2
.	.	.
.	.	.
.	.	.
t	I_t	C_t

The bare land value can then be calculated as

$$BLV_t = \frac{\sum_{j=0}^{t} (I_j - C_j)(1 + i)^{t-j}}{(1 + i)^t - 1} \tag{8.6}$$

Note that this approach simply calculates net incomes for each year, compounds these to the end of the rotation, and sums the resulting values to obtain the net return at harvest. Division by $[(1 + i)^t - 1]$ provides the discounted sum of the continuing series. The use of equation (8.6) can be illustrated by considering a variation of the calculations used to produce the results of Table 8.2. The previous computations assumed that the initial regeneration costs were incurred immediately and that subsequent regeneration costs occurred in the same years that stands were harvested. This, in turn, implied that the age of harvest stands was t years if the rotation length was t years. In actual forest practice, there is often a delay between the harvest of one stand and the regeneration of the next. The economic effects of such delays can be expressed and evaluated through appropriate use of equation (8.6).

Again, assume that $S = \$35.00$ per cunit, $R = \$100.00$ per acre, $i = 0.04$, and $T = \$1.50$ per acre per year. The total regeneration cost of $\$100.00$ per acre is composed of $\$75.00$ per acre for site preparation plus $\$25.00$ per acre for planting. On the average, site preparation takes place 1 year following harvest and planting occurs 2 years after harvest. If the rotation age is to be 25 years, the rotation length must now be 27 years. The bare land value for this plantation sequence is

$$BLV = \frac{-\$75(1.04)^{26} - \$25(1.04)^{25} + \$35(50.91)}{(1.04)^{27} - 1} - \frac{\$1.50}{0.04}$$

$$= \$800.30 - \$37.50$$

$$= \$762.80$$

where the per-acre yield at harvest is 50.91 cunits per acre. The corresponding value with immediate regeneration (from Table 8.2) is $872.11, so that, in this case, the per-acre reduction in net present value arising from regeneration delay is $872.11 - $762.80 = $109.31.

8.3   SELECTION OF THE OPTIMUM ROTATION AGE

The problem of selecting an optimum rotation age offers an opportunity for application of the decision-making techniques previously described in Chapter 7. In order to make this selection, the manager must define the management regimes (strategies) to be considered and specify the decision criterion to be used. Once these steps have been taken, the decision criterion can be evaluated for each management regime and the optimum regime can be selected.

It has already been pointed out that mean annual increment is the appropriate decision criterion to use in selecting the rotation age if the objective is maximum total volume production. If there is only one stand type (i.e., one yield curve) to be considered in the selection process, then the procedure is simply a matter of calculating mean annual increment for each candidate rotation age. This process can be defined notationally as

$$\max_{t} [MAI_t] = \max_{t} [Y_t/t]$$

where the notation

$$\max_{t} [\ \ ]$$

means find the value of t that maximizes the quantity in brackets. In practice, the process is seldom this simple since several stand types will usually need to be considered. The existence of several stand types results from differences in such factors as species, type and intensity of site preparation, and initial spacing. In a situation involving k stand types, the decision process is

$$\max_{k} \left[\max_{t_k} [Y_{t_k}/t_k] \right]$$

where Y_{t_k} equals the per-acre yield of stand type k at age t_k. The second max operator is defined to operate over a range of ages "t_k" to indicate that the range considered may be different for each stand type. This process simply amounts to identifying the maximum MAI for each stand type and then selecting the largest of these values. As a simple example of this procedure, consider a situation where either of two stand types can be grown.

1. The growth curve for stand type 1 is

$$Y_t = 100(1 - e^{-0.05t})^{2.0}$$

2. The growth curve for stand type 2 is

$$Y_t = 90(1 - e^{-0.08t})^{2.0}$$

The *MAI* values for the stand type 1 growth curve have already been calculated and tabulated in Table 8.1. The maximum *MAI* value of 2.0363 cunits per acre per year occurs with a rotation age of 25 years. A similar set of computations with the stand type 2 growth curve shows the maximum *MAI* value is 2.9319 cunits per acre per year for a rotation of 16 years. Thus, physical productivity would be maximized by growing stand type 2 with a rotation age of 16 years.

As has been previously pointed out, few managers can ignore economic considerations when making decisions. As a result, rotation ages are seldom selected on a volume maximization basis. Although several possible economic criteria for optimizing rotation age can be proposed, the most popular, by far, is maximization of net present value. Use of this criterion means that the optimum rotation is that harvest age which produces the cash flow with maximum net present value. Since it makes little sense to compare single rotation cash flows for alternatives with different rotation lengths, the standard procedure is to compare cash flows for continuing series of plantations. The present value of cash flows for a continuing series of rotations (starting with immediate establishment of the first rotation) has already been defined in the previous section and is termed the bare land value.

Maximization of present value is accomplished by selecting the rotation age with maximum bare land value. This rotation is commonly referred to as the *optimum economic rotation*. If a single stand type is involved, the decision process is

$$\max_t [BLV_t]$$

This procedure can be illustrated by reference to Table 8.2, where bare land values have been computed for rotation ages 10 years through 40 years using the yield function specified in equation (8.1). Inspection of the bare land values shows that the maximum value of $967.73 occurs at age 17. Hence, 17 years is the optimum economic rotation for this stand type. This value also implies that, for the economic conditions specified, a firm could pay $967.73 per acre for land that would produce the yield implied by the yield curve, grow plantations using a 17-year rotation with the specified cost and income values, and earn an inflation-free rate of return of 4 percent. If the land could be purchased for less than $967.73, the rate of return would be greater than 4 percent. For this same stand type, the rotation of maximum mean annual increment is 25 years. This illustrates the general rule that the optimum economic rotation is usually shorter than the rotation of maximum mean annual increment.[3] The difference between the two rotations grows larger with an increase in the interest rate.

When determining an optimum economic rotation, the manager will usually want to consider several stand types. If k stand types are involved, the decision process is

$$\max_{k} \left[\max_{t_k} [BLV_{t_k}] \right]$$

where

BLV_{t_k} = bare land value for stand type k with a rotation age of t_k years

This amounts to finding the optimum economic rotation for each stand type and, from these, selecting the stand type where the optimum economic rotation bare land value is largest.

Situations occasionally exist in which rotation age decisions should not be based on comparisons of continuing series of plantations. The best example of such situations is a lease of fixed duration. Under such an agreement, the lessee (usually a forest products firm) purchases the right to grow and harvest timber during the period of the lease. At the end of the lease period, the landowner (lessor) reassumes responsibility for management of the property. The lessee's rotation age decisions in such a case should clearly not be based on continuing series cash flow comparisons, but instead should consider cash flow comparisons for the lease period only.

8.4 DECISIONS CONCERNING INTERMEDIATE HARVESTS

Timber managers are often involved in analyses to determine the desirability of intermediate harvests. The ultimate effects of intermediate harvests are a function of their type, timing, and intensity, and a considerable body of mensurational and economic information is required to analyze these effects properly. Although the details of the analysis can be quite complex, the conceptual procedure is identical to that discussed in the previous section. For each combination of stand type, thinning regime, and final harvest age, a bare land value is calculated. The best alternative is the one with maximum bare land value.

---

[3] This rule only holds if stumpage price does not increase with increasing age. If stumpage prices rise as age increases, the optimum economic rotation may not be shorter than the rotation of maximum mean annual increment.

Clutter et al. (1981) have carried out economic analyses of thinning operations in old-field slash pine plantations and their data (with some augmentation) can be used to illustrate the decision process concerning intermediate harvests. Consider two strategies.

1. An unthinned management regime with a rotation age of 30 years. The stand is assumed to have 400 stems per acre at age 20.

2. A thinned management regime with a thinning at age 20 and final harvest at age 30. The stand is assumed to have 400 stems per acre prior to the thinning. which is applied from below and removes 30 percent of the merchantable volume.

The mensurational predictions are based on methodology developed by Clutter and Jones (1980) and. for the example given here. assume a site index of 70 feet (index age of 25 years). Values for some pertinent economic inputs are

i = inflation-free interest rate = 0.03

TC = per-cord transportation cost = \$4.00

R = regeneration cost = \$100/acre

T = per-acre tax and administration cost = \$1.50/acre/year

Final harvest harvesting costs and delivered prices by dbh class are shown in Table 8.3. Predicted harvests by dbh class for the two regimes considered are

TABLE 8.3

Delivered Price per Cord and Harvesting Cost per Cubic Foot by dbh Classes

dbh Class (inches)	Delivered Price per Cord (dollars)	Final Harvest Harvesting Cost per Cubic Foot (dollars)
5	\$40.00	\$0.515
6	40.00	0.328
7	40.00	0.249
8	40.00	0.208
9	40.00	0.182
10	50.00	0.166
11	50.00	0.155
12	60.00	0.148
13	60.00	0.142
14	70.00	0.138

Source: From Clutter et al.. 1981.

shown in Table 8.4. A conversion factor of 92 cubic feet per cord is used where required. Harvesting costs by dbh class for thinnings are assumed to be 25 percent higher than the final harvest values shown in Table 8.3. Summaries of the per-acre net returns from harvest are shown here for the thinned and unthinned regimes.

1. Unthinned regime:

Total income	$2829.63
Less harvesting costs	− 964.56
Less transportation costs	− 236.29
Net return from final harvest	$1628.78

2. Thinned regime:
    (a) Thinning:

Total income	$446.21
Less harvesting costs	− 353.75
Less transportation costs	− 44.62
	$ 47.84

    (b) Final harvest:

Total income	$2360.14
Less harvesting costs	− 660.84
Less transportation costs	− 180.88
Net return from final harvest	$1518.42

The bare land values for the two regimes are calculated as

1. Unthinned regime:

$$BLV_1 = \frac{\$1628.78 - \$100(1.03)^{30}}{(1.03)^{30} - 1} - \frac{\$1.50}{0.03}$$

$$= \$921.13$$

2. Thinned regime:

$$BLV_2 = \frac{\$1518.42 + \$47.84(1.03)^{10} - \$100(1.03)^{30}}{(1.03)^{30} - 1} - \frac{\$1.50}{0.03}$$

$$= \$888.85$$

TABLE 8.4

Harvest Volume Predictions by dbh Class for Thinned and Unthinned Regimes in Old-Field Slash Pine Plantations; Site Index 70 Feet, 400 Stems per Acre, at Age 20

dbh Class (inches)	Outside-Bark Volumes Removed		
	Thinning at Age 20 (cubic feet/acre)	From Thinned Stand at Age 30 Final Harvest (cubic feet/acre)	From Unthinned Stand at Age 30 Harvest (cubic feet/acre)
5	68.82	10.46	25.25
6	231.61		95.07
7	502.80		313.84
8	223.06		645.38
9		437.45	1000.70
10		1041.57	1235.77
11		1344.18	1178.97
12		1057.38	759.17
13		235.96	180.49
14		33.26	
Totals	1026.29	4160.26	5434.64

Source: From Clutter and Jones, 1980.

This result shows that, for the mensurational and economic inputs used, the unthinned regime would be preferable to the thinned regime. The analysis illustrates well some of the tradeoffs that commonly exist in thinned versus unthinned comparisons.

1. The thinning provides income early in the rotation. However, the volume removed in the thinning has a low selling price and a high harvesting cost.

2. Total yield for the thinned regime is often no greater than that for the unthinned regime. However, the volume removed from the thinned stand by the final harvest has a higher average per-cord selling price and a lower average per-cubic-foot harvesting cost.

It should also be pointed out that thinning decisions often involve risk considerations that are not dealt with in analyses similar to that just presented. In some stands with high levels of stand density, a decision not to thin may significantly increase the probability of severe damage from insect and disease attack. On the other hand, recently thinned stands will be more susceptible to wind and ice damage than comparable unthinned stands. In addition, the thinning operation may create conditions favorable to insect or disease attack such as bark beetles of *Fomes annosus*. All things considered, it is perhaps not surprising that, for many species, the desirability of thinning is a matter on which reasonable managers often disagree.

8.5 DECISIONS CONCERNING EXISTING STANDS

The previous sections have discussed procedures for selecting an optimum management regime consisting of a continuing series of similar rotations. Once such a series is underway, all future management activities are scheduled until changes in economics or mensurational inputs make a different continuing series optimal. However, if the existing stand on a particular site differs from the optimal continuing series stand, a decision problem exists. How long should the existing stand be left before it is harvested and the first stand of the continuing series established? Although the details of the appropriate analysis may be complex, the concept involved is familiar and straightforward. The optimum length of time to hold the existing stand is the specific period that maximizes the present value of all future cash flows.

For example, consider a land area for which the optimum bare land strategy consists of plantations whose growth is defined by equation (8.1). The economic values appropriate to the situation are those previously used in Section 8.2.

S = per-cunit stumpage price = \$35.00

R = per-acre regeneration cost = \$100.00

i = inflation-free interest rate = 0.04

T = annual per-acre tax and administration cost = \$1.50

For these conditions, it has already been established that the optimum economic rotation is 17 years and the bare land value is \$967.73. The stand currently in existence on the land area under consideration has a current standing volume of 10.1 cunits per acre. Projected future volumes for the next 10 years are shown in Table 8.5. If the current stand is harvested 5 years from now, the continuing plantation series would begin at that time and the present value 5 years hence, of all subsequent cash flows, would be \$967.73. The cash flow summary for the strategy of holding the current stand for 5 years is shown in Table 8.6. With an interest rate of 4 percent, this cash flow pattern has a present value of \$1309.42.

A general formula for the present value of a strategy involving harvest n years hence is

$$V_n = \frac{\$35.00 Y_n}{(1.04)^n} + \frac{\$967.73}{(1.04)^n} - \$1.50 \frac{(1.04)^n - 1}{0.04(1.04)^n} \qquad (8.7)$$

where

V_n = present value of the strategy involving harvest of the present stand n years hence

Y_n = per-acre yield in cunits from harvest of the present stand n years from now

The meaning of the three terms on the right of equation (8.7) should be clearly understood. The first term is simply the present value of the income received from harvest of the present stand, whereas the second term contains the present value of all cash flows generated by the continuing series of subsequent plantations. The third term includes the present value of tax and administrative costs through the year of harvest of the present stand. All tax and administrative costs following that year are included in the bare land value. Table 8.7 summarizes solutions of equation (8.7) for values of 0 (immediate harvest) to 10 years. Values for each of the three component terms are listed separately. Inspection of Table 8.7 shows that the maximum cash flow present value of $1335.22 occurs when the current stand is cut 2 years from now. Thus, the optimum strategy is to harvest the existing stand 2 years hence and begin the continuing series of plantation rotations.

It is not uncommon for decision makers to oversimplify the situation described above and make bad judgments as a result. For example, the existing stand was expected to increase in volume from 13.7 cunits per acre to 15.2 cunits per acre during the third year. Some might argue that, since this constitutes approximately a 10 percent growth rate and the interest rate is only 4 percent, the stand should

TABLE 8.5

Projected Future Volumes for a Currently Existing Stand

Years Hence	Volume/Acre (cunits)
1	11.8
2	13.7
3	15.2
4	16.7
5	18.1
6	19.3
7	20.3
8	21.1
9	21.8
10	22.5

TABLE 8.6

Cash Flow Summary for a Strategy Involving Harvest of the Present Stand 5 Years Hence

Year	Cash Flow
1	$-1.50
2	-1.50
3	-1.50
4	-1.50
5	18.1(35.00) + 967.73 - 1.50 = 1599.73

be left to grow. Such an argument would be fallacious, however, because it is equivalent to only considering the first term in equation (8.7). For the situation just described, holding the stand for another year rather than cutting it after year 2 would increase the first term of equation (8.7) from $443.32 to $472.95. However, the sum of the second and third terms decreases from $891.89 to $856.44. Therefore, the increase in value of the existing stand resulting from one more year's growth is not enough to justify delaying all subsequent cash flows by 1 year.

The example just presented can also be used to illustrate the determination of value components for an acre of land and timber. With the optimum strategy of harvest 2 years hence, the current value of land and timber is $1335.22 per acre. What portion of this total value is properly ascribed to the land and what part should be considered timber value? Regardless of the timber stand characteristics, the value of the land is always given by the bare land value which, in this case, is $967.73 per acre. The total timber value must therefore equal $1335.22 - $967.73, or $367.49 per acre. If the existing merchantable timber was harvested immediately, the income would be 10.1 cunits times $35.00 per cunit, or $353.50. This merchantable timber value is one component of the total timber value. The remaining $13.99 ($367.49 - $353.50) is the *incremental growing stock value* and the fact that it is positive confirms the conclusion that immediate harvest is not the optimum strategy.

8.6 THE COST OF GROWING TIMBER

A statistic of considerable significance in some timber management situations is the per-unit volume cost of timber production. This cost includes cash disbursements plus opportunity costs. The formula for unit volume growing cost for any specified management regime is most easily obtained by equating the present value of all costs involved in growing the timber (PVC_1) to the present value of a series of open market stumpage purchases that would generate the

TABLE 8.7

Present Values for Strategies with Various Times to Initial Harvest

Years until Initial Harvest (n)	Initial Harvest Volume (cunits) (Y_n)	Present Value of Initial Harvest $\left(\dfrac{\$35.00 Y_n}{1.04^n}\right)$	Present Value of Continuing Series Cash Flows $\left(\dfrac{\$967.73}{1.04^n}\right)$	Present Value Tax & Administrative Costs $\left(-\$1.50 \dfrac{1.04^n - 1}{0.04(1.04)^n}\right)$	Total Present Value (V_n)
0	10.1	$353.50	$967.73	$ −0.00	$1321.23
1	11.8	397.12	930.51	−1.44	1326.18
2	13.7	443.32	894.72	−2.83	1335.22
3	15.2	472.95	860.60	−4.16	1329.09
4	16.7	499.63	827.22	−5.44	1321.41
5	18.1	520.69	795.40	−6.68	1309.42
6	19.3	533.86	764.81	−7.86	1290.81
7	20.3	539.92	735.40	−9.00	1266.31
8	21.1	539.61	707.11	−10.10	1236.63
9	21.8	536.07	679.91	−11.15	1204.83
10	22.5	532.01	653.76	−12.17	1173.60

same pattern of timber flows (PVC_2). An illustration of this approach for a continuing series of plantations with no intermediate harvests is provided here. Let:

t = rotation age in years

Y_t = per-acre yield at age t

R = per-acre regeneration cost

i = inflation-free interest rate

T = annual per-acre ad valorem tax and administrative cost

L = land cost per acre

The present value per acre of all costs involved in growing such a series of plantations is

$$PVC_1 = L + \frac{R(1 + i)^t}{(1 + i)^t - 1} + \frac{T}{i} \qquad (8.8)$$

The per-acre wood flows produced by this regime would amount to harvests of Y_t volume units every t years, with the first harvest occurring t years hence. If these same wood flows were obtained by purchasing Y_t volume units of stumpage every t years at a cost of C dollars per volume unit, the present value of these stumpage purchases would be

$$PVC_2 = \frac{CY_t}{(1 + i)^t - 1} \qquad (8.9)$$

If PVC_1 and PVC_2 are equated and solved for C, the resulting formula is

$$C = \frac{[(1 + i)^t - 1]\left(L + \dfrac{T}{i}\right) + R(1 + i)^t}{Y_t} \qquad (8.10)$$

and C is interpreted as the growing cost per unit of volume. By making PVC_1 and PVC_2 equal and solving for C, we obtain the stumpage price at which a wood user would be indifferent between growing his own timber and purchasing outside stumpage. Since the wood user would be indifferent to these two alternatives, C must also be the production cost per unit of volume. Table 8.8 shows values of growing cost per unit for rotation lengths of 10 through 40 years for the growth curve defined by equation (8.1) and the following economic values.

TABLE 8.8

Per-Cunit Growing Costs for Various Rotation Lengths

Rotation Length (years)	Per-Acre Yield (cunits)	Growing Cost per Cunit (dollars)
10	15.48	$35.54
11	17.90	33.84
12	20.36	32.59
13	22.84	31.68
14	25.34	31.02
15	27.84	30.56
16	30.32	30.29
17	32.79	30.15
18	35.22	30.14
19	37.61	30.25
20	39.96	30.45
21	42.26	30.73
22	44.51	31.10
23	46.70	31.55
24	48.83	32.06
25	50.91	32.64
26	52.92	33.29
27	54.87	34.00
28	56.76	34.77
29	58.59	35.61
30	60.35	36.51
31	62.06	37.46
32	63.70	38.48
33	65.28	39.57
34	66.80	40.71
35	68.26	41.93
36	69.67	43.20
37	71.02	44.55
38	72.32	45.96
39	73.57	47.44
40	74.76	49.00

$R = \$100.00$ per acre

$i = 0.04$

$T = \$1.50$ per acre per year

$L = \$800.00$ per acre

The minimum per-cunit growing cost value of $30.14 is achieved with a rotation length of 18 years. Growing cost can be used as a decision criterion for setting rotation length, but it is only applicable in certain uncommon situations. In particular, selecting a rotation based on growing cost values alone partially ignores the consideration that different annual quantities of wood will be produced per acre with different rotations. Thus, the only situations in which the criterion is fully appropriate are those where a fixed amount of wood must be marketed or utilized each year. Some discussion of such situations is provided in Chapter 9.

*8.7 TAX CONSIDERATIONS

All of the economic analyses previously presented in this chapter have been carried out on a before-tax basis; in other words, all income tax considerations have been ignored. This approach is pedagogically useful since the basic concepts involved are more easily grasped in the absence of the complexities introduced by tax computations. However, the unpleasant realities of life can be ignored for only so long. At this point, some previously developed formulations will be revised for use by individuals and firms operating in a tax-paying environment.

Several additional economic inputs are required for after-tax economic analysis. These are

OIR = tax rate on ordinary income

CGR = tax rate on capital gains income

D_t = per-unit-volume depletion rate in year t

It will be assumed throughout that all incomes from timber sales qualify for capital gains treatment and that sufficient amounts of ordinary income are available for complete deduction of ordinary expenses.

Section 8.2 contains several important equations that are often needed on an after-tax basis. The after-tax versions are given immediately following equation numbers of the before-tax versions. Thus, equation (8.11) is the after-tax equivalent of equation (8.2).

Equation (8.2)

$$N_t = SY_t - CGR(S - D_t)Y_t - R(1 + i)^t \\ - (1 - OIR)T[(1 + i)^t - 1]/i \tag{8.11}$$

Equation (8.3)

$$BLV_t = \frac{SY_t - CGR(S - D_t)Y_t - R(1 + i)^t - (1 - OIR)T[(1 + i)^t - 1]/i}{(1 + i)^t - 1}$$

$$\tag{8.12}$$

Equation (8.4)

$$BLV_t = -R + \frac{SY_t - CGR(S - D_t)Y_t - R}{(1 + i)^t - 1} - \frac{(1 - OIR)T}{i} \quad (8.13)$$

Equation (8.5)

$$BLV_t = \frac{SY_t - CGR(S - D_t)Y_t - R(1 + i)^t}{(1 + i)^t - 1} - \frac{(1 - OIR)T}{i} \quad (8.14)$$

Calculation of bare land values for more complex management regimes on a before-tax basis is accomplished through use of equation (8.6). This equation cannot be easily modified for after-tax situations since the basic cash flow components must be identified in more detail. For after-tax computations, the following cash flow components are defined.

I_j = timber sale income received in year j

CE_j = capitalized expenses incurred in year j

OE_j = ordinary expenses incurred in year j

D_j = depletion expense incurred in year j

The bare land value is calculated as

$$BLV_t = \frac{\sum_{j=0}^{t} [I_j - CGR(I_j - D_j) - CE_j - (1 - OIR)OE_j](1 + i)^{t-j}}{(1 + i)^t - 1}$$

$$(8.15)$$

When optimum economic rotations are calculated for taxpaying individuals or organizations, the bare land values involved in the analyses should be calculated on an after-tax basis. The procedures discussed in Sections 8.4 and 8.5 for decisions concerning intermediate harvests and existing stands are conceptually unchanged by the inclusion of tax considerations. However, the cash flows analyzed must be after-tax rather than before-tax cash flows.

The formulas presented in Section 8.6 for timber growing costs are also affected by tax considerations. Using the notation defined in Section 8.6, and assuming that the per-acre depletion cost will equal the per-acre regeneration costs, the present value of all timber growing costs is

$$PVC_1 = L + \frac{(Y_tS - R)CGR + R(1 + i)^t}{(1 + i)^t - 1} + \frac{T(1 - OIR)}{i} \quad (8.16)$$

where S equals stumpage price per unit of volume. The present value of purchase costs for equivalent wood flows is given by the equation

$$PVC_2 = \frac{Y_t C(1 - OIR)}{(1 + i)^t - 1} \tag{8.17}$$

By making PVC_1 equal to PVC_2 and solving for C, we obtain

$$C = \frac{[(1 + i)^t - 1]\left(L + \dfrac{T(1 - OIR)}{i}\right) + (Y_t S - R)CGR + R(1 + i)^t}{Y_t(1 - OIR)}$$

$$\tag{8.18}$$

which is the equation for the after-tax unit-volume growing cost.[4]

*8.8   SOME IMPORTANT ANALYTIC RESULTS

Several of the topics introduced in previous sections of this chapter can be more fully developed through the use of some elementary calculus. Perhaps the best examples involve the definitions of current annual increment (CAI) and mean annual increment (MAI), and the relationship between the two. The stand volume development curve, or yield curve, has been defined as

$$Y_t = f(t) \tag{8.19}$$

The first derivative of this function is

$$\frac{dY_t}{dt} = f'(t) \tag{8.20}$$

which, by the definition of dY_t/dt, is the instantaneous growth rate function. Since growth rate and current annual increment are essentially synonymous, equation (8.20) is the equation for current annual increment.

Mean annual increment is defined as

$$MAI = Y_t/t \tag{8.21}$$

---

[4] This formula is not correct for forest products firms that process timber from fee lands in their own mills. In such situations, Section 631a of the Internal Revenue Code provides for additional tax savings that are not considered in equation (8.18).

The value of t at which MAI is a maximum must occur when

$$\frac{d(MAI)}{dt} = 0 \tag{8.22}$$

Setting the derivative of equation (8.21) equal to zero gives

$$f'(t)/t - f(t)/t^2 = 0$$

which is equivalent to

$$f'(t) = f(t)/t \tag{8.23}$$

This proves that the maximum MAI value occurs when CAI and MAI are equal. To illustrate the points just developed, consider the hypothetical yield curve

$$Y_t = 21,850e^{-41.006t^{-1}} \tag{8.24}$$

where Y_t is per-acre merchantable cubic foot volume (outside bark) to a 4-inch top. The equation for current annual increment is

$$\begin{aligned} CAI &= dY_t/dt \\ &= 895,981e^{-41.006t^{-1}}t^{-2} \end{aligned} \tag{8.25}$$

Mean annual increment is defined as

$$MAI = 21,850e^{-41.006t^{-1}}/t \tag{8.26}$$

so that

$$\frac{d(MAI)}{dt} = -21,850e^{-41.006t^{-1}}t^{-2} + t^{-3}895,981e^{-41.006t^{-1}} \tag{8.27}$$

By setting this derivative equal to zero and solving for t, we obtain $t = 41.006$, which means that the maximum MAI occurs at 41.006 years, at which time the associated MAI value is

$$\begin{aligned} MAI &= 21,850e^{-41.006(41.006)^{-1}}/41.006 \\ &= 196.0 \text{ cubic feet/acre/year} \end{aligned}$$

At an age of 41.006 years, the *CAI* value is

$$CAI = 895,981e^{-41.006(41.006)^{-1}}(41.006)^{-2}$$

$$= 196.0 \text{ cubic feet/acre/year}$$

The fact that the rotation of maximum *MAI* equals -1 times the coefficient of *t* in the yield function [equation (8.24)] is not a coincidence. It is easy to show that for any yield function of the form

$$Y_t = \alpha e^{-\beta t^{-1}}$$

the rotation age that maximizes *MAI* is equal to β.

Another important maximization problem involves determining the rotation age that maximizes bare land value (optimum economic rotation). Bare land value can be defined using continuous interest notation as

$$BLV = \frac{SY_t - Re^{it}}{e^{it} - 1} - \frac{T}{e^i - 1} \qquad (8.28)$$

or

$$BLV = PV_1 - PV_2$$

where PV_1 is the present value of all future timber incomes and regeneration costs, PV_2 is the present value of all future tax and administrative costs, and *i* is the continuous interest rate. Since PV_2 is unaffected by the rotation age, the rotation age that maximizes PV_1 will also maximize the bare land value. Hence, the optimum economic rotation must occur at the value of *t* where

$$\frac{d(PV_1)}{dt} = 0$$

The resulting equation cannot be directly solved for the optimum value of *t*, but can be reduced to

$$S\left(\frac{dY_t}{dt}\right) = i(SY_t + PV_1) \qquad (8.29)$$

This result states that the optimum economic rotation occurs at that age where the instantaneous value growth rate is equal to the instantaneous opportunity cost incurred by delaying the harvest.

REFERENCES

Clutter, J. L., and E. P. Jones. 1980. Prediction of growth after thinning in old-field slash pine plantations. *U.S.D.A. For. Serv., Res. Paper SE-127.*

Clutter, J. L., T. R. Dell, and G. H. Brister. 1981. Application of available growth and yield data for management decisions. In *Proceedings of a Symposium on the Managed Slash Pine Ecosystem.* Univ. of Fla., Gainesville.

Davis, K. P. 1966. *Forest management: regulation and valuation.* 2nd ed. McGraw-Hill, New York.

Duerr, W. A., D. E. Teeguarden, N. B. Christiansen, and S. Guttenberg. 1979. *Forest resource management.* Saunders, Philadelphia.

Johnston, D. R., A. J. Grayson, and R. T. Bradley, 1967. *Forest planning.* Faber, London.

9

Forest-Level Management Planning: Basic Concepts

The preceding chapter has dealt with methods for timber management planning that apply when each stand can be considered as a separate and independent decision-making situation. These methods are primarily applicable in the management of small tracts of forestland where there is no particular need for stabilizing, or smoothing over time, the timber yields and cash flows produced from the property. On the other hand, managers of larger tracts typically must be concerned with the production of timber harvests and profits that are relatively stable from year to year. To achieve this stability, the forest must be treated as a single entity and more complex planning and analysis procedures must be utilized.

The process we are referring to as *forest-level planning* has traditionally been called *forest regulation*. However, the objectives of the process and the techniques involved have changed so dramatically in recent years that adoption of a new name is appropriate to emphasize the differences between the older methodology and the approaches used today. Traditional forest regulation procedures were based on the existence of some "target forest" structure. Attainment and subsequent maintenance of this structure were assumed to be important management objectives. We do not believe a static balance forest constitutes a

238

very reasonable goal for today's forest manager (Thompson, 1966; Ware and Clutter, 1971) and, instead, contend that the real role of the manager is the intelligent management of *imbalanced* forest structures. It is hoped that the full meaning of this statement will be clarified in the subsequent discussion.

9.1 THE FULLY REGULATED FOREST

Forest regulation target forests were originally referred to as *normal forests*. Like many entities qualified by the adjective "normal," such forests existed only as mental constructs. The traditional normal forest is a collection of evenaged stands that are being managed on a rotation age of R years. Yields for these stands are given by some normal yield table, so that all stands are assumed to be normally (i.e., fully) stocked. All stands are considered as growing on equi-productive sites and the age class distribution in the forest is assumed to be *balanced*. A *balanced age class distribution* exists when there are equal acreages of 1-year-old stands, 2-year-old stands, . . . , R-year-old stands. More recent discussions of forest regulation (e.g., Davis, 1966; Clawson, 1977) have abandoned the term *normal forest* and instead consider *fully regulated forests*. The concept of a fully regulated forest in no way involves any reference to normal stocking. In a fully regulated forest, the yields attainable at various ages are simply assumed to be given by some known yield function that is applicable for the type and intensity of management being applied. Although a fully regulated structure is seldom an achievable, or even desirable, status for real forests, the concept of a fully regulated forest is a useful construct, and a sound understanding of the dynamic relationships involved in any fully regulated forest is a necessary prerequisite to a study of the changes through time that occur in forests with more complex structures.

9.1.1 The Structure of Fully Regulated Forests

Many of the fundamental principles of forest dynamics are based on relationships present in fully regulated forests. It is therefore worthwhile to discuss the structure of fully regulated forests in some detail. Consider a forest of A acres managed with a rotation age of R years. The forest consists of R 1-year age classes with equal areas in all age classes. The average per-acre volume for each age class is known from an appropriate yield table. Stands in the R-year age class are assumed to enter the 1-year age class after harvest.[1] To achieve a precise statement of the situation, the following variables are defined.

---

[1] This does not necessarily imply immediate regeneration since the average regeneration delay can easily be included in the yield table. For example, if the expected average regeneration delay is 1 year, the per-acre volume shown in the yield table for, say, age class 25 would be the volume per acre for a 24-year-old stand.

Y_i = per-acre volume in age class i

V_i = total volume in age class i

a = acres per age class

g = average annual per-acre growth for the forest

G = total annual growth for the forest

H = total annual harvest for the forest

MAI_R = mean annual increment for rotation age stands

Each year, stands of the oldest age class in the forest are harvested and these acres become the age class 1 stands for the next year. All other stands move up one age class each year. Since all age classes have equal acreages, the distribution of acres by age classes is unchanged from year to year and, since all acres are equally productive, the distribution of volume by age classes is also unchanged. These circumstances dictate the dominant characteristic of a fully regulated forest—so long as the oldest age class is harvested each year, the structure of the forest is unchanged. Here are some important relationships for such a forest.

1.   The number of acres in each class is

$$a = A/R \tag{9.1}$$

2.   The total volume of growing stock in the forest V_{gs} is[2]

$$V_{gs} = V_1 + V_2 + \cdots + V_R = \sum_{i=1}^{R} V_i \tag{9.2}$$

   or

$$V_{gs} = aY_1 + aY_2 + \cdots + aY_R = a \sum_{i=1}^{R} Y_i \tag{9.3}$$

3.   The annual harvest is the volume of the oldest age class, so that

$$H = V_R = aY_R \tag{9.4}$$

4.   Since the structure of the forest remains unchanged from one year to the next, annual growth and annual harvest for the forest must be equal, so

---

[2] The statement of this relationship can be expressed in several ways depending on when the harvest is assumed to occur. Financial analysts normally show annual cash flows as occurring in their entirety at the end of the year. The equation shown for V_{gs} is based on an equivalent, simplifying assumption for timber flows.

that

$$G = H \tag{9.5}$$

or, equivalently,

$$G = aY_R \tag{9.6}$$

5. From equation (9.1) it is known that $A = aR$, so that equation (9.6) can be rewritten as

$$\frac{G}{A} = \frac{aY_R}{aR}$$

or

$$g = MAI_R \tag{9.7}$$

This important result means that the average annual per-acre growth for the entire forest is equal to the mean annual increment for rotation age stands. It also follows from equations (9.5) and (9.6) that

$$H = aY_R$$
$$= (A/R)Y_R$$
$$= (Y_R/R)A$$

or

$$H = (MAI_R) \times (A) \tag{9.8}$$

Thus, the total annual harvest is the product of total forest acreage and the mean annual increment for rotation age stands.

9.1.2   Some Examples of Fully Regulated Forests

Table 9.1 shows a hypothetical tabular yield table for a rapid-growth, short-rotation plantation species. Table 9.1 will be used to illustrate the composition of a number of fully regulated forests. All of these forests are assumed to grow according to the yield relationship shown in this table, and all will produce the same total annual harvest. The forests considered will, however, have different rotation ages. The important structural characteristics of these forests for rotation ages of 6 through 30 years are summarized in Table 9.2. Each forest shown is capable of supporting a sustained annual harvest of 400,000 cunits per year.

To illustrate the steps involved in the calculation of Table 9.2, consider the fully regulated forest with a rotation age of 25 years. Since age class 25 stands

TABLE 9.1

Hypothetical Example of a Yield Table

Age Class	Yield (cunits/acre)
6	4.80
7	10.50
8	16.64
9	22.95
10	29.10
11	34.98
12	40.80
13	46.67
14	52.22
15	57.00
16	61.60
17	65.96
18	70.20
19	73.91
20	77.60
21	81.06
22	84.26
23	87.40
24	90.24
25	92.75
26	94.90
27	96.93
28	98.56
29	100.05
30	100.80

contain an average of 92.75 cunits per acre and the annual harvest must be 400,000 cunits, the area harvested annually must be

$$a = \frac{400,000}{92.75} = 4312.67 \text{ acres}$$

With 25 age classes and 4312.67 acres per age class, the total size of the forest is

$$A = 25(4312.67) = 107,817 \text{ acres}$$

The total volume of growing stock for the forest can be calculated as

$$V_{gs} = 4312.67(4.80 + 10.50 + 16.64 + \cdots + 92.75)$$

$$= 4,746,697 \text{ cunits}$$

TABLE 9.2

Characteristics of Various Fully Regulated Forests Providing a Sustainable Harvest of 400,000 Cunits per Year

Rotation Length (R)	Annual Cutting Area a (acres)	Total Forest Area A (acres)	Total Growing Stock V_{gs} (cunits)	Annual Percent Harvest	MAI for Harvest Stands MAI_R (cunits/acre/year)
6	83.333	500,000	400,000	100.0	0.80
7	38,095	266,667	582,857	68.6	1.50
8	24,038	192,308	767,788	52.1	2.08
9	17,429	156,863	956,688	41.8	2.55
10	13,746	137,457	1,154,502	34.8	2.91
11	11,435	125,786	1,360,435	29.4	3.18
12	9,804	117,647	1,566,373	25.5	3.40
13	8,571	111,421	1,769,359	22.6	3.59
14	7,660	107,239	1,981,310	20.2	3.73
15	7,018	105,263	2,215,158	18.1	3.80
16	6,494	103,896	2,449,740	16.3	3.85
17	6,064	103,093	2,687,811	14.9	3.88
18	5,698	102,564	2,925,470	13.7	3.90
19	5,412	102,828	3,178,623	12.6	3.89
20	5,155	103,093	3,427,474	11.7	3.88
21	4,935	103,627	3,681,174	10.9	3.86
22	4,747	104,439	3,941,372	10.1	3.83
23	4,577	105,263	4,199,771	9.5	3.80
24	4,433	106,383	4,467,598	9.0	3.76
25	4,313	107,817	4,746,697	8.4	3.71
26	4,215	109,589	5,039,157	7.9	3.65
27	4,127	111,421	5,333,622	7.5	3.59
28	4,058	113,636	5,645,414	7.1	3.52
29	3,998	115,942	5,961,339	6.7	3.45
30	3,968	119,048	6,316,984	6.3	3.36

so that the percent of total growing stock harvested each year is

$$\text{Percent harvest} = 100 \left(\frac{400,000}{4,746,697} \right)$$

$$= 8.43 \text{ percent}$$

The mean annual increment for rotation age stands is obtained as

$$MAI_R = \frac{92.75}{25} = 3.71 \text{ cunits/acre/year}$$

A number of interesting comparisons can be made with the data contained in Table 9.2. As previously mentioned, all the forests shown are equivalent in one respect—each can support a sustained annual harvest of 400,000 cunits per year. In other respects, the forests are quite different. Annual cutting areas vary from 83,333 acres to 3968 acres and total forest size ranges from a maximum of 500,000 acres to a minimum of 102,564 acres. The minimum rotation length forest contains a total growing stock volume of only 400,000 cunits, while the maximum rotation length forest has a total growing stock volume of 6,316,984 cunits. Percent harvest for the various forests varies from 100.0 percent to 6.3 percent. Mean annual increment ranges from 0.80 to 3.90 cunits per acre per year.

The obvious question at this point, of course, is: "Which of the forest structures shown is best?" This is not an easy question to answer. Some might contend that the 18-year rotation forest is preferable because it requires the smallest land base (102,564 acres). It should not be surprising that the minimum land base forest is managed at the rotation of maximum mean annual increment. Equation (9.8) states that

$$H = (MAI_R)\,(A)$$

In this case H is specified as 400,000 cunits and the minimum A value satisfying the equality must then be associated with the maximum MAI_R value. However, selection of the minimum land base forest at best ignores all economic considerations (with the possible exception of land purchase costs), and this alternative would probably constitute an optimum strategy only if the decision criterion selected was minimum forest size. Of the economic criteria which could be considered, minimum per-unit growing cost is probably most appropriate in this situation. Since the forests are controlled for an annual production of 400,000 cunits, it is reasonable to believe that the forest is associated with a processing facility having a 400,000 cunit annual wood requirement and that other markets are not available. In this situation, the optimal *operating* forest for the owner would be that forest with minimum annual growing cost. It is important to note, however, that the preceding statement still does not completely settle the question. If one could move directly into an operational situation, the best alternative would be the one involving the rotation of minimum growing cost. However, if the forest must be established prior to the startup of the processing facility, it is by no means certain that the optimum strategy would involve a forest managed at the rotation of minimum per-unit growing cost.

For example, suppose, for the economic conditions involved, that the minimum per-unit growing cost occurs with a rotation of 15 years. If a firm started immediately from bare land (or noncommercial forest) to establish the forest and processing facility, it would receive no income until a point in time 15 years hence, but it would incur considerable expenses during each of those 15 years. If a considerable annual profit is expected from the processing facility, the strategy maximizing the present value of future cash flows would almost certainly involve a forest based, at least initially, on a shorter rotation than 15 years, with the profits generated from earlier mill startup more than compensating for the higher growing costs associated with the shorter rotation.

Although combined afforestation/mill establishment ventures of the type described above may be unfamiliar to North American foresters, many such projects have been undertaken in other parts of the world.[3] Given the increasing interest among developing countries in forestry activities, it can be reasonably anticipated that investments of this type will be even more common in the future.

9.1.3 A Generalization of the Fully Regulated Forest Concept

It is now appropriate to reconsider some of the results shown in Table 9.2. In particular, note that the MAI_R value for the 24-year rotation forest is 3.76 cunits per acre per year, while the MAI_R value for the 25-year rotation forest is 3.71 cunits per acre per year. Is there then no fully regulated forest with a harvest of 400,000 cunits per year that will produce, say, an MAI of 3.73 cunits per acre per year? In fact, there is such a forest if the concept of a fully regulated forest is generalized somewhat. In this generalization, the restriction requiring all age classes to have the same number of acres is abandoned and a fully regulated forest is defined as any forest that permanently retains a constant age-class structure under some constant level of harvest.

A forest that satisfies this definition, provides an annual harvest of 400,000 cunits, and has an MAI_R value of 3.73 cunits per acre per year is shown in Figure 9.1. Age classes 1 to 24 each contain 4359.86 acres, while age class 25 contains 2615.57 acres. The harvest each year is obtained by cutting all the age class 25 acres plus 1744.29 acres of age class 24. The total acreage harvested annually is

$$2615.57 + 1744.29 = 4359.86 \text{ acres}$$

The annual volume harvested is

$$2615.57(92.75) + 1744.29(90.24) = 400,000 \text{ cunits}$$

and the average MAI_R value for the stands harvested is

$$\frac{2615.57(3.71) + 1744.29(3.76)}{4359.86} = 3.73 \text{ cunits/acre/year}$$

---

[3] Relatively well-known examples of such enterprises are the state-owned forest industries of South Australia, N. Z. Forest Products Ltd. of New Zealand, the Usutu Project in Swaziland, the Fiji Pine Commission in the Fiji Islands, and the much-publicized Jari Project in equatorial Brazil.

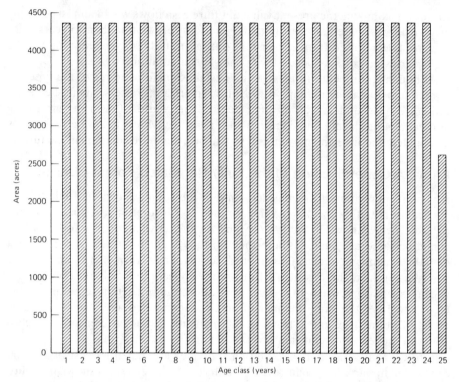

Figure 9.1 The structure of a fully regulated forest with an annual harvest of 400,000 cunits and an average *MAI* of 3.73 cunits per acre per year.

After the harvest,

$$4359.86 - 1744.29 = 2615.57$$

acres are left in age class 24 so that, when all age classes are advanced and harvest acres are put in age class 1, the structure is identical to that of the initial forest. It is also of interest to note that the average rotation age is

$$R = \frac{2615.57(25) + 1744.29(24)}{4359.86} = 24.6 \text{ years}$$

and that the ratio (p) of acres in the 25-year age class to acres in the 24-year age class is

$$p = \frac{2615.57}{4359.86} = 0.6$$

This same ratio value is also involved in the MAI relationship where

$$\frac{3.73 - 3.76}{3.71 - 3.76} = 0.6$$

These results are not coincidental. The general relationships may be stated as follows. If a fully regulated forest has an average rotation age equal to $n + p$ where $0 < p < 1$, then the following relationships hold.

1. $a_{n+1} = pa_n$

   where

   a_{n+1} = number of acres in the oldest age class

   a_n = number of acres in the next-to-oldest age class

2. $MAI_R = MAI_n + p(MAI_{n+1} - MAI_n)$

   where

   MAI_R = average mean annual increment for harvested stands

   MAI_n = mean annual increment for stands of age n

   MAI_{n+1} = mean annual increment for stands of age $n + 1$

It should be noted that with this more general balanced structure the total annual growth of the forest is no longer exactly equal to the product of the total acres and the average harvest stand *MAI*. (However, the result is still approximately correct.) For the forest of Figure 9.1, the total annual growth is 400,000 cunits per year since the forest is stable under an annual cut of 400,000 cunits. However, the product of the total acres and the average harvest stand *MAI* is 107,252.21 acres times 3.73 cunits per acre per year, which equals 400,051 cunits.

9.1.4 Changing the Harvest in a Fully Regulated Forest

Table 9.2 shows the characteristics of a number of fully regulated forests, any one of which is capable of supporting a sustained annual harvest of 400,000 cunits. Under a continuing annual harvest of 400,000 cunits, each of these forests would have a constant structure. What happens to such forests when the equilibrium harvest level is increased or decreased?

For example, consider a 50,000 acre fully regulated forest with a 25-year rotation. All stands in the forest are assumed to grow according to the yield relationship given in Table 9.1. Some of the important characteristics of this forest are

Acres per age class = 2000

Equilibrium harvest = 185,500 cunits/year

Harvest stand *MAI* = 3.71 cunits/acre/year

Suppose that the annual harvest for this forest is increased to a continuing level of 193,000 cunits per year. During the first year of operation at the increased harvest level, the entire 25-year age class would be harvested and sufficient acres in the 24-year age class would have to be harvested to produce the additional 7,500 cunits. Since age-class 24 stands average 90.24 cunits per acre, 7500/90.24 = 83.11 acres of age-class 24 would be harvested during the first year. In the next year, less than 185,500 cunits would be available in the 25-year age class, and an increased acreage would have to be harvested from the 24-year age class. One might intuitively suspect, from this limited examination of the situation, that continuation of the increased harvest would, in time, lead to the complete removal of all the growing stock. In fact, this would not happen for the case considered here. Table 9.3 shows the development of the forest structure through time. It can be seen that imposition of the increased cut leads to a decrease in the average rotation age and a decline in the total growing stock volume. However, as time passes, the forest slowly assumes an increasingly regular structure until, at the end of 400 years, it is, for all practical purposes, fully regulated on a 21-year rotation. (If the simulation were carried forward long enough, the 22-year age class would finally disappear and the remaining age classes would each contain 2380.95 acres.) In this new structure, the forest could perpetually sustain the 193,000 cunit annual harvest level. A realization of what has happened here is fundamental to a basic understanding of forest dynamics. In the situation just described, the increase in harvest level has produced an associated increase in forest productivity. This has occurred because the average rotation age for the new forest is closer to the rotation of maximum mean annual increment than was the rotation for the original forest.

The ultimate results of any harvest pattern can always be explored through a computer simulation similar to that reported in Table 9.3. However, for the type of situation reported here, the ultimate result of a change in harvest level can be determined by an examination of the mean annual increment/rotation age relationship. A graph of harvest stand *MAI* over rotation age for the yield relationship involved is shown in Figure 9.2. The *MAI* value for the initial fully regulated forest of Table 9.3 is shown as point A. The increased harvest produces a new balanced forest structure with a rotation age of 21 years and an associated mean annual increment of 3.86 cunits per acre per year (point B in Figure 9.2). Since total annual forest growth in a balanced forest is obtainable as the product of total acreage and rotation age *MAI*, the annual growth for the new balanced

TABLE 9.3

Changes in Forest Structure for an Initially Fully Regulated Forest Subjected to an Annual Harvest of 193,000 Cunits

Age Class (years)	Acreage by Age Class at End of Year						
	1	2	25	50	100	200	400
1	2083	2085	2167	2234	2315	2368	2380
2	2000	2083	2164	2232	2314	2368	2380
3	2000	2000	2159	2230	2313	2368	2380
4	2000	2000	2154	2228	2312	2368	2380
5	2000	2000	2149	2225	2311	2368	2380
6	2000	2000	2145	2223	2309	2367	2380
7	2000	2000	2138	2220	2308	2367	2380
8	2000	2000	2133	2218	2307	2367	2380
9	2000	2000	2129	2215	2306	2367	2380
10	2000	2000	2125	2212	2305	2366	2380
11	2000	2000	2122	2208	2303	2366	2380
12	2000	2000	2119	2204	2302	2366	2380
13	2000	2000	2116	2202	2301	2366	2380
14	2000	2000	2112	2199	2300	2365	2380
15	2000	2000	2109	2196	2298	2365	2380
16	2000	2000	2106	2194	2297	2365	2380
17	2000	2000	2104	2192	2296	2365	2380
18	2000	2000	2101	2189	2294	2364	2380
19	2000	2000	2098	2186	2293	2364	2380
20	2000	2000	2095	2183	2291	2364	2380
21	2000	2000	2093	2180	2289	2364	2380
22	2000	2000	2090	2178	1638	312	11
23	2000	2000	2088	1452			
24	2000	2000	1183				
25	1917	1831					
Total acres	50,000	50,000	50,000	50,000	50,000	50,000	50,000
Total volume (cunits)	2,193,571	2,185,648	2,037,537	1,947,481	1,851,301	1,790,468	1,776,684

forest is

$$G = 50,000(3.86) = 193,000 \text{ cunits/year}$$

which will perpetually sustain the increased harvest level.

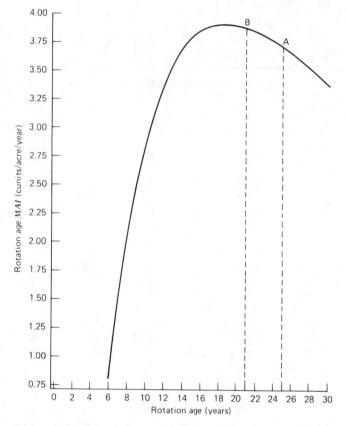

Figure 9.2 Rotation age *MAI* in relation to rotation age
for the yield relationship in Table 9.1.

To this point, we have only considered a particular example case. A general
statement governing such situations is possible. If the harvest in a fully regulated
forest is changed to a new sustained level, one of three eventualities will result
(Allison, 1978).

1. The forest structure will restabilize with a new average rotation age.
2. The forest will be totally depleted.
3. The forest will become unmanaged.

For any given situation, the outcome can be determined from the *MAI* relationship. Consider again the initial 25-year rotation fully regulated forest of
Table 9.3 as a starting point, and suppose that a continuing harvest of 225,000
cunits per year is imposed on such a forest. Since this forest contains 50,000

acres, an average rotation age MAI of 4.50 cunits per acre per year (225,000 cunits per year/50,000) would be required to sustain this harvest in perpetuity. Reference to Table 9.2 shows there is no rotation age that produces an MAI value this large. Thus it will be impossible to develop a stable forest structure that would produce 225,000 cunits per year, and a continued harvest of 225,000 cunits per year will, in time, completely deplete the growing stock. (Simulation shows that, in this case, the last growing stock would be cut in the 43rd year of increased harvest.)

On the other hand, suppose the same 25-year rotation fully regulated forest is subjected to a continuing harvest of 172,500 cunits per year. In this case, the average harvest age will initially increase, leading to a decrease in rotation age MAI. The MAI required for a sustained growth of 172,500 cunits per year is 172,500/50,000 = 3.45 cunits per acre per year. Reference to Table 9.2 or Figure 9.2 shows that this MAI is produced in a fully regulated forest with a rotation age of 29 years. Hence, continued imposition of the 172,500 cunits per year harvest would ultimately result in a stable forest structure with a rotation age of 29 years.

Finally, consider a situation where a 25-year rotation fully regulated forest has a cut of 50,000 cunits per year imposed on it. The MAI value required to produce this level of growth is 50,000/50,000 = 1.00 cunit per acre per year. Under the 50,000 cunits harvest level, harvest ages will increase from 25 years, but no older harvest age within the range of the yield table produces an MAI as low as 1.00 cunit per acre per year. Thus, harvest ages will continue to increase to some unpredictable maximum, at which point mortality from natural causes will probably have a greater impact on forest structure than the harvest. When this occurs, the forest has become unmanaged.

The relationships just illustrated have some significant management implications. First, it should be noted that a fully regulated forest managed on a rotation longer than the rotation of maximum MAI has some desirable characteristics. If the cut is increased from the equilibrium cut level, such a forest becomes more productive and may restabilize at a lower average rotation age. Even in cases where restabilization is impossible, the depletion of growing stock often takes place very slowly so that the firm has adequate time to establish additional forest, which can become merchantable prior to depletion of the original forest. Therefore, a fully regulated forest with rotation age greater than the maximum MAI rotation is a valuable asset to a firm contemplating expansion of its harvest. On the other hand, creation of such a forest involves significantly greater economic costs than those associated with other equally productive forests.

It has already been pointed out that economic considerations usually result in the selection of rotation ages less than the rotation of maximum MAI. Fully regulated forests managed on rotations less than the rotation of maximum MAI have very undesirable characteristics in harvest expansion situations. When the harvest is increased above the equilibrium level, average rotation age decreases and moves further below the age of maximum *MAI*. This produces an associated decrease in forest productivity, which, in turn, results in an increasingly rapid reduction in growing stock. Forests of this type can be depleted very rapidly when annual harvest volumes exceed the sustainable equilibrium harvest.

9.2 PREDICTING STRUCTURE CHANGES IN NONFULLY REGULATED FORESTS

This section presents methodology for predicting subsequent events when a constant continuing annual harvest is imposed on a forest of any initial structure. We will continue to simplify the situation by assuming that all stands in the forest are now growing and will, in the future, grow according to the yield relationship shown in Table 9.1. We now, however, no longer assume that equal numbers of acres are initially present in each age class but, instead, only assume that the number of acres in each age class is known. This situation is much more complex than that previously discussed, but some technology for dealing with the problem is available.

First, it is possible to make the following general statement. If a significant, constant annual harvest is imposed on a forest of even-aged stands (with oldest stands harvested first), one of two eventualities will occur (Allison, 1978):

1. The forest will be completely depleted.
2. A fully regulated forest will eventually be developed.

The term *significant* has been included as a qualifier on the harvest level to rule out the uninteresting case in which the average age of the forest increases to the point where the forest is essentially unmanaged. The fact that alternative 1 can occur should come as no surprise to anyone, but the fact that, if 1 does not occur, a fully regulated forest will eventuate is not intuitively obvious and has not been widely reported in the literature.

There are two essential aspects to this situation; one involves short-term considerations and the other is a matter of long-term developments. The short-term aspects are almost entirely related to the amount and distribution by age class of the initial growing stock, while the long-term aspects depend on the growth potential present in the forest. The nature of the fully regulated forest that develops if the growing stock is not depleted can be predicted without resorting to voluminous calculations. As before, the nature of this forest is a function of the harvest level and the *MAI* curve.

Consider, for example, a 100,000-acre forest in which a continuing harvest level of 390,000 cunits per year is imposed. A fully regulated forest producing this quantity of annual growth would have a rotation age *MAI* of 3.90 cunits per acre per year. Table 9.2 (or Figure 9.2) shows that the only rotation age that will produce this *MAI* is 18 years (the age of maximum *MAI*). Thus, if a harvest of 390,000 cunits per year is removed from *any* 100,000-acre forest in which the stands grow according to the yield relationship shown in Table 9.1, and if the forest is not depleted by this level of harvest, the forest that will eventuate is a fully regulated forest with an 18-year rotation.

As a second example, suppose a 100,000-acre forest is harvested at a constant and continuing rate of 359,000 cunits per year. Annual growth of this amount in a fully regulated forest would require a rotation age *MAI* of 3.59 cunits per acre per year. This *MAI* is produced in a fully regulated forest with a rotation age of 13 years and also in a fully regulated forest with a rotation age of 27 years. Therefore, if a harvest of 359,000 cunits per year is imposed on *any* 100,000-acre forest in which the previously referred to yield relationship applies, and if the forest sustains this harvest, the long-term result will be either a 13-year rotation fully regulated forest or a 27-year rotation fully regulated forest. Which of the two would occur depends on the amount and distribution by age class of the initial growing stock.

Determining whether the growing stock will be depleted prior to stabilization of the forest is a more difficult matter and can only be accomplished by carrying out computations that impose the harvest and update the age-class distribution on a year-by-year basis. Table 9.4 shows some of the details of such a forest simulation for a 10-year period. The forest involved contains 100,000 acres and the oldest age class in the initial distribution is 23 years. During each of the 10 years, a harvest volume of 375,000 cunits is removed. Figure 9.3 shows a graphic comparison of the initial age-class distribution with the distribution at the end of the 10-year harvest period.

The computations in Table 9.4 are easily programmed for implementation with a computer, and it is only through use of a computer that such calculations can be practically accomplished. The results from computer simulations with four different forests are shown in Figure 9.4. All four forests are 100,000 acres in size and have an initial growing stock volume of 2,400,000 cunits. All four simulations impose a constant harvest of 385,000 cunits per year. Two of the forests shown are incapable of supporting this harvest level, and total depletion of the forest occurs in the 14th year of harvest in one case and in the 93rd year of harvest in the other. Each of the other forests is capable of sustaining the 385,000 cunits per year harvest level, and both ultimately become fully regulated forests with a 21.32-year average rotation. However, the speeds with which the two forests approach the equilibrium structure are considerably different. This example illustrates the important point that it is, in general, impossible to tell, without resorting to simulation, whether a forest with a given total growing stock volume will sustain some specified harvest level.

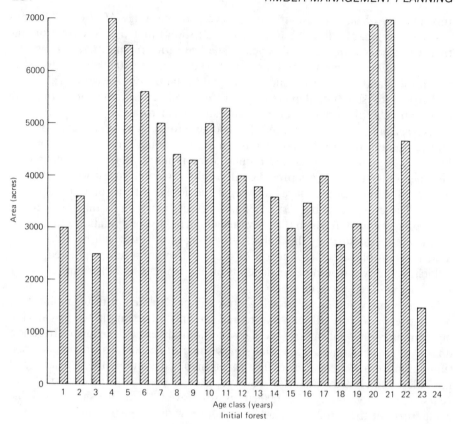

Figure 9.3   Age-class distributions before and after a 10-year harvest period.

9.3 DETERMINING MAXIMUM SUSTAINABLE HARVEST

A problem of considerable practical significance involves determination of the maximum continuing constant harvest level that can be imposed on a given forest and sustained in perpetuity. This level is referred to as the *maximum sustainable harvest* or *maximum sustained yield*. Determination of the maximum sustainable harvest requires repeated computer simulations with varying harvest levels. Two cases are of interest. The first considers the determination of maximum sustainable harvest with a constant land base. In the second case, only the beginning growing stock level is fixed, with various amounts of additional bare land available for use in maximizing the sustainable harvest. Both of these procedures are illustrated with a hypothetical short rotation forest.

Table 9.5 shows the yield relationship for the example forest about to be considered. The initial distribution of acres by age class is shown in Table 9.6.

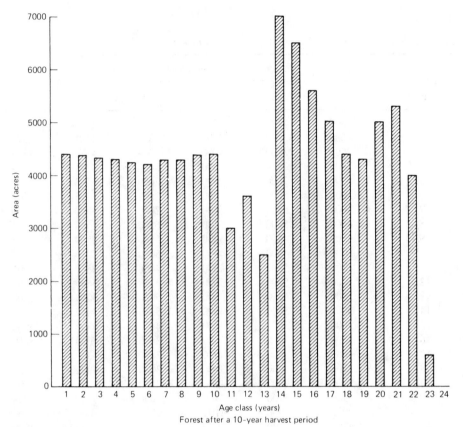

Figure 9.3 (continued)

The total size of the forest is 50,000 acres. Inspection of Table 9.5 indicates that the maximum *MAI* value for the yield table occurs at age 10 where a value of 4.60 cunits per acre per year is obtained. Hence, no matter how much growing stock is currently present, the maximum sustainable harvest cannot possibly exceed 50,000(4.60) = 230,000 cunits per year if the land base is held fixed. Table 9.7 shows the results of repeated simulation using the initial structure shown in Table 9.6 and varying harvest levels. The results show that a continuing harvest level of 213,000 cunits/year will totally deplete the growing stock in 38 years. However, a harvest level of 212,000 cunits per year can be sustained in perpetuity. Thus, the maximum sustainable harvest (to the nearest 1000 cunits) is 212,000 cunits per year.

We now consider the determination of maximum sustainable yield with an augmentable land base. In this situation, the possibility of increasing the maximum sustainable harvest through the addition of bare land is analyzed. The result is a maximum sustainable harvest value for each level of land augmen-

TABLE 9.4

Age-Class Distributions During a 10-Year Harvest Period

Age Class (years)	Acreage by Age Class (years)					
	0	**1**	**2**	**3**	**6**	**10**
1	3000	4395	4383	4291	4237	4405
2	3600	3000	4395	4383	4201	4377
3	2500	3600	3000	4394	4286	4327
4	7000	2500	3600	3000	4291	4294
5	6500	7000	2500	3600	4383	4237
6	5600	6500	7000	2500	4395	4201
7	5000	5600	6500	7000	3000	4286
8	4400	5000	5600	6500	3600	4291
9	4300	4400	5000	5600	2500	4383
10	5000	4300	4400	5000	7000	4395
11	5300	5000	4300	4400	6500	3000
12	4000	5300	5000	4300	5600	3600
13	3800	4000	5300	5000	5000	2500
14	3600	3800	4000	5300	4400	7000
15	3000	3600	3800	4000	4300	6500
16	3500	3000	3600	3800	5000	5600
17	4000	3500	3000	3600	5300	5000
18	2700	4000	3500	3000	4000	4400
19	3100	2700	4000	3500	3800	4300
20	6900	3100	2700	4000	3600	5000
21	7000	6900	3100	2700	3000	5300
22	4700	7000	6900	3100	3500	4000
23	1500	1805	4422	6900	4000	604
24				132	107	
Total acres	100,000	100,000	100,000	100,000	100,000	100,000
Total volume (cunits)	3,809,796	3,824,268	3,854,745	3,881,367	3,933,555	3,978,454

tation. From a computational standpoint, the forest simulations must be iteratively repeated, varying both harvest level and acreage added to the current forest. This latter quantity will be referrred to as *age class 0 acreage*, since these acres can be treated in the initial age-class distribution as belonging to a "0-year" age class. Acres in the 0-year age class move into the 1-year age class after the first year's harvest. Harvested acres also move into the 1-year age class.

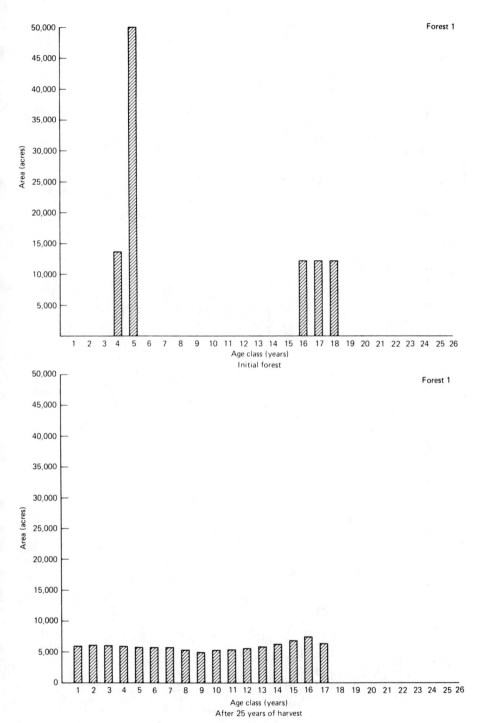

Figure 9.4 Simulation results for four 100,000-acre forests.

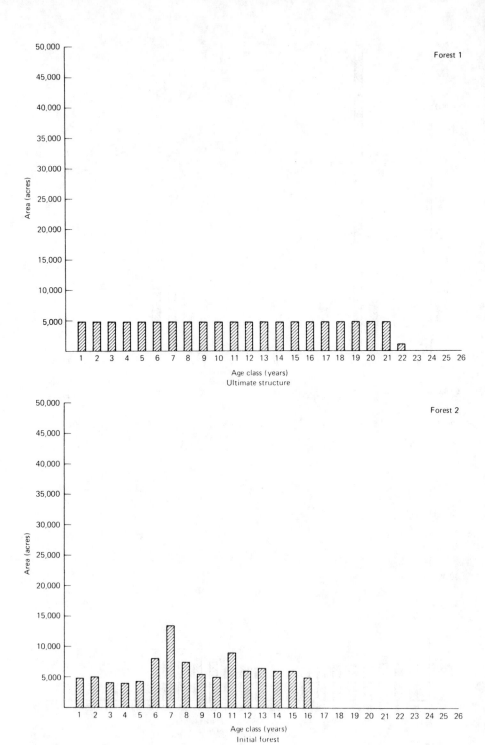

Figure 9.4 (continued)

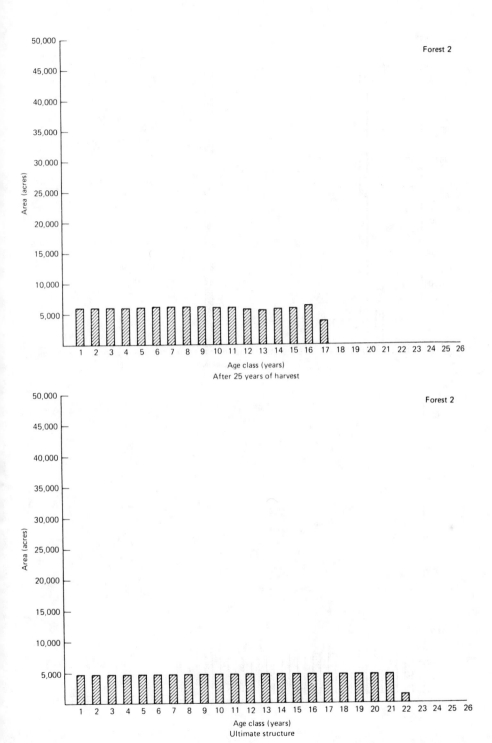

Figure 9.4 (continued)

259

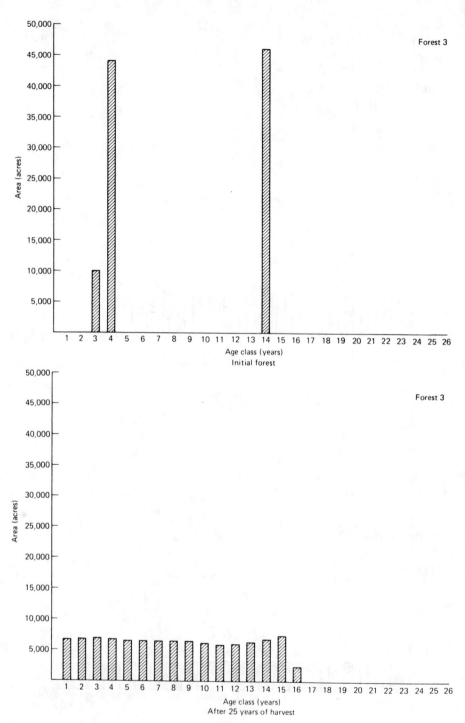

Figure 9.4 (continued)

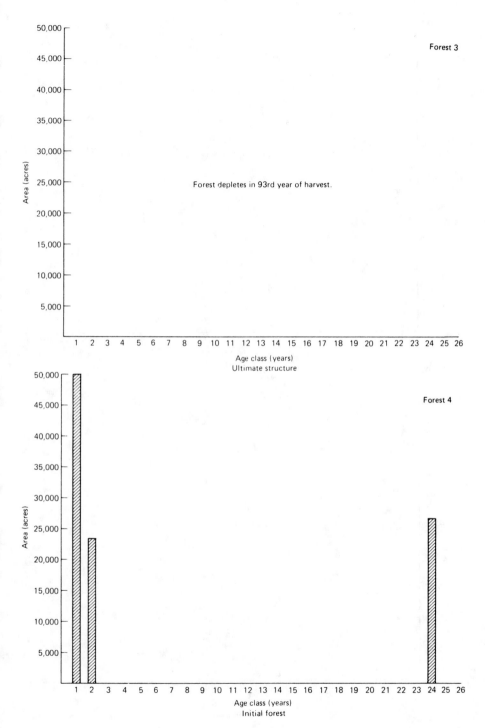

Figure 9.4 (continued)

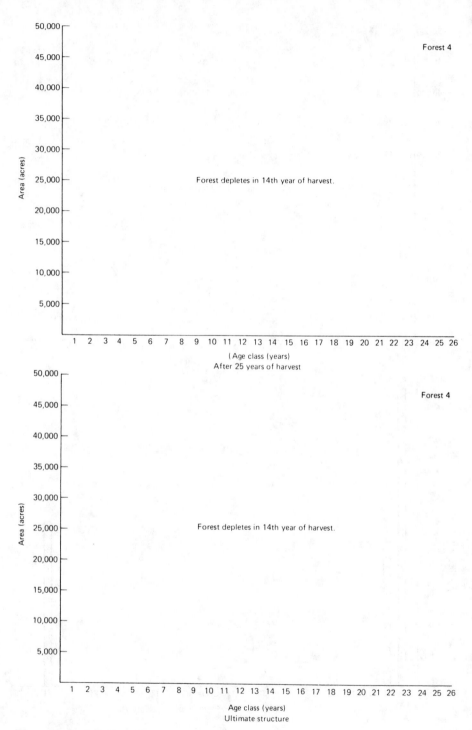

Forest 4

Area (acres)

Forest depletes in 14th year of harvest.

(Age class (years)
After 25 years of harvest

Forest 4

Area (acres)

Forest depletes in 14th year of harvest.

Age class (years)
Ultimate structure

Figure 9.4 (continued)

262

TABLE 9.5

Yield Table for a Hypothetical Short Rotation Forest

Age Class (years)	Yield (cunits/acre)	Mean Annual Increment (cunits/acre/year)
3	3.00	1.00
4	8.40	2.10
5	14.10	2.82
6	20.40	3.40
7	26.95	3.85
8	33.60	4.20
9	40.32	4.48
10	46.00	4.60
11	50.05	4.55
12	54.00	4.50
13	57.46	4.42
14	58.80	4.20
15	60.00	4.00
16	60.80	3.80
17	61.20	3.60
18	61.50	3.42
18 +	61.50	

TABLE 9.6

Initial Age Structure of a Hypothetical Short Rotation Forest

Age class (years)	Area (acres)
1	6100
2	7200
3	7900
4	6700
5	5800
6	4400
7	3600
8	3000
9	2600
10	2200
11	500
Total	50,000

TABLE 9.7

Harvest Simulation Results for the Initial Forest Shown in Table 9.6

Harvest Level (cunits/year)	
200.000	Harvest can be sustained
210.000	Harvest can be sustained
211.000	Harvest can be sustained
212.000	Harvest can be sustained
213.000	Growing stock depletes in year 38
214.000	Growing stock depletes in year 28
215.000	Growing stock depletes in year 24
220.000	Growing stock depletes in year 16
230.000	Growing stock depletes in year 11

Age class 0 acres constitute land that could be immediately acquired and afforested in time to be included in the 1-year age class at a point in time 1 year hence. In the present analysis, such acres exist only in the statement of the initial forest characteristics.

This procedure is illustrated using the initial forest structure shown in Table 9.6 and the yield relationship given in Table 9.5. The outcomes of simulations with various combinations of harvest level and age class 0 acres are shown in Table 9.8. The results shown in Table 9.7 indicated that the maximum sustainable

TABLE 9.8

Harvest Simulation Results for the Initial Forest Shown in Table 9.6

Harvest Level (cunits/year)	Acres of Age Class 0					
	0	10,000	20,000	30,000	40,000	50,000
215.000	D-24	S	S	S	S	S
225.000	D-13	S	S	S	S	S
235.000	D-10	D-22	S	S	S	S
245.000	D-8	D-11	S	S	S	S
255.000	D-7	D-8	D-13	S	S	S
265.000	D-6	D-7	D-9	D-20	S	S
275.000	D-5	D-6	D-7	D-8	S	S
285.000	D-5	D-5	D-6	D-7	D-8	S
295.000	D-5	D-5	D-5	D-6	D-6	D-8

Note: "D-*n*" indicates depletion of the growing stock in year *n*. "S" indicates that the harvest level can be sustained.

harvest for the currently existing forest is 212,000 cunits per year. The Table 9.8 simulations show that higher harvest levels could be immediately imposed if the forest is immediately expanded. For example, if 20,000 acres were immediately acquired and planted, a harvest of 245,000 cunits per year could be imposed immediately and sustained. A continued annual harvest of 245,000 cunits would, in the long run, result in the development of a fully regulated forest with an 18.53-year average rotation.

One might well question the wisdom of the forest expansion that has just been analyzed. The size of the forest has been expanded by 40 percent but the maximum sustainable harvest has increased by only about 16 percent. However, it is important to remember that the maximum sustainable harvest is not a static quantity. In any realistic forest, this value will never remain constant from one year to the next. Analysis shows that the new 70,000-acre forest, managed at a harvest level of 245,000 cunits per year, would, 10 years hence, have a maximum sustainable harvest (without further land augmentation) of 280,000 cunits per year. Thus, the immediate acquisition of 20,000 acres not only makes possible an immediate 33,000-cunit increase in sustainable annual harvest but also generates a further expansion capability of 35,000 cunits per year 10 years hence. This example well illustrates the major problem facing managers of real-world forests: How is the forest best managed to meet immediate demand obligations and to simultaneously undergo changes in structure that will prepare for future circumstances? This is a far more realistic and interesting problem than the traditional forest regulation problem of creating a fully regulated forest.

It should now be obvious that maximum sustainable harvest is a statistic of great practical importance for forest enterprises whose mills are totally dependent on wood from their own forests. If such an enterprise ever places itself in a situation where mill consumption exceeds the maximum sustainable harvest, one of two events must subsequently occur:

1. Mill consumption will have to be reduced by closing some facilities.
2. The forest will be totally depleted.

For most firms, neither of these outcomes would be considered a welcome development.

It should also be noted that maximum sustainable harvest is bound to become a significant statistic in management of the national forests of the United States since the National Forest Management Act of 1976 (Public Law 94-588) requires that (with certain limited exceptions) the annual cut from each national forest must not be greater than the maximum sustainable harvest.

The results shown in Table 9.8 can also be used to illustrate a concept that has recently come to be known as the *allowable cut effect* (ACE; Schweitzer et al., 1972). The forest to which Table 9.8 applies has a maximum sustainable harvest, without land base augmentation, of 212,000 cunits per year. The maximum sustainable harvest with a land base augmentation of 20,000 acres is 245,000 cunits per year. A conventional economic analysis concerning the purchase of the additional land would look at the initial acquisition cost and the cash flows generated by subsequent silvicultural costs and timber harvest incomes from activities on the purchased land. However, if the forest is being managed in an environment where the harvest in any year must be greater than or equal to the harvest for the preceding year (nondeclining sustained yield), it can be argued that purchase of the additional land will permit an immediate increase in the annual harvest from 212,000 cunits per year to 245,000 cunits per year, so that the economic benefits generated by the new harvest level should be legitimately included in the land purchase analysis. Since these benefits are immediate in their effect, the justifiable land purchase cost, with the ACE included, will generally be considerably greater than the result obtained by discounting the cash flows directly generated by the land in question. It should also be noted that other activities, besides land base augmentation, produce the allowable cut effect. For example, any silvicultural practice (fertilization, drainage, competing vegetation control, etc.) that changes the yield relationship given in Table 9.5 will affect the maximum sustainable harvest values in Table 9.8 and, in a nondeclining sustained yield environment, such a practice would generate an allowable cut effect.

Several authors (e.g., Teeguarden, 1973; Walker, 1977; Clawson, 1977) have questioned the validity of economic analyses based on the allowable cut effect. Although a detailed examination of the question is inappropriate here, we offer the general comments that (1) the controversies concerning the allowable cut effect are more a matter of semantics than economics, and (2) the principal objections to ACE analyses usually stem from the analyst's failure to include all relevant strategies rather than from the allowable cut linkage per se. For example, consider a forest that has been established over a period of years to support a future processing facility. Suppose that the forest, under current practices, is capable of supporting the minimum-size facility in perpetuity starting 5 years hence. However, if fertilization of certain stands is immediately undertaken, growth rates will be increased to the point where the facility could be constructed immediately and sustained. If waiting without fertilization and operating immediately with fertilization are indeed the only strategies available, no error is made by ascribing the economic benefits of immediate operation to the fertilization activity. However, if the mill could be opened immediately by simply buying the necessary wood on the open market, the linkage of immediate opening to fertilization is clearly unjustified and fallacious. If all feasible strategies are identified and the cash flows that will eventuate from each are correctly specified, calculation of the present values associated with the various strategies will properly express any allowable cut effects that legitimately exist.

9.4 DEALING WITH MORE COMPLEX FOREST STRUCTURES

The discussion previously presented in this chapter has dealt with hypothetical forests of relatively simple structure. Although most real-world forests are considerably more complex, a sound conceptual understanding of forest dynamics for the idealized cases provides considerable insight concerning the behavior of more realistic forest structures. However, any thorough analysis of dynamic structure in a complex forest will require techniques more general than those thus far considered.

The procedures previously presented have assumed that all stands in the forest have a common yield curve. This is obviously not an assumption that is commonly satisfied in realistic situations. Several techniques can be applied in situations where multiple yield functions are involved. Some of these techniques are applicable only in fairly specialized situations. Others are more general.

Perhaps the simplest generalization of the single yield function situation is a forest involving only a single species (or type) in which several yield functions exist because of site variability within the forest. In such cases, the relationship between any two yield curves is often one of approximately equal proportionality. When this occurs, stands can be measured in terms of *standard acres*, an initial distribution of standard acres by age class can be prepared, and the forest simulation procedures previously discussed can be applied. As an example of this technique, consider the yield curves shown in Figure 9.5 for three different site quality classes. The initial age-class distributions for the three site quality classes are shown in Table 9.9.

Figure 9.5 shows that site class I yields are roughly one-third greater than those for site class II at the same age, while site class III yields are roughly half of those for site class II. Any one of the three site classes could be used as the standard to which the others are compared. Site class II will be used as the standard here. This amounts to defining a standard acre as "that unit of land required to produce 60 cunits at age 30." (The choice of age 30 is also arbitrary; use of any other age and its associated site class II yield would be equivalent.) This gives the following relationships.

0.75 acres of site class I land   = 1 standard acre

1.00 acres of site class II land   = 1 standard acre

2.00 acres of site class III land   = 1 standard acre

These conversions have been applied to Table 9.9 to obtain the age-class distribution of standard acres shown in Table 9.10. The forest shown in Table 9.10 is essentially a site class II forest, which is equivalent, from a forest dynamics standpoint, to the mixed site class forest of Table 9.9. Forest simulations of the type described in Section 9.3 can be used to establish the maximum sustainable

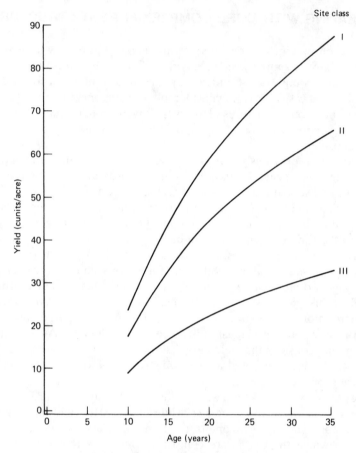

Figure 9.5 Yield curves for three site quality classes.

harvest for the forest defined in Table 9.10. The value obtained will also be the maximum sustainable harvest for the mixed site class forest of Table 9.9.

In many situations, the yield curves appropriate for various strata of the forest will not be proportional, in which case a consolidation by standard acres is inappropriate. The proper procedure then depends on the nature of the situation. If the strata represent species or significant age-class differences (e.g., old-growth versus second-growth), the yields from one stratum may not be substitutable for those from another. In this situation, the maximum sustainable harvests by strata are probably of more interest than an overall figure, and each stratum is simply treated as an independent forest for simulation purposes.

In cases where it is inappropriate to treat the strata as separate forests, the only alternative is to utilize a more complex simulation program that iteratively imposes the specified harvests and maintains a separate age-class distribution

TABLE 9.9

Acreage Distribution for a Hypothetical Forest with Three Site Quality Classes

Age Class	Site Class			
	I	**II** (acres)	**III**	
1	500	240	90	
2	160	210	150	
3	140			
4	600	650	210	
5		326	200	
6		404	456	
7	712	602	515	
8		1100	320	
9		850	716	
10	432	114	490	
11	505	196	321	
12	380	305	204	
13	916	471	187	
14	780	492	138	
15	412	517		
16		602		
17		520		
18		488		
19		390		
20		367		
Totals	5537	8844	3997	18,378

for each stratum. Conceptually, this is not difficult, but two problems arise in practice. First, the number of strata may be quite large. Second, no natural order of assigning harvests to age-class stratum combinations is apparent. By way of illustration, a forest might be divided into strata based on stand density-site index-forest type combinations. If 3 density classes, 5 site index classes, and 8 forest types are defined, there will be 120 strata with a separate distribution of acres by age classes for each one. With contemporary computing equipment, the amount of calculations involved is still manageable, but what priorities should be used in allocating each year's harvest among the various strata is, by no means, obvious. It will still, in general, be advantageous to cut older stands first, but ages in different forest types will not be directly comparable. One must also consider that higher harvest priority should be given to low-density strata so that these areas can be regenerated to stands that will more fully utilize the productive potential of the land areas involved. In general, if the current stands

TABLE 9.10

*Distribution of Standard Acres for the Mixed
Site Class Forest Defined in Table 9.9*

Age Class	Number of Standard Acres
1	951.67
2	498.33
3	186.67
4	1555.00
5	426.00
6	632.00
7	1808.83
8	1260.00
9	1208.00
10	935.00
11	1029.83
12	913.67
13	1785.83
14	1601.00
15	1066.33
16	602.00
17	520.00
18	488.00
19	390.00
20	367.00
Total	18.225.16

are to be replaced by stands with greater productivity (e.g.. natural stands being replaced by plantations). it is obvious that some harvest priority should be accorded to high site quality strata since the productivity gained by conversion will be greatest in these strata. Ordering of the harvest in this situation is now obviously a matter of some complexity. In fact. determination of the optimum ordering is. for complex forests. an economic problem of overwhelming importance. Methods for solving this problem are considered in the next chapter.

It is possible to simulate the development of complex forests through time without aggregating the component stands into strata. Each stand can be treated as an independent entity that is regenerated following harvest and grown according to whatever yield curve is appropriate. In any realistic forest. the total number of stands may. of course. be quite large. However. the principal problem in obtaining meaningful results from such a simulation again involves the ordering of stands for harvest. Many orderings are possible. and the optimum sequencing is seldom, if ever, intuitively obvious. Trial-and-error methods are sometimes used to evaluate alternative sequences, but productive approaches to this problem generally require application of the methodology presented in the next chapter.

REFERENCES

Allison, B. J. 1978. *Some aspects of forest planning.* N. Z. Forest Products Ltd., Auckland.

Clawson, M. 1977. Decision making in timber production, harvest, and marketing. *Resources for the Future, Res. Paper R-4.* Washington.

Davis, K. P. 1966. *Forest management: regulation and valuation.* 2nd ed. McGraw-Hill, New York.

Duerr, W. A., D. E. Teeguarden, N. B. Christiansen, and S. Guttenberg. 1979. *Forest resource management.* Saunders, Philadelphia.

Johnston, D. R., A. J. Grayson, and R. T. Bradley. 1967. *Forest planning.* Faber, London.

Schweitzer, D. L., R. W. Sassaman, and C. H. Schallau. 1972. Allowable cut effect: some physical and economic implications. *J. For.* **70**:415–418.

Teeguarden, D. E. 1973. The allowable cut effect: a comment. *J. For.* **71**:224–226.

Thompson, E. F. 1966. Traditional forest regulation model: an economic critique. *J. For.* **64**:750–752.

Walker, J. L. 1977. Economic efficiency and the National Forest Management Act of 1976. *J. For.* **75**:715–718.

Ware, G. O., and J. L. Clutter. 1971. A mathematical programming system for the management of industrial forests. *For. Sci.* **17**:428–445.

10

Forest-Level Management Planning: Current Techniques

The vehicle for implementing forest-level management planning is a document known as a *harvest schedule* or a *cutting schedule*. This document lists the stands to be harvested during each year of a planning period that extends some specified number of years into the future. Data on the types and intensities of harvests intended for each stand are included in such a schedule along with a timetable for regenerating currently nonproductive areas and stands scheduled for subsequent clearcutting. Both the operating characteristics of the forest (e.g., annual harvest volumes, annual cash flows, age-class distribution in any given year) and the structure of the terminal forest that will exist at the end of the planning period are direct outcomes of the activities specified in the harvest schedule. The extent to which any given forest satisfies the objectives of the owner or owners is therefore largely dependent on the harvest schedule used to manage the forest.

Prior to the availability of recently developed techniques, harvest schedule preparation was closely linked to the target-forest concept, and the final choice of a specific harvest sequence was heavily influenced by the ultimate structure of the target forest. Current procedures for harvest schedule preparation do not generally include any steady-state, long-term, structural goal and are instead more concerned with immediate, rather than distant future, characteristics of the forest. Present-day harvest scheduling techniques assume that the harvest-scheduling problem can be stated as follows (Ware and Clutter, 1971).

1. The ultimate goal of forest management is the maximization of the utility of the forest to the owner. For profit-oriented owners, this goal is usually equivalent to maximizing the present value of future cash flows.

2. Certain considerations restrict the manager's choice of a strategy for achieving this goal. These considerations may reflect practical feasibility restrictions (e.g., annual harvest and cash flow stability) or they may be imposed as a result of owner policy (e.g., nondeclining sustained yield for the National Forests).

Any problem involving an optimization subject to restrictions is known as a *mathematical programming problem*. Great progress has been made over the past three decades in developing efficient solution procedures for mathematical programming problems. Particularly effective techniques now exist for an important subclass known as *linear programming problems*.[1] The practical implementation of these techniques is almost totally dependent on the availability of modern, high-speed computing equipment.

10.1 FOREST-LEVEL PLANNING AS A LINEAR PROGRAMMING PROBLEM

Although the simplex procedure for solving linear programming problems[2] was developed during the 1940s (Dantzig, 1951), practical applications of the procedure were initially limited by the amount of computation required to solve problems of realistic size. However, as improved computing equipment became available in the late 1950s and 1960s, applications for linear programming techniques were identified and implemented in a variety of applied fields. A number of papers published during the 1960s suggested possible approaches to solving forest-level planning problems with linear programming methods (e.g., Curtis, 1962; Donnelly et al., 1963; Leak, 1964; Loucks, 1964; Wardle, 1965; Kidd et al., 1966; Liittschwager and Tcheng, 1967; Nautiyal and Pearse, 1967; Navon and McConnen, 1967).

Two fairly general approaches to linear-program-based harvest-scheduling models eventually emerged. One of these, known as Timber RAM (Resource

---

[1] All linear programming problems have the following structure.
  Maximize or minimize

$$Z = c_1 X_1 + c_2 X_2 + \cdots + c_n X_n$$

Allocation Model), was developed by the U.S. Forest Service (Navon, 1971) for harvest scheduling in western National Forests. The second system, MAX-MILLION, was developed at the University of Georgia in collaboration with a number of industrial cooperators (Clutter, 1968; Ware and Clutter, 1971). Timber RAM served as the prototype for several generations of U.S. Forest Service models, the most recent of which is the FORPLAN (Forest Planning) system. (Johnson et al., 1980). MAX-MILLION has been implemented with various modifications by industrial forestry concerns in the Southeast, the Lake States, the Inland Empire, and the Pacific Northwest. Although the mathematical structures of Timber RAM and MAX-MILLION are quite similar, there are considerable differences between the two in information requirements and report content. To a large extent, these differences stem from the fact that one model was intended for application in the public forestry sector, while the other was oriented toward usage by forest industry.

The remaining topics of this section discuss the concepts involved in developing a linear-program-based harvest-scheduling model of the type exemplified by Timber RAM and MAX-MILLION. Although most of the presentation is equally applicable to either Timber RAM or MAX-MILLION, a few variants are mentioned that, to our knowledge, have only been implemented in certain companies' individual proprietary versions of MAX-MILLION. The terminology used is basically that employed by Ware and Clutter (1971).

---

subject to the restrictions

$$a_{11}X_1 + a_{12}X_2 + \cdots + a_{1n}X_n \gtreqless b_1$$

$$a_{21}X_1 + a_{22}X_2 + \cdots + a_{2n}X_n \gtreqless b_2$$

$$\cdot \qquad\qquad\qquad\qquad \cdot$$

$$\cdot \qquad\qquad\qquad\qquad \cdot$$

$$\cdot \qquad\qquad\qquad\qquad \cdot$$

$$a_{m1}X_1 + a_{m2}X_2 + \cdots + a_{mn}X_n \gtreqless b_m$$

with $X_j \geq 0$ for $(j = 1, \ldots, n)$. The notation "$\gtreqless$" is meant to imply that the restriction may involve either $\geq$, $\leq$, or $=$.

[2] The simplex procedure involves iterative application of an interesting algorithm. If a candidate solution to a properly formulated problem is provided as input to the algorithm, the algorithm will either (1) produce as output a new candidate solution with an equally good or better Z value, or (2) conclude that the candidate solution is the optimal solution. A candidate solution must satisfy the restrictions and possess certain other mathematical properties. A computerized procedure is available for generating an initial candidate solution. It can be shown that repetitive application of the simplex algorithm, with the output solution from one iteration providing the input solution for the next iteration, must eventually lead to the optimum solution.

10.1.1 Specifying Management Regimes[3]

The concept of a *management regime* is a key component in formulating harvest-scheduling problems. Basically, each management regime defines a strategy involving a series of harvesting/silvicultural practices that can be implemented during the planning period. Because of the long-term nature of forestry activities, it is usually neither conceptually desirable nor computationally feasible to schedule harvests and silvicultural practices for periods as short as 1 year. Instead, the planning period is divided into p component cutting periods. The planning period is defined to be n years long and, in practice, the values used for n are typically 1.5 to 2 times the length of a typical rotation for the forest types being managed. The cutting periods may be of unequal length, in which case the length of cutting period j is denoted by m_j and

$$n = \sum_{j=1}^{p} m_j \tag{10.1}$$

(If the cutting periods all have a common length of m years, then $n = mp$.)

It is assumed that all harvests and silvicultural activities (e.g., fertilization, precommercial thinning, site preparation, and planting) occur at the midpoints of cutting periods. Thus, a harvest or cultural activity scheduled to take place in some particular period j' ($j' \leq p$) is assumed to occur $y_{j'}$ years in the future, where

$$y_{j'} = \sum_{j=1}^{j'-1} m_j + (m_{j'}/2) \tag{10.2}$$

(If all $m_j = m$ ($j = 1, \ldots, p$), then $y_j = m(j' - 1) + m/2$.) Any unique pattern of harvests and silvicultural activities by cutting periods constitutes a management regime. Table 10.1 shows several example management regimes for a situation involving eight cutting periods. Harvest activities considered are

C = clearcut followed by site preparation and replanting

T = thin by some specified rule (e.g., remove 30 percent of the volume in a thinning from below)

Silvicultural activities involved are

F = fertilize according to some specified treatment

P = precommercial thin to some given number of trees per acre

---

[3] In U.S. Forest Service planning, management regimes are referred to as *prescriptions*.

TABLE 10.1

Some Example Management Regimes

Regime	Cutting Period							
Number	1	2	3	4	5	6	7	8
1	C	P				C		
2	C	P			T		C	
3	C	F				C		
4	C	P + F		T		C		
5		C				T		C
6			C				T	
7		T		C				

Regime number 1, for example, involves a clearcut followed by site preparation and planting in period 1, a precommercial thinning in period 2, followed in period 6 by another clearcut with subsequent site preparation and planting. Regime number 4, in comparison, calls for clearcuts and regeneration in periods 1 and 6, fertilization and precommercial thinning in period 2, and a commercial thinning in period 4.

Since the regimes included in Table 10.1 are given only to exemplify the variety of possible patterns, all possible regimes are not included. However, in any actual application, the set of management regimes should include all possible pertinent strategies. For example, consider a simpler management situation in which the only activity involved is clearcutting followed by site preparation and planting. In addition, assume the following.

1. The length of the planning period is 32 years.
2. The planning period is divided into eight cutting periods, each one having a length of 4 years.
3. The minimum subsequent rotation length is 20 years.

All possible management regimes for this situation are shown in Table 10.2, where, as before, C indicates a clearcut with subsequent site preparation and planting. Regime number 1, for example, calls for harvest of the existing stand at the middle of cutting period 1 (i.e., 2 years hence). The stand established following that harvest will be clearcut in the middle of period 6 (i.e., 22 years hence). The stand in existence at the end of the planning period will be 10 years old if it is assumed that regeneration also takes place in the middle of period 6. If a regeneration delay exists, the stand can still be referred to as a 10-year age-class stand (meaning 10 years since previous harvest), and the regeneration delay can be built into the yield table (e.g., 10-year age-class stands may actually use the per-acre yields for age 8 stands).

TABLE 10.2

A Typical Set of Management Regimes

Regime Number	Cutting Period							
	1	2	3	4	5	6	7	8
1	C					C		
2	C						C	
3	C							C
4	C							
5		C					C	
6		C						C
7		C						
8			C					C
9			C					
10				C				
11					C			
12						C		
13							C	
14								C
15								

10.1.2 Cutting Units

Forests are typically divided, for management purposes, into mutually exclusive and geographically identifiable areas. Various names are used for these basic management units (e.g., compartments, working areas, management units). They will be referred to here as *cutting units*. (The equivalent U.S. Forest Service term is *analysis areas*.) Several methods for creating cutting units are in common use.

1. Each currently existing stand constitutes a cutting unit.

2. Cutting units are created by consolidating geographically contiguous stands that, after the initial harvest, are managed as one stand. The initial stands involved in the consolidation may differ considerably in species, density, and, to some extent, age. It is, however, assumed that the consolidated subsequent stands are sufficiently homogeneous to be managed as a single stand.

3. Cutting units are created by pooling similar but noncontiguous stands, which are close enough together geographically to be managed as a single unit.

4. Cutting units are created by combining similar stands over the entire ownership. In this situation, a single cutting unit might contain all slash

pine plantations with $18 \leq$ age ≤ 20, $61 \leq$ site index ≤ 65, and $401 \leq$ number of trees per acre ≤ 500. Cutting units formed in this way are usefully referred to as *forest strata*.

Application of one (or a combination) of these procedures to any particular forest results in a subdivision of the forest into N cutting units. The development of a harvest schedule then involves the assignment of a management regime to each cutting unit. If each cutting unit could be treated as an independent decision situation, the problem would reduce to stand-level management planning, and optimum assignments could be developed by a straightforward economic analysis of each regime as applied to each cutting unit. However, if forest-level restrictions are operational, such an approach is inadequate and other procedures must be used to make the assignments. The magnitude of the problem involved can be made evident by noting that, if M management regimes are used, there are M possible choices for cutting unit 1, M possible choices for cutting unit 2, . . . , and M possible choices for cutting unit N. Thus, a total of M^N different assignments of management regimes to cutting units can be made. (For $M = 15$ and $N = 50$, $M^N = 6.38 \times 10^{58}$.) Of the M^N possible harvesting schedules, some will satisfy the constraints that are operational and some will not. The problem thus involves identifying the set of schedules that satisfies the constraints and picking, from this set, the schedule that is economically most desirable.

10.1.3 Evaluating Management Regimes

For any given cutting unit, some regimes produce more favorable economic results than others. For example, a cutting unit containing a well-stocked, premerchantable plantation should not be managed with a regime that involves a clearcut in cutting period 1. The desirability of each management regime as applied to a particular cutting unit can be evaluated with a discounted cash flow analysis.

The major income components in this analysis arise from predicted harvest yields. Predicted yields for harvests of the initially existing stand can be obtained from knowledge of the forest type, site index, initial age, and initial stand density. Predicted yields for harvests of subsequent stands can be calculated from specifications concerning the nature of subsequent stands (species, initial planting density, or expected basal area at some fixed age for natural regeneration) and the elapsed time since the previous clearcut. The mensuration programs used in some harvest scheduling systems predict yields by *product classes* rather than an overall volume total. Product classes generally represent a separation of the total volume into species group-tree size classes.

The estimated periodic yields must be multiplied by appropriate per-unit-volume values to obtain predicted gross incomes by cutting periods. If the forest involved sells stumpage, the unit-volume values should be expected stumpage prices. On the other hand, if the forest provides raw material for processing in the organization's own mills, then the values used should reflect the value of the raw material to the mills involved. Per-unit values used in this situation are referred to as *transfer prices*. If certain product classes produce greater mill profits, this fact should be recognized in the specification of transfer prices so that the harvest-scheduling procedure can recognize the economic gains associated with the processing of these categories of timber. For each regime the gross incomes by cutting periods are combined with the silvicultural costs incurred in each period to obtain net cash flows by cutting periods. Depending on the circumstances, these net cash flows may be on a before-tax or an after-tax basis.

Another important component that must be considered in the evaluation of each management regime is the terminal value of land and growing stock existing at the end of the planning period. Some firms approach this problem by assuming a hypothetical sellout at the end of the planning period and by specifying the selling price they would expect to receive. A second alternative involves the methods described in Section 8.5 after establishing the following assumptions.

1. If the age of the stand in existence at the end of the planning period is greater than or equal to the optimum economic rotation, the stand will be cut at the end of the planning period.

2. If the age of the stand in existence at the end of the planning period is less than the optimum economic rotation, the stand will be harvested when it reaches the optimum economic rotation age.

3. After harvest of the stand existing at the end of the planning period, the cutting unit will be used to grow a continuing series of rotations with each one harvested at the optimum economic rotation age. Hence, after harvest of the stand in existence at the end of the planning period, the value of all future cash flows will be equal to the bare land value.

With this second approach, the terminal value of land and growing stock for management regime k can be calculated as

$$TV_k = \frac{NTHI_k + BLV + \dfrac{T}{i}}{(1 + i)^{a_k}} \tag{10.3}$$

where

TV_k = per-acre value (either before tax or after tax) of land and growing stock in existence at the end of the planning period (exclusive of annual tax and administrative costs)

$NTHI_k$ = net per-acre income (either before tax or after tax) from harvest of the stand in existence at the end of the planning period

BLV = per-acre bare land value (either before tax or after tax) for the cutting unit being evaluated

T = annual per-acre ad valorem tax and administrative costs (either before tax or after tax)

i = discount rate

a_k = number of years elapsing between the end of the planning period and harvest of the stand existing at the end of the planning period for regime k

If OER is the optimum economic rotation and A_k is the age of the stand in existence at the end of the planning period with regime k, a_k can be determined as follows.

$$\text{If } A_k \geqslant OER, \qquad a_k = 0$$

$$\text{If } A_k < OER, \qquad a_k = OER - A_k$$

The final component of management regime value arises from annual ad valorem tax and administrative costs. This component is most simply included as the perpetuity value T/i. [This necessitates the inclusion of the T/i term in equation (10.3) to cancel out the negative T/i term included in the bare land value.]

The above components can now be combined into a single formula for computing the present value of the cash flows produced by implementation of regime k in the cutting unit under consideration. The result is

$$PV_k = \sum_{j=1}^{p} \frac{NHI_{jk} - NE_{jk}}{(1 + i)^{y_j}} + \frac{TV_k}{(1 + i)^n} - \frac{T}{i} \tag{10.4}$$

where

PV_k = per-acre present value of cash flows generated by implementation of management regime k

NHI_{jk} = per-acre net income from timber harvest in period j if regime k is used

NE_{jk} = per-acre net expense of silvicultural practices in period j if regime k is used

TV_k = per-acre value of land and timber in existence at the end of the planning period with regime k

T = annual ad valorem tax and administrative costs

p = number of cutting periods involved

i = discount rate

y_j = number of years between the beginning of the planning period and the midpoint of cutting period j

n = number of years in the planning period

A detailed example problem that illustrates the application of this formula is included in Section 10.2.

10.1.4 The Model I Linear Programming Formulation

Johnson and Scheurman (1977) have classified the various linear programming approaches to harvest scheduling into two basic types known as Model I and Model II. The concepts previously developed in this section apply most directly to Model I formulations. Of the various Model I harvest-scheduling systems, MAX-MILLION and Timber RAM are probably the best known and most widely used. The basic structure of the Model I linear programming formulation is described in the remainder of this section. A discussion of the Model II formulation is contained in Section 10.3.

Discussion of the Model I formulaton involves the following quantities developed during the analysis of yields and economic values associated with the possible use of each management regime on each cutting unit.

N = number of cutting units

M = number of management regimes

p = number of cutting periods

A_i = number of acres contained in cutting unit i

X_{ik} = number of acres of cutting unit i that are assigned to management regime k

D_{ik} = per-acre present value of cutting unit i if management regime k is used

V_{ijk} = per-acre volume harvested from cutting unit i in period j if management regime k is used[4]

F_{ijk} = per-acre net cash flow for cutting unit i in period j if management regime k is used

---

[4] If yields by product classes are involved, this would appear as V_{ijkl} where

V_{ijkl} = per-acre product class l volume harvested from cutting unit i in period j if management regime k is used

Separate volume restrictions by product classes could then be specified.

H_{ijk} = number of acres on which harvesting activities occur for cutting unit i in period j if management regime k is used

R_{ijk} = number of acres on which regeneration activities occur for cutting unit i in period j if management regime k is used

For the subscripts used above,

$$i = 1, 2, \ldots, N$$

$$j = 1, 2, \ldots, p$$

$$k = 1, 2, \ldots, M$$

Some harvest-scheduling analyses may require all the information defined above, while others will use only a subset thereof.

With the quantities defined above, the objective function to be maximized is

$$Q = \sum_{i=1}^{N} \sum_{k=1}^{M} D_{ik} X_{ik} \qquad (10.5)$$

where Q represents the present value of all future cash flows that will be produced by the forest involved. The restrictions imposed can represent required maximum and minimum values by period for harvest acres, regeneration acres, volume harvested, and cash flow generated. Constraints must also be provided to force the total acres assigned to management regimes for any cutting unit to equal the specified cutting unit acreage. These latter restrictions will be referred to as *unit summation restrictions*. Correct forms for the various restrictions follow.

1. Unit summation restriction for cutting unit i.

$$\sum_{k=1}^{M} X_{ik} = A_i \qquad (10.6)$$

where A_i is the number of acres contained in cutting unit i. A restriction of this type must be provided for each cutting unit ($i = 1, 2, \ldots, N$).

2. Harvest acreage restrictions for cutting period j.
    (a) Maximum harvest acreage:

$$\sum_{i=1}^{N} A_i^{-1} \sum_{k=1}^{M} H_{ijk} X_{ik} \leq HMAX_j \qquad (10.7)$$

    (b) Minimum harvest acreage:

$$\sum_{i=1}^{N} A_i^{-1} \sum_{k=1}^{M} H_{ijk} X_{ik} \geq HMIN_j \qquad (10.8)$$

If desired, both a maximum and minimum restriction of this type can be provided for each cutting period ($j = 1, 2, \ldots, p$)

3. Regeneration acreage restrictions for cutting period j.
   (a) Maximum regeneration acreage:

   $$\sum_{i=1}^{N} A_i^{-1} \sum_{k=1}^{M} R_{ijk} X_{ik} \leq RMAX_j \qquad (10.9)$$

   (b) Minimum regeneration acreage:

   $$\sum_{i=1}^{N} A_i^{-1} \sum_{k=1}^{M} R_{ijk} X_{ik} \geq RMIN_j \qquad (10.10)$$

   If desired, both a maximum and minimum regeneration acreage restriction can be included for each cutting period ($j = 1, 2, \ldots, p$).

4. Harvest volume restrictions for cutting period j.
   (a) Maximum harvest volume:

   $$\sum_{i=1}^{N} \sum_{k=1}^{M} V_{ijk} X_{ik} \leq VMAX_j \qquad (10.11)$$

   (b) Minimum harvest volume:

   $$\sum_{i=1}^{N} \sum_{k=1}^{M} V_{ijk} X_{ik} \geq VMIN_j \qquad (10.12)$$

   Both a maximum and a minimum restriction of this type can be included, if desired, for each cutting period ($j = 1, 2, \ldots, p$).

5. Cash flow restrictions for cutting period j.
   (a) Maximum cash flow:

   $$\sum_{i=1}^{N} \sum_{k=1}^{M} F_{ijk} X_{ik} \leq FMAX_j \qquad (10.13)$$

   (b) Minimum cash flow:

   $$\sum_{i=1}^{N} \sum_{k=1}^{M} F_{ijk} X_{ik} \geq FMIN_j \qquad (10.14)$$

   Both a maximum and a minimum cash flow restriction can be included, if desired, for each cutting period.

The quantities appearing as the right-hand sides of equations (10.7) through (10.14) are defined as follows.

$HMAX_j$ = maximum permissible harvest acreage in cutting period j

$HMIN_j$ = minimum permissible harvest acreage in cutting period j

$RMAX_j$ = maximum permissible regeneration acreage in cutting period j

$RMIN_j$ = minimum permissible regeneration acreage in cutting period j

$VMAX_j$ = maximum permissible harvest volume in cutting period j

$VMIN_j$ = minimum permissible harvest volume in cutting period j

$FMAX_j$ = maximum permissible cash flow in cutting period j

$FMIN_j$ = minimum permissible cash flow in cutting period j

Values for these quantities must be assigned by the analyst for the particular forest under study. Few analyses require all of the restrictions shown in equations (10.7) through (10.14) and, in most cases, only a small subset of the possible restrictions is involved.

The size of the linear programming problem defined by the above equations is determined by the number of cutting units involved (N), the number of management regimes specified (M), and the number of cutting periods used (p). The number of decision variables involved is equal to the product of N and M. A total of N unit summation restrictions will always be involved. The number of additional restrictions present depends on how many of the restrictions given by equations (10.7) through (10.14) are included and whether the various maxima and minima are specified in all, or only some, of the cutting periods. If all the restrictions defined above are included for every cutting period, the total number of restrictions involved in the problem will be equal to $N + 8p$.[5] Problems with as many as 500 restrictions and 30,000 decision variables can be handled routinely with currently available computing equipment. However, the costs involved for processing a job of this size may be significant (several hundred dollars or more depending on the details of the problem involved).

Harvest-scheduling systems with a Model I structure are composed of three linked computer programs. The first of these is the *matrix generator*. This program accepts inventory and economic data as input, calculates the quantities A_i, D_{ik}, V_{ijk}, F_{ijk}, H_{ijk}, and R_{ijk}, and passes these data, along with such user-specified information as N, M, p, $HMAX_j$, $HMIN_j$, . . ., $FMIN_j$, to the second-phase program. The second component is usually a system software program for solving linear programming problems. This program accepts the input prepared by the phase 1 program and then calculates and outputs the optimum values for the

---

[5] Some computer programs for solving linear programming problems include a feature known as *right-hand-side ranging*, which makes it possible to specify both a maximum and a minimum for a given quantity in a single restriction. With a program of this type, the maximum total number of restrictions would be $N + 4p$.

X_{ik} decision variables. The final program is referred to as the *report writer*. The report writer uses most of the information produced by the matrix generator together with the optimum values of the X_{ik} decision variables to produce reports that show the regimes assigned to the various cutting units along with the subsequent wood flows and cash flows that will be produced. Readers interested in the details of such systems should consult the user manuals that have been published for MAX-MILLION (Clutter, 1968), Timber RAM (Navon, 1971), and FORPLAN (Johnson et al., 1980). Several forest industry firms use significantly enhanced versions of the original MAX-MILLION system, but the details concerning the structure and use of these programs are usually considered to be proprietary. Some other companies, most of them located in the western United States, have used Timber RAM and other Forest Service developed systems for harvest scheduling.

Although much of the original work on the development of computerized harvest-scheduling systems took place in the United States, several noteworthy applications have been developed in other countries. In Australia, Paine (1966) used linear programming procedures to develop harvest schedules for a 15,000-acre mixed eucalypt forest in Victoria. Subsequent work by the Victoria Forests Commission has produced a more general optimization model known as MASH (from *mountain-ash*), which is used to schedule harvests on some 300,000 acres of State-owned forestland (Weir, 1972). A system has also been developed by the Forestry Commission of New South Wales for scheduling harvests in about 250,000 acres of State-owned Monterey pine plantations (Australian Forestry Council, 1978). Dargavel (1978) has reported on the harvest-scheduling system developed by A.P.M. Forests Pty., Ltd. for management of that company's Monterey pine plantations in central Victoria. In Canada, the British Columbia Forest Service has developed a system called CARP (Computer Assisted Resource Planning) for scheduling harvests on forestland owned by the Province. CARP was originally developed from Timber RAM but now includes many original extensions and additional features.

*10.1.5 Some Modifications of the Model I Formulation

Several possible modifications to the problem structure described in the previous section are worthy of some discussion. One such modification involves a minimization of discounted costs rather than a maximization of discounted cash flows. This approach is sometimes appropriate for a wood-using organization that produces some of its required raw material from harvest of its own lands and purchases the remaining requirements on the open market. In this situation, the organization can specify the total amounts of wood required by cutting periods and then solve for the optimum amounts of fee-land wood and open-market wood in each period. Some additional quantities must be defined before the problem can be formulated.

Y_{jl} = amount of open-market wood purchased at price level l in period j (l = 1, . . . , L)

W_{jl} = maximum amount of open-market wood that can be purchased in period j at price level l

C_{jl} = per-unit cost of price-level l open-market wood in period j (C_{jl} < $C_{j,l+1}$; l = 1, . . . , L − 1)

In addition, the D_{ik} values (D_{ik} = per-acre present value of cutting unit i if management regime k is used) must be modified by omitting any positive contributions arising from fictitious sale of wood to the mill.[6] This amounts to defining NHI_{jk} in equation (10.4) as

NHI_{jk} = net per-acre cost of timber harvest (including transportation cost to the mill) in period j if regime k is used

The cost minimization problem with minimum wood production requirements can now be formulated. Minimize

$$Q = \sum_{i=1}^{N} \sum_{k=1}^{M} D_{ik} X_{ik} + \sum_{j=1}^{p} \sum_{l=1}^{L} C_{jl} Y_{jl} \qquad (10.15)$$

subject to

$$\sum_{k=1}^{M} X_{ik} = A_i \qquad (i = 1, \ldots, N) \qquad (10.16)$$

$$\sum_{i=1}^{N} \sum_{k=1}^{M} V_{ijk} X_{ik} + \sum_{l=1}^{L} Y_{jl} \geq WMIN_j \qquad (j = 1, \ldots, p) \qquad (10.17)$$

$$Y_{jl} \leq W_{jl} \qquad (j = 1, \ldots, p; l = 1, \ldots, L) \qquad (10.18)$$

where L is the number of price levels considered and $WMIN_j$ is the total amount of wood required by the mill in period j. The number of restrictions of the form shown in equation (10.17) is equal to the number of cutting periods. The number of equation (10.18) restrictions equals $p \times L$ (the number of cutting periods times the number of price levels). The above model can easily be generalized to provide separate requirements for various product classes of raw material.

A second useful modification of the standard Model I formulation involves

---

[6] With U.S. tax laws, the fictitious sale generates a tax deduction (cost of raw material) against ordinary income. The net effect of this tax benefit should be included in each D_{ik} value.

the use of period-to-period change restrictions. In many situations, there are no absolute a priori upper and lower limits on such quantities as periodic harvest volumes and periodic cash flows, but there may well be limits on how much change can be accepted from one period to the next. Restrictions limiting the amount and direction of permissible change can be used in addition to, or instead of, the simple maximum and minimum restrictions previously defined. Period-to-period change restrictions can be expressed on an absolute or relative basis. Both types are illustrated here for periodic harvest volume changes.

1. Absolute change restrictions.
    (a) Restrictions on maximum amounts of increase:

$$\sum_{i=1}^{N} \sum_{k=1}^{M} V_{i,j+1,k} X_{ik} - \sum_{i=1}^{N} \sum_{k=1}^{M} V_{ijk} X_{ik} \leq MAXINC_j \qquad (10.19)$$

   where $MAXINC_j$ is the maximum permissible harvest volume increase between period j and period $j + 1$. Restrictions of this type can be provided for any or all sequential pairs of periods.
    (b) Restrictions on maximum amounts of decrease:

$$\sum_{i=1}^{N} \sum_{k=1}^{M} V_{ijk} X_{ik} - \sum_{i=1}^{N} \sum_{k=1}^{M} V_{i,j+1,k} X_{ik} \leq MAXDEC_j \qquad (10.20)$$

   where $MAXDEC_j$ is the maximum permissible harvest volume decrease between period j and period $j + 1$. Restrictions of this type can be provided for any or all sequential pairs of periods. Inclusion of a restriction of this type for all sequential pairs (i.e., for $j = 1$, 2, . . . , $p - 1$), with $MAXDEC_j = 0$ for all j, mandates a non-declining sustained yield solution over the length of the planning period.

2. Percentage change restrictions.
    (a) Restrictions on maximum percentage increase:

$$(1 + \beta) \sum_{i=1}^{N} \sum_{k=1}^{M} V_{ijk} X_{ik} - \sum_{i=1}^{N} \sum_{k=1}^{M}$$
$$V_{i,j+1,k} X_{ik} \geq 0 \qquad (10.21)$$

   where β is the maximum proportional increase in harvest volume from period j to period $j + 1$. For example, if $\beta = 0.20$, the harvest in period $j + 1$ could, at most, be 20 percent greater than the harvest in period j. Restrictions of this type could be provided for any or all sequential pairs of periods or, if desired, for any set of nonsequential pairs of periods.

(b) Restrictions on maximum percentage decrease:

$$(1 - \alpha) \sum_{i=1}^{N} \sum_{k=1}^{M} V_{ijk} X_{ik} - \sum_{i=1}^{N} \sum_{k=1}^{M} V_{i,j+1,k} X_{ik} \leq 0 \qquad (10.22)$$

where α is the maximum proportional decrease in harvest volume from period j to period $j + 1$. For example, if $\alpha = 0.10$, the harvest in period $j + 1$ could be no more than 10 percent less than the harvest in period j. Restrictions of this type can be provided for any or all sequential pairs of periods or, if desired, for any set of non-sequential pairs of periods.

Appropriate changes in the above formulas can be easily made to obtain period-to-period change restrictions for harvest acreages, regeneration acreages, and cash flows.

A third variation of the standard formulation is obtained when the harvest-scheduling model is combined with a mill-scheduling model in a single linear programming system. Systems of this type have been under consideration for some time but they have not been widely implemented. A typical harvest scheduler/mill scheduler model includes activity variables that assign regimes to cutting units, activity variables that provide for outside-wood purchases, activity variables that assign harvested wood to various mill complexes, and activity variables that define the amounts of end products produced by each processing facility at each mill complex. A given amount of a particular end product at a certain facility requires allocation of sufficient wood of specified product classes to that facility. This allocation can be made only if the required amount of wood has been harvested or purchased and transported to the mill complex involved. An interesting aspect of such models is the fact that no transfer prices need to be specified for wood harvested from fee lands.[7] Income is generated when end products are produced and this income is reduced by the costs associated with fee-land timber production, outside-wood purchase, and transportation of wood to the various mill complexes. Combination harvest scheduler/mill scheduler systems tend to be very large models and their solution can require large amounts of computing time. However, such a model realistically expresses the resource allocation problems involved in an integrated forest products company and, if it is well constructed, the model can provide management information of great economic value.

---

[7] In this case, certain outputs from the linear programming analysis (shadow prices) give the appropriate tranfer price values.

10.2 AN EXAMPLE PROBLEM

In this section, we consider an example problem designed to illustrate the use of the Model I linear programming formulation. The problem involved is, of necessity, small in terms of number of variables and number of restrictions but is sufficiently realistic to exemplify the calculations required. Consider the following scenario.

> *Behemoth Pulp Company has just completed construction of a 10,000 ton/ day pulp mill. However, Behemoth owns no land in the vicinity of this mill, and the supply of raw material to the mill is considered to be a matter of some concern. Since the XYZ Timber Co. owns 155,000 acres nearby, Behemoth has agreed to buy wood from XYZ. The contract requires XYZ to provide at least 500,000 cunits per year for harvest by Behemoth in each of the next 16 years. The agreed-on stumpage price is $25 per cunit. If XYZ wishes to provide more than 500,000 cunits in any year, Behemoth will purchase the additional wood at the same price.*

XYZ Timber is now faced with the problem of scheduling harvests and regeneration so that the agreed-on 500,000 cunits can be provided in each of the next 16 years. The forest involved is composed of 90,000 acres of age-13 plantations and 65,000 acres of nonproductive brushland. Both current and subsequent plantations follow the yield table shown in Table 10.3. Regeneration costs the XYZ Timber Co. $150 per acre and the company has annual ad valorem tax and administrative costs of $1.50 per acre. The interest rate used for financial analysis is 5 percent.

The linear programming formulation decided on by XYZ involves a planning period of 16 years, with eight 2-year cutting periods. Specification of a minimum permissible harvest age of 10 years leads to the definition of the 15 management regimes shown in Table 10.4. The symbol C in Table 10.4 indicates a clearcut followed by immediate regeneration. A harvest operation applied to brushland produces no volume but results in plantation establishment. Two cutting units are defined. Cutting unit 1 contains the 90,000 acres of 13-year-old plantations and cutting unit 2 contains the 65,000 acres of brushland. The harvest yields produced by implementation of each management regime in the two cutting units are shown in Table 10.5. These yields are taken directly from Table 10.3 for the ages involved. Regime 1 in cutting unit 1, for example, involves the harvest of an age-14 plantation in period 1 (yield = 52.22 cunits per acre) and the harvest of an age-10 plantation in period 6 (yield = 29.10 cunits per acre).

Bare land values for rotation ages of 10 through 30 years can be calculated as

$$BLV_t = -\$150 + \frac{\$25Y_t - \$150}{1.05^t - 1} - \frac{\$1.50}{0.05} \qquad (10.23)$$

TABLE 10.3

Yield Table for Lands Owned by the XYZ Timber Co.

Plantation Age (years)	Yield (cunits/acre)
10	29.10
11	34.98
12	40.80
13	46.67
14	52.22
15	57.00
16	61.60
17	65.96
18	70.20
19	73.91
20	77.60
21	81.06
22	84.26
23	87.40
24	90.24
25	92.75
26	94.90
27	96.93
28	98.56
29	100.05
30	100.80

where

t = length of the rotation

Y_t = per-acre yield at the end of the rotation

BLV_t = bare land value for a continuing series of rotations of length t

The maximum value of BLV_t occurs when $t = 15$, with

$$BLV_{15} = -\$150 + \frac{\$25(57.00) - \$150}{1.05^{15} - 1} - \frac{\$1.50}{0.05}$$

$$= \$1001.73$$

The optimum economic rotation is, therefore, 15 years with an associated bare land value of \$1001.73. These values can now be used with equation (10.3) to

TABLE 10.4

Management Regimes Used for Harvest Scheduling of XYZ Timber Co. Lands

Management Regime	Cutting Period							
	1	2	3	4	5	6	7	8
1	C					C		
2	C						C	
3	C							C
4	C							
5		C					C	
6		C						C
7		C						
8			C					C
9			C					
10				C				
11					C			
12						C		
13							C	
14								C
15								

C = clearcut followed by immediate regeneration.

calculate the terminal value of land and timber for each regime in each cutting unit. The computations involved are summarized in Table 10.6. The terminal value entry for management regime 1 in cutting unit 1 is, for example, calculated as

$$TV_1 = \frac{\$25(57.00) + \$1001.73 + \dfrac{\$1.50}{0.05}}{1.05^{10}}$$

$$= \$1508.22$$

Table 10.7 shows the data required for calculation of the cash flow present values for each management regime/cutting unit combination using equation (10.4). The results shown for management regime 1 in cutting unit 1 are calculated as follows.

Period 1 net cash flow:

$$\text{Timber harvest income} = \$25(52.22) = \quad \$1305.50$$

$$\text{Less regeneration costs} \qquad\qquad \underline{-\ 150.00}$$

$$\$1155.50$$

TABLE 10.5

Predicted Harvest Yields by Cutting Unit, Management Regime, and Cutting Period

Management Regime	Cutting Period Yields (cunits)							
	1	2	3	4	5	6	7	8
				Cutting Unit 1				
1	52.22					29.10		
2	52.22						40.80	
3	52.22							52.22
4	52.22							
5		61.60				29.10		
6		61.60						40.80
7		61.60						
8			70.20					29.10
9			70.20					
10				77.60				
11					84.26			
12						90.24		
13							94.90	
14								98.56
15								
				Cutting Unit 2				
1	0.00					29.10		
2	0.00						40.80	
3	0.00							52.22
4	0.00							
5		0.00				29.10		
6		0.00						40.80
7		0.00						
8			0.00					29.10
9			0.00					
10				0.00				
11					0.00			
12						0.00		
13							0.00	
14								0.00
15								

TABLE 10.6

Computation of Per-Acre Terminal Values by Management Regime and Cutting Unit

Management Regime (k)	Stand Age at Planning Period End (A_k)	Years until Terminal Stand Harvest (a_k)	Yield from Terminal Stand Harvest (cunits)	Terminal Value (TV_k)
		Cutting Unit 1		
1	5	10	57.00	$1508.22
2	3	12	57.00	1368.00
3	1	14	57.00	1240.82
4	15	0	57.00	2456.73
5	3	12	57.00	1368.00
6	1	14	57.00	1240.82
7	13	2	57.00	2228.33
8	1	14	57.00	1240.82
9	11	4	57.00	2021.16
10	9	6	57.00	1833.25
11	7	8	57.00	1662.81
12	5	10	57.00	1508.22
13	3	12	57.00	1368.00
14	1	14	57.00	1240.82
15	29	0	100.05	3532.98
		Cutting Unit 2		
1	5	10	57.00	1508.22
2	3	12	57.00	1368.00
3	1	14	57.00	1240.82
4	15	0	57.00	2456.73
5	3	12	57.00	1368.00
6	1	14	57.00	1240.82
7	13	2	57.00	2228.33
8	1	14	57.00	1240.82
9	11	4	57.00	2021.16
10	9	6	57.00	1833.25
11	7	8	57.00	1662.81
12	5	10	57.00	1508.22
13	3	12	57.00	1368.00
14	1	14	57.00	1240.82
15	—	—	—	1031.73

TABLE 10.7

Computation of Per-Acre Present Values by Management Regime and Cutting Unit

Management Regime	Cutting Period Per-Acre Cash Flows ($)								Per-Acre Terminal Value (TV)	Per-Acre Present Value (PV)
	1	2	3	4	5	6	7	8		
				Cutting Unit 1						
1	$1155.50					$ 577.50			$1508.22	$2099
2	1155.50						$ 870.00		1368.00	2159
3	1155.50							$1155.50	1240.82	2195
4	1155.50								2456.73	2196
5		$1390.00					577.50		1368.00	2104
6		1390.00						870.00	1240.82	2158
7		1390.00							2228.33	2192
8			$1605.00					577.50	1240.82	2074
9			1605.00						2021.16	2153
10				$1790.00					1833.25	2082
11					$1956.50				1662.81	1993
12						2106.00			1508.22	1892
13							2222.50		1368.00	1775
14								2314.00	1240.82	1652
15									3532.98	1589

Cutting Unit 2

1	$−150.00				$577.50		$1508.22	$856
2	−150.00					$870.00	1368.00	915
3	−150.00					$1155.50	1240.82	951
4	−150.00						2456.73	953
5		$−150.00			577.50		1368.00	773
6		−150.00				870.00	1240.82	827
7		−150.00					2228.33	861
8			$−150.00		577.50		1240.82	699
9			−150.00				2021.16	778
10				$−150.00			1833.25	703
11					$−150.00		1662.81	635
12							1508.22	573
13						−150.00	1368.00	517
14						−150.00	1240.82	466
15							1031.73	443

Period 6 net cash flow:

$$\text{Timber harvest income} = \$25(29.10) = \quad \$727.50$$
$$\text{Less regeneration costs} \qquad\qquad \underline{-\ 150.00}$$
$$\qquad\qquad\qquad\qquad\qquad\qquad\qquad \$577.50$$

$$PV = \frac{\$1155.50}{1.05^1} + \frac{\$577.50}{1.05^{11}} + \frac{\$1508.22}{1.05^{16}} - \frac{\$1.50}{0.05}$$

$$= \$2099$$

All quantities needed for complete formulation of the linear programming problem are now available. The decision variables are defined as

$X_{i,k}$ = number of acres in cutting unit i (i = 1, 2) assigned to management regime k (k = 1, . . ., 15)

The objective is to maximize

$$Q = 2099X_{1.1} + 2159X_{1.2} + \cdots + 1589X_{1.15} \tag{10.24}$$
$$+ 856X_{2.1} + 915X_{2.2} + \cdots + 443X_{2.15}$$

subject to unit summation restrictions and a minimum harvest volume restriction for each cutting period. The unit summation restrictions are

$$\sum_{k=1}^{15} X_{1.k} = 90,000$$

$$\sum_{k=1}^{15} X_{2.k} = 65,000 \tag{10.25}$$

while the minimum harvest volume restrictions can be written as

$$
\begin{array}{l}
52.22X_{1.1} \ + \ 52.22X_{1.2} \ + \ 52.22X_{1.3} \ + \ 52.22X_{1.4} \ \geqslant \ 1{,}000{,}000 \\
\qquad\qquad\quad\ 61.60X_{1.5} \ + \ 61.60X_{1.6} \ + \ 61.60X_{1.7} \ \geqslant \ 1{,}000{,}000 \\
\qquad\qquad\qquad\qquad\qquad\ 70.20X_{1.8} \ + \ 70.20X_{1.9} \ \geqslant \ 1{,}000{,}000 \\
\qquad\qquad\qquad\qquad\qquad\qquad\qquad\ 77.60X_{1.10} \ \geqslant \ 1{,}000{,}000 \\
\qquad\qquad\qquad\qquad\qquad\qquad\qquad\ 84.26X_{1.11} \ \geqslant \ 1{,}000{,}000 \\
\qquad\qquad\quad\ 29.10X_{1.1} \ + \ 90.24X_{1.12} \ + \ 29.10X_{2.1} \ \geqslant \ 1{,}000{,}000 \\
40.80X_{1.2} \ + \ 29.10X_{1.5} \ + \ 94.90X_{1.13} \ + \ 40.80X_{2.2} \ + \ 29.10X_{2.5} \ \geqslant \ 1{,}000{,}000 \\
52.22X_{1.3} \ + \ 40.80X_{1.6} \ + \ 29.10X_{1.8} \ + \ 98.56X_{1.14} \\
\qquad\qquad\qquad\ + \ 52.22X_{2.3} \ + \ 40.80X_{2.6} \ + \ 29.10X_{2.8} \ \geqslant \ 1{,}000{,}000
\end{array}
$$

$$\tag{10.26}$$

The problem thus involves 30 activity variables and 10 restrictions.

TABLE 10.8

Optimum Solution for the XYZ Timber Co. Harvest-Scheduling Problem

Management Regime	Acres Assigned in Cutting Unit	
	1	2
1	—	34,364
2	24,510	—
3	10,257	8,893
4	—	21,743
5	—	—
6	—	—
7	16,234	—
8	—	—
9	14,245	—
10	12,886	
11	11,868	—
12	—	—
13	—	—
14	—	—
15	—	—
Total	90,000	65,000

The optimum solution is shown in Table 10.8. Six different regimes are used for the management of cutting unit 1 and three different regimes are applied in cutting unit 2. Data concerning periodic wood flows, cash flows, acres harvested, and acres regenerated for the optimum solution are shown in Table 10.9. The age class distribution at the end of the planning period is given in Table 10.10. The present value of the forest with the optimum solution is $250,761,009, or $1617.81 per acre.

*10.3   AN ALTERNATIVE MODEL FORMULATION

Previous sections of this chapter have provided a detailed discussion of the Model I linear programming formulation for harvest-scheduling problems. In this section, we provide an example of a Model II formulation. Readers interested in a more general and complete coverage of Model II procedures should consult the excellent presentation of the procedure provided by Johnson and Scheurman (1977). The principal difference between the Model I and Model II formulations lies in the definition of the activity variables. With Model I, each activity variable

TABLE 10.9

Periodic Harvest Volumes, Cash Flows, Harvest Areas, and Regeneration Areas for the Optimum Solution to the XYZ Timber Co. Harvest-Scheduling Problem

Cutting Period	Volume Harvested (cunits)	Cash Flow (thousands of dollars)	Area Harvested (acres)	Area Regenerated (acres)
1	1,815.512	$29,958	34,767	99,767
2	1,000.000	22,100	16,234	16,234
3	1,000.000	22,398	14,245	14,245
4	1,000.000	22,601	12,886	12,886
5	1,000.000	22,755	11,868	11,868
6	1,000.000	19,380	34,364	34,364
7	1,000.000	20,859	24,510	24,510
8	1,000.000	21,625	19,150	19,150

is associated with a particular pattern of forest operations that spans the entire planning period. In the Model II formulation, each harvesting opportunity is represented by a separate activity variable. This difference can be illustrated by considering management regime 1 in the XYZ Timber Co. problem given in the previous section (see Table 10.4). With a Model I formulation, the pattern of clearcut and plant in period 1, clearcut and plant in period 6, and ownership of a 5-year-old plantation at the end of the planning period is associated with a

TABLE 10.10

Age-class Distribution for XYZ Timber Co. Forestlands at the End of the Planning Period after Management with the Optimum Solution

Plantation Age	Number of Acres
1	19,150
3	24,510
5	34,364
7	11,868
9	12,886
11	14,245
13	16,234
15	21,743
Total	155,000

single-activity variable. In a Model II formulation, three activity variables would be required to describe this same pattern—one to provide for harvest of the initially existing stand in period 1, another to provide for harvest of the second stand in period 6, and a third to define the existence of the 5-year-old stand at the end of the planning period.

The use of Model II procedures is illustrated by reconsidering the XYZ Timber Co. harvest-scheduling problem originally presented in Section 10.2. The important aspects of the problem are summarized here.

1. Initial forest consists of 90,000 acres of age-13 plantations and 65,000 acres of nonproductive brushland.

2. Planning period length = 16 years.

3. Number of cutting periods = 8.

4. Cutting period length = 2 years.

5. Minimum harvest per period = 1,000,000 cunits.

6. Stumpage price = $25 per cunit.

7. Regeneration cost = $150 per acre.

8. Interest rate = 5 percent.

9. Minimum harvest age = 10 years.

10. Ad valorem tax and administrative cost = $1.50 per acre per year.

The yield table for XYZ Timber Co. plantations is shown in Table 10.3. In the previous formulation, the 13-year-old plantations and the brushland were referred to as cutting unit 1 and cutting unit 2. With a Model II formulation, the initial subdivisions of the forest do not retain their identity through the planning period. The two initial forest types are therefore referred to as *initial strata*. (In most Model II formulations, the initial strata are the various age classes in existence at the beginning of the planning period.)

A Model II formulation of the XYZ Timber Co. problem requires definition of the following activity variables. Let:

Y_{ij} = acres of initial stratum i that are harvested in cutting period j ($i = 1$, 2; $j = 1, \ldots, 8$)

X_{jk} = acres regenerated in cutting period j and harvested in cutting period k ($j = 1, 2, 3$; $k = j + 5, \ldots, 8$); if $j > 3$, then $X_{jk} = 0$

W_i = acres of initial stratum i that are left unharvested through the planning period ($i = 1, 2$)

U_j = acres regenerated in period j and subsequently left unharvested until the end of the planning period ($j = 1, \ldots, 8$)

The following economic inputs are required.

D_{ij} = per-acre present value of all costs and incomes associated with stands from initial stratum i that are harvested in cutting period j ($i = 1, 2; j = 1, \ldots, 8$)

E_{jk} = per-acre present value of all costs and incomes associated with stands that are regenerated in cutting period j and harvested in cutting period k ($j = 1, 2, 3; k = j + 5, \ldots, 8$)

T_i = per-acre present value of leaving a stand from initial stratum i unharvested at the end of the planning period ($i = 1, 2$)

Z_j = per-acre present value of leaving a stand that was regenerated in cutting period j unharvested at the end of the planning period

Ad valorem tax and administrative costs could be included in the above costs but such an approach is unwieldy. It is simplest to calculate the present value of all future tax and administrative costs and to subtract this quantity from the linear programming objective function value for the optimum solution. Since the annual ad valorem tax and administrative costs are a fixed $1.50 per acre, the present value of all such future payments is

$$PV_{ta} = 155,000(\$1.50/0.05)$$

$$= \$4,650,000$$

The Model II objective function can be written as follows. Maximize

$$Q = \sum_{i=1}^{2} \sum_{j=1}^{8} D_{ij}Y_{ij} + \sum_{j=1}^{3} \sum_{k=j+5}^{8} E_{jk}X_{jk}$$
$$+ \sum_{i=1}^{2} T_i W_i + \sum_{j=1}^{8} Z_j U_j \qquad (10.27)$$

Constraints must be provided to ensure feasibility of the area assignments and to specify the minimum periodic harvest requirements. The area constraints are

$$\sum_{j=1}^{8} Y_{ij} + W_i = A_i \qquad (i = 1, 2) \qquad (10.28)$$

$$\sum_{k=j+5}^{8} X_{jk} + U_j - \sum_{i=1}^{2} Y_{ij} = 0 \qquad (j = 1, \ldots, 8) \qquad (10.29)$$

where A_i is the number of acres in initial stratum i. Equation (10.28) defines two constraints that require the assignment acreages from each initial stratum to sum to the number of acres originally present in that initial stratum. Eight constraints are defined by equation (10.29). The jth of these requires the acreage of stands originating in cutting period j to equal the acreage of stands assigned for harvest in period j. The periodic harvest constraints are

$$\sum_{i=1}^{2} V_{ij}Y_{ij} + \sum_{m=1}^{j-5} H_{mj}X_{mj} \geq 1,000,000 \qquad (j = 1, \ldots, 8) \qquad (10.30)$$

where

V_{ij} = volume per acre harvested in period j from stands belonging to initial stratum i

H_{mj} = volume per acre harvested in period j from stands regenerated in period m (if $j < m + 5$, then $H_{mj} = 0$)

Equation (10.30) defines a restriction for each cutting period that requires the volume harvested in the period to be greater than 1,000,000 cunits.

Computation of the D_{ij}, E_{jk}, W_i, and Z_j values needed in the analysis is shown in Tables 10.11, 10.12, 10.13, and 10.14. Correct values for the V_{ij} terms are included in Table 10.11 and appropriate H_{mj} values are given in Table 10.15. Substitution of the numeric values in equations (10.27) through (10.30) results in a linear programming problem with 32 variables and 18 restrictions. The optimum solution to this problem includes the following nonzero activity variable values (all in acres).

$Y_{11} = 34,767$	$X_{18} = 19,150$
$Y_{12} = 16,234$	$U_1 = 21,743$
$Y_{13} = 14,245$	$U_2 = 16,234$
$Y_{14} = 12,886$	$U_3 = 14,245$
$Y_{15} = 11,868$	$U_4 = 12,886$
$Y_{21} = 65,000$	$U_5 = 11,868$
$X_{16} = 34,364$	$U_6 = 34,364$
$X_{17} = 24,510$	$U_7 = 24,510$
	$U_8 = 19,150$

TABLE 10.11

Calculation of D_{ij} Values for the XYZ Timber Co. Harvest-Scheduling Problem

Initial Stratum (i)	Harvest Period (j)	Harvest Yield (cunits/acre) (V_{ij})	Harvest Income	Present Value (D_{ij})
1	1	52.22	$1305.50	$1243
1	2	61.60	1540.00	1330
1	3	70.20	1755.00	1375
1	4	77.60	1940.00	1379
1	5	84.26	2106.50	1358
1	6	90.24	2256.00	1319
1	7	94.90	2372.50	1258
1	8	98.56	2464.00	1185
2	1	0	0	0
2	2	0	0	0
2	3	0	0	0
2	4	0	0	0
2	5	0	0	0
2	6	0	0	0
2	7	0	0	0
2	8	0	0	0

These values define the same optimum strategy indicated by previous solution of the Model I formulation. The periodic harvest volumes, cash flows, harvest areas, and regeneration areas associated with the above solution are identical with those given for the Model I problem in Table 10.9. The objective function value associated with the optimum Model II solution is $255,325,644. Subtraction of the $4,650,000 adjustment for all future ad valorem tax and administrative

TABLE 10.12

Calculation of E_{jk} Values for the XYZ Timber Co. Harvest-Scheduling Problem

Period Regenerated (j)	Period Harvested (k)	Age at Harvest (years)	Harvest Yield (cunits/ acre) (H_{jk})	Per-Acre Present Value of Regeneration Costs	Per-Acre Present Value of Harvest Income	Per-Acre Total Present Value (E_{jk})
1	6	10	29.10	$ – 142.86	$425.35	$282
1	7	12	40.80	– 142.86	540.93	398
1	8	14	52.22	– 142.86	627.97	485
2	7	10	29.10	– 129.58	385.81	256
2	8	12	40.80	– 129.58	490.64	361
3	8	10	29.10	– 117.53	349.94	232

TABLE 10.13

Calculation of T_i Values for the XYZ Timber Co. Harvest-Scheduling Problem

Initial Stratum (i)	Stand Age at Planning Period End (years)	Per-Acre Value at Planning Period End[a]	Present Value per Acre (T_i)
1	29	$3532.98	$1619
2	—	1031.73	473

[a] These values were previously calculated in Table 10.6.

TABLE 10.14

Calculation of Z_j Values for the XYZ Timber Co. Harvest-Scheduling Problem

Period Regenerated (j)	Stand Age at Planning Period End (years)	Terminal Value at Planning Period End[a]	Present Value of Terminal Value	Present Value of Regeneration Costs in Period j	Total Present Value (Z_j)
1	15	$2456.73	$1125.46	$142.86	$983
2	13	2228.33	1020.82	129.58	891
3	11	2021.16	925.92	117.53	808
4	9	1833.25	839.83	106.60	733
5	7	1662.81	761.75	96.69	665
6	5	1508.22	690.93	87.70	603
7	3	1368.00	626.70	79.55	547
8	1	1240.82	568.43	72.15	496

[a] These values were previously calculated in Table 10.6.

TABLE 10.15

Determination of H_{mj} Values for the XYZ Timber Co. Harvest-Scheduling Problem

Period Regenerated (m)	Period Harvested (j)	Harvest Age (years)	Per-Acre Yield (cunits/acre) (H_{mj})
1	6	10	29.10
1	7	12	40.80
1	8	14	52.22
2	7	10	29.10
2	8	12	40.80
3	8	10	29.10

costs reduces this to $250,675,644, which differs only by rounding error from the corresponding Model I value of $250,761,009.

Model II linear programming formulations have not as yet been widely used for the actual solution of operational harvest-scheduling problems, although Nautiyal and Pearse (1967) and Hallanger (1973) suggested model structures that are very similar to the Model II approach. It seems probable that some harvest-scheduling problems can be handled with greater computational efficiency through a Model II formulation and it may well be that the Model II approach will become more popular as time passes. The FORPLAN harvest-scheduling system currently used by the U.S. Forest Service (Johnson et al., 1980) has the capability of obtaining optimum solutions with either Model I or Model II methods. The Model II option has been generally used in FORPLAN runs for the Southern Region of the Forest Service (Region 8) because the minimum rotations involved (40 years or less) in combination with the Forest Service's standard 150-year planning period produce a very large number of management regimes with a Model I formulation.

*10.4   OTHER APPROACHES TO FOREST-LEVEL PLANNING

In addition to linear programming, a number of other computerized iterative techniques have been used or suggested for use in solving harvest-scheduling problems. Applications of these models have been almost exclusively concerned with harvest scheduling in old-growth forests of the Pacific Northwest. The best known of these models are the following.

1.   SORAC—Short Run Allowable Cut (Chappelle, 1966).

2.   SIMAC—Simulating Intensively Managed Allowable Cut (Sassaman et al., 1972).

3.   TREES—Timber Resource Economic Estimation System (Tedder et al., 1979).

4.   ECHO—Economic Harvest Optimization Model (Walker, 1976).

All four systems involve a computational approach known as *binary search*. Basically, this is a trial-and-error procedure for deciding whether the acres contained in forest stratum *i* will or will not be harvested in cutting period *j*. In all four models, the binary search approach is made possible by invoking an assumption that the harvesting priorities for the various forest strata are known a priori. (With a linear programming approach, the determination of these priorities is an output of the analysis; with binary search procedures, the priorities must be provided as an input to the analysis.) Once the strata are listed in order by harvesting priority, the determination of the optimum harvest schedule is simply a matter of establishing the points in the list where period 1 harvest stops, where period 2 harvest stops, and so forth.

SORAC, SIMAC, and TREES are essentially simulation procedures for calculating a level of harvest that can be sustained through a finite-length planning period subject to certain conditions. All three are basically procedures for determining maximum sustained yield and are conceptually very similar to the techniques previously discussed in Section 9.3 for determining maximum sustainable harvest. In the ECHO model, the objective is maximization of present net value, and the formulation recognizes that stumpage price received may be a function of the quantity sold. Johnson and Scheurman (1977) have shown that the sustained yield maximization problems considered in SORAC and SIMAC are special cases of the general Model II linear programming formulation. The simulation procedures generally require less computer time than solution of the Model II linear programming problem, but the solutions produced by such programs as SORAC, SIMAC, or TREES are optimal only if the a priori harvesting priorities assigned to the various forest strata are identical to those that would be established by linear programming. A discussion of the decision algorithm used in ECHO is also provided by Johnson and Scheurman. Their analysis shows that the ECHO optimization problem can be formulated as a slightly generalized form of the Model II linear programming formulation, and this greatly clarifies the assumptions that are implicit in the use of the ECHO algorithm.

REFERENCES

Australian Forestry Council. 1978. Techniques of Australian forest planning. In *U.S.D.A. For. Serv., General Tech. Report PSW-32.*

Chappelle, D. E. 1966. A computer program for scheduling allowable cut using either area or volume regulation during sequential planning periods. *U.S.D.A. For. Serv., Res. Paper PNW-33.*

Clutter, J. L. 1968. MAX-MILLION—a computerized forest management planning system. *School of For. Res., Univ. of Ga.*

Curtis, F. H. 1962. Linear programming the management of a forest property. *J. For.* **60**:611–616.

Dantzig, G. B. 1951. Maximization of a linear function of variables subject to linear inequalities. In T. C. Koopmans (ed.). *Activity analysis of production and allocation.* Wiley, New York.

Dargavel, J. B. 1978. A model for planning the development of industrial plantations. *Austral. For.* **41**:95–107.

Donnelly, R. H., R. W. Gardner, and H. R. Hamilton. 1963. Integrating woodlands activities by mathematical programming. *Amer. Pulpwood Assoc.*

Hallanger, W. 1973. The linear programming structure of the problem. In Sustainable harvest analysis 1971 and 1972. *State of Washington, Dept. of Nat. Res., Harvest Regulation Report 5.*

Johnson, K. N., and H. L. Scheurman. 1977. Techniques for prescribing optimal timber harvest and investment under different objectives—discussion and synthesis. *For. Sci. Monograph 18.*

Johnson, K. N., D. B. Jones, and B. M. Kent. 1980. *Forest planning model (FORPLAN): user's guide and operations manual* (draft copy). U.S.D.A. For. Serv., Land Management Planning, Fort Collins.

Kidd, W. E., E. F. Thompson, and P. H. Hoepner. 1966. Forest regulation by linear programming—a case study. *J. For.* **64**:611–613.

Leak, W. B. 1964. Estimating maximum allowable timber yields by linear programming. *U.S.D.A. For. Serv., Res. Paper NE-17.*

Liittschwager, J. M., and T. H. Tcheng. 1967. Solution of a large scale forest scheduling problem by linear programming decomposition. *J. For.* **65**:644–646.

Loucks, D. P. 1964. The development of an optimal program for sustained-yield management. *J. For.* **62**:485–490.

Nautiyal, J. C., and P. H. Pearse. 1967. Optimizing the conversion to sustained-yield—a programming solution. *For. Sci.* **13**:131–139.

Navon, D. I., and R. J. McConnen. 1967. Evaluating forest management policies by parametric linear programming. *U.S.D.A. For. Serv., Res. Paper PSW-42.*

Navon, D. I. 1971. Timber RAM . . . a long-range planning method for commercial timber lands under multiple-use management. *U.S.D.A. For. Serv., Res. Paper PNW-70.*

Paine, D. W. M. 1966. Analysis of a forest management situation by linear programming. *Austral. For.* **30**:293–303.

Sassaman, R. W., E. Holt, and K. Bergsvick 1972. User's manual for a computer program for simulating intensively managed allowable cut. *U.S.D.A. For. Serv., General Tech. Report PNW-1.*

Tedder, P. L., J. S. Schmidt, and J. Gourley. 1979. TREES; timber resource economic estimation. Vol. I. A user's manual for forest management and harvest scheduling. *Oreg. State Univ., For. Res. Lab. Bull. 312.*

Walker, J. L. 1976. ECHO: solution technique for a nonlinear economic harvest optimization model. In *Systems analysis and forest resource management.* Soc. Amer. Foresters, Washington.

Wardle, P. A. 1965. Forest management and operational research: a linear programming study. *Ser. B, Mgmt. Sci.* **11**:260–270.

Ware, G. O., and J. L. Clutter. 1971. A mathematical programming system for the management of industrial forests. *For. Sci.* **17**:428–445.

Weir, I. C. A. 1972. Planning of wood production using systems analysis. *AP-PITA* **26**(2):107–112.

APPENDIX A

Common and Scientific Names of Tree Species Referenced

All of the following names are listed according to: W. M. Harlow, E. S. Harrar, and F. M. White. 1979. *Textbook of Dendrology.* 6th ed. McGraw-Hill, New York.

black oak	*Quercus velutina* Lam.
Douglas-fir	*Pseudotsuga menziesii* (Mirb.) Franco
eastern white pine	*Pinus strobus* L.
Jeffrey pine	*Pinus jeffreyi* Grev. and Balf.
loblolly pine	*Pinus taeda* L.
lodgepole pine	*Pinus contorta* Dougl. ex Loud.
longleaf pine	*Pinus palustris* Mill.
Monterey pine	*Pinus radiata* D. Don
northern red oak	*Quercus rubra* L.
ponderosa pine	*Pinus ponderosa* Dougl. ex Laws.
quaking aspen	*Populus tremuloides* Michx.
red pine	*Pinus resinosa* Ait.
scarlet oak	*Quercus coccinea* Muenchh.

shortleaf pine	*Pinus echinata* Mill.
Sitka spruce	*Picea sitchensis* (Bong.) Carr.
slash pine	*Pinus elliottii* Engelm.
southern red oak	*Quercus falcata* Michx.
western hemlock	*Tsuga heterophylla* (Raf.) Sarg.
western white pine	*Pinus monticola* Dougl. ex D. Don
white ash	*Fraxinus americana* L.
white oak	*Quercus alba* L.
white spruce	*Picea glauca* (Moench) Voss
yellow-poplar	*Liriodendron tulipifera* L.

APPENDIX B

Factors for Converting Selected English Measurement Units to Corresponding Metric Measurement Units

1. Length

    1 inch = 2.540 centimeters
    1 foot = 0.3048 meters

2. Area

    1 square inch = 6.452 square centimeters
    1 square foot = 0.09290 square meters
    1 acre = 0.4047 hectares

3. Volume

    1 cubic inch = 16.39 cubic centimeters
    1 cubic foot = 0.02832 cubic meters

4. Weight

    1 pound = 0.4536 kilograms
    1 ton (2000 pounds) = 907.2 kilograms

5. Compound units

1 square foot per acre = 0.2296 square meters per hectare
1 cubic foot per acre = 0.06997 cubic meters per hectare
1 pound per cubic foot = 16.02 kilograms per cubic meter
1 pound per acre = 1.121 kilograms per hectare
1 ton per acre = 2242 kilograms per hectare
1 item (e.g., 1 tree) per acre = 2.471 items per hectare

APPENDIX C

Linear Regression Procedures

The general linear regression model can be written as

$$Y_j = \beta_0 + \beta_1 X_{1j} + \beta_2 X_{2j} + \cdots + \beta_m X_{mj} + \varepsilon_j \qquad (C.1)$$

where

$$\beta_0, \beta_1, \ldots, \beta_m \quad = \text{parameters of the model}$$

$$X_{1j}, X_{2j}, \ldots, X_{mj} = \text{values of the predictor (independent) variables for the } j\text{th population element}$$

$$Y_j = \text{value of the dependent variable for the } j\text{th population element}$$

The quantity ε_j represents the value of a random variable that expresses the difference between Y_j and the average of all Y values associated with the specific combination of predictor variable values $X_{ij}, X_{2j}, \ldots, X_{mj}$. The random variable ε is assumed to be additive to the model and randomly distributed with mean 0 and constant variance σ^2. From an analysis standpoint, $\beta_0, \beta_1, \ldots, \beta_m$ and σ^2 are unknown parameters to be estimated from the data, while the values of the predictor variables are treated as known constants. The random variable Y is therefore distributed with a mean of $\beta_0 + \beta_1 X_1 + \cdots + \beta_m X_m$ and a variance of σ^2.

The first step in any regression analysis is data collection. A sample of n elements is selected from the population, and values for the dependent and independent variables are determined for each of the sample elements. Sample relationships are expressed by writing equation (C.1) as

$$Y_i = \beta_0 + \beta_1 X_{1i} + \beta_2 X_{2i} + \cdots + \beta_m X_{mi} + \varepsilon_i \qquad (C.2)$$

where

$$X_{1i}, X_{2i}, \ldots, X_{mi} = \text{values of the predictor variables for the } i\text{th sample element}$$

$$Y_i = \text{value of the dependent variable for the } i\text{th sample element}$$

$$\varepsilon_i = \text{value of the random variable } \varepsilon \text{ that is associated with the } i\text{th sample element } (i = 1, \ldots, n)$$

When predicted values of $\beta_0, \beta_1, \ldots, \beta_m$ are available (these predicted values are denoted as $\hat{\beta}_0, \hat{\beta}_1, \ldots, \hat{\beta}_m$), predicted values of the response variable can be obtained as

$$\hat{Y}_i = \hat{\beta}_0 + \hat{\beta}_1 X_{1i} + \hat{\beta}_2 X_{2i} + \cdots + \hat{\beta}_m X_{mi} \qquad (C.3)$$

and predicted values of the ε_i values can be calculated as

$$\hat{\varepsilon}_i = Y_i - \hat{Y}_i$$
$$= Y_i - \hat{\beta}_0 - \hat{\beta}_1 X_{1i} - \hat{\beta}_2 X_{2i} - \cdots - \hat{\beta}_m X_{mi} \qquad (C.4)$$

The $\hat{\varepsilon}_i$ values are referred to as *residuals*. Although several different approaches can be used to develop formulas for calculating the $\hat{\beta}_k$ values ($k = 0, 1, \ldots, m$), the so-called *least-squares method* is the standard procedure. With a least-squares approach, the "best" estimates of $\beta_0, \beta_1, \ldots, \beta_m$ are defined to be those values of $\hat{\beta}_0, \hat{\beta}_1, \ldots, \hat{\beta}_m$ that minimize the quantity

$$Q = \sum_{i=1}^{n} \hat{\varepsilon}_i^2 = \sum_{i=1}^{n} (Y_i - \hat{Y}_i)^2$$

$$= \sum_{i=1}^{n} (Y_i - \hat{\beta}_0 - \hat{\beta}_1 X_{1i} - \cdots - \hat{\beta}_m X_{mi})^2 \qquad (C.5)$$

Equations defining the values of $\hat{\beta}_0, \hat{\beta}_1, \ldots, \hat{\beta}_m$ that minimize Q can be obtained from equation (C.5) using standard differential calculus optimization procedures. These equations are known as the *normal equations* and they can be written as follows.

$$\hat{\beta}_0 n + \hat{\beta}_1 \sum X_{1i} + \hat{\beta}_2 \sum X_{2i} + \cdots + \hat{\beta}_m \sum X_{mi} = \sum Y_i$$

$$\hat{\beta}_0 \sum X_{1i} + \hat{\beta}_1 \sum X_{1i}^2 + \hat{\beta}_2 \sum X_{1i} X_{2i} + \cdots + \hat{\beta}_m \sum X_{1i} X_{mi} = \sum X_{1i} Y_i$$

$$\hat{\beta}_0 \sum X_{2i} + \hat{\beta}_1 \sum X_{1i} X_{2i} + \hat{\beta}_2 \sum X_{2i}^2 + \cdots + \hat{\beta}_m \sum X_{2i} X_{mi} = \sum X_{2i} Y_i$$

$$\vdots \qquad\qquad\qquad\qquad\qquad \vdots$$

$$\hat{\beta}_0 \sum X_{mi} + \hat{\beta}_1 \sum X_{1i} X_{mi} + \hat{\beta}_2 X_{2i} X_{mi} + \cdots + \hat{\beta}_m \sum X_{mi}^2 = \sum X_{mi} Y_i \qquad (C.6)$$

where all summations are taken over the sample observations ($i = 1, \ldots, n$).

The relationships shown as formulas (C.6) constitute a set of $m + 1$ linear equations with $m + 1$ unknowns. These equations are solved simultaneously to produce the least-squares parameter estimates $\hat{\beta}_0, \hat{\beta}_1, \ldots, \hat{\beta}_m$.[1] The estimate of the variance parameter is calculated as

$$\hat{\sigma}^2 = \frac{\sum_{i=1}^{n} (Y_i - \hat{\beta}_0 - \hat{\beta}_1 X_{1i} - \hat{\beta}_2 X_{2i} - \cdots - \hat{\beta}_m X_{mi})^2}{n - (m + 1)} \qquad (C.7)$$

Procedures for constructing confidence interval statements concerning the values of the unknown parameters and for testing hypotheses about parameter values are contained in most textbooks on statistical methods.

C.1   RESIDUAL ANALYSIS

An examination of the calculated residuals ($Y_i - \hat{Y}_i$ values) is useful in judging whether the assumptions basic to the estimation procedure have been satisfied. Most analysts proceed as follows.

1.   For each independent variable, a plotting of the residual values over the independent variable values is prepared. The residual values should be randomly scattered around a horizontal line representing a residual value of zero. If the points show any nonrandom trend in relation to the zero line, the relationship

---

[1] All subsequent discussions in this Appendix apply specifically to least-squares regression analysis. All references to the term *linear regression* in the body of the text should be taken to imply *least-squares* linear regression.

between the dependent variable and the independent variable is not being properly expressed by the regression model and appropriate modifications to the model must be made. Such modifications usually involve (a) transformation of the dependent variable, (b) transformation of the independent variable involved, or (c) the inclusion of additional terms in the model.

2. Each of the plottings obtained in step 1 should display a relatively constant dispersion of the residuals across the range of the independent variable involved. If a clear pattern is present (e.g., dispersion increasing as X increases), the assumption of constant variance for the random variable ε does not hold for the model that has been fitted.

3. In addition to the plottings described above, it is usually advisable to plot the residual values over the predicted values.[2] The residual plottings should be randomly dispersed about the zero residual line with no discernible trend and a relatively constant dispersion.

If any of the plottings discussed in steps 1 and 2 show unacceptable patterns, the step 3 plotting will also usually display some undesirable characteristic. A puzzling situation can arise when the step 1 and 2 plottings show acceptable patterns but the step 3 plotting is unacceptable. In this case, the analyst knows that the model fitted is unacceptable, but no information is available to indicate what changes must be made to obtain an acceptable model. Frequently, this situation arises because one or more important variables have been omitted or because one or more variables expressing interaction effects need to be added to the model. Some analysts use plottings of observed over expected values as an alternative to plotting residuals over expected values. An acceptable plotting of this type will show the observed values randomly dispersed vertically around a 45-degree line, with no discernible trends and relatively constant dispersion.

C.2 PROCEDURES FOR STABILIZING THE VARIANCE

Intelligent use of a priori knowledge concerning the phenomenon being modeled often leads to specification of a model that properly expresses the relationship between average Y and the predictor variable values. However, the model may not satisfy the constant variance assumption previously introduced. This same situation can evolve through model modification processes. The same procedures can be used to obtain a satisfactory model in either case.

---

[2] It is never appropriate to plot either residuals or predicted values over observed Y values. Such plottings will, in general, show nonrandom patterns for models that fit the data correctly. See Section 3.3 of Draper and Smith (1981).

Consider first the following simple linear model.

$$Y_i^* = \beta_0^* + \beta_1^* X_i^* + \varepsilon_i^* \tag{C.8}$$

where ε^* is distributed with mean 0 and variance σ^{*2}, where σ^{*2} is not constant but is instead proportional to $f(X^*)$. In this situation, all terms in the model must be divided by $\sqrt{f(X^*)}$ which is referred to as the *weighting factor*. This produces a new model

$$Y_i = \beta_1 X_{1i} + \beta_2 X_{2i} + \varepsilon_i \tag{C.9}$$

where

$$Y_i = Y_i^* / \sqrt{f(X_i^*)}$$

$$X_{1i} = 1 / \sqrt{f(X_i^*)}$$

$$X_{2i} = X_i^* / \sqrt{f(X_i^*)}$$

For the new model, ε_i is distributed with mean zero and a constant variance.[3] In most applications of this procedure, simple forms for $\sqrt{f(X_i^*)}$ suffice to satisfactorily stabilize the variance. (Division of the model by X_i^* and division by $\sqrt{X_i^*}$ are the two most commonly applied variations.) Information on the appropriate weighting factor can be extracted from plottings of Y_i^* on X_i^* or of residuals from model (C.8) on X_i^*. Alternatively, the data can be broken into classes based on the values of X_i^*, and the variance of the Y_i^* values in each class can be calculated. A plotting of these variances over the average X_i^* values for the various classes usually shows the form of the variance relationship quite clearly.

When unequal variance problems are encountered with a model that involves several independent variables, the appropriate course of action is less clearly defined. If the existing model is suitable in other respects, some pattern of transformations to stabilize the variance can usually be worked out. When the residuals show unequal variance patterns in all plottings against the independent variables, the ε variable may be operating multiplicatively rather than additively. In this case, the use of $\ln(Y^*)$ rather than Y^* as the independent variable may cure the problem. (Transformation of some or all of the independent variables to logarithmic form may also be required to achieve linearity.) In many (perhaps

---

[3] Some textbooks do not use a transformation approach in dealing with heterogeneous variance problems and, instead, present "weighted regression" formulas for estimating the regression coefficients. Both methods produce identical end results and are simply different procedures for carrying out the same computations.

most) regression analysis problems, correlations exist between various pairs of the independent variables. As a result, an unequal variance situation arising from the form of the relationship between the dependent variable and one of the independent variables may result in unequal dispersion patterns for several, or even all, of the independent variables. However, specification of a new model using a weighting factor involving the particular independent variable causing the problem will stabilize the variance in all plottings based on residuals from the new model. In other more complex situations, use of a weighting factor that is a function of more than one independent variable may be required. Some examples of the use of weighting factors are shown in Section 1.4 of Chapter 1.

C.3 SPECIFICATION OF THE INITIAL REGRESSION MODEL

The fitting of a specific regression model to a set of suitable data is a matter of simple arithmetic that can be quickly and economically accomplished with modern computing equipment. However, the complete regression analysis process is far from being a matter of simple arithmetic, and the successful completion of such an analysis often requires considerable technical skill and sound judgment on the part of the analyst. The data available for a regression analysis can be defined as consisting of values for the variables $U_1, U_2, \ldots, U_q$. Values for these variables are the basic measurement data provided as input for the analysis. The objective of the analysis, in almost all cases, is the development and analysis of an equation to predict values of one of the U variables from given values for some or all of the other U variables. After collection of the basic data, any regression analysis proceeds by fitting one or more regression models of the form

$$Y_i = \beta_0 + \beta_1 X_{1i} + \beta_2 X_{2i} + \cdots + \beta_m X_{mi} + \varepsilon_i \qquad (C.10)$$

where

$$Y_i = f_1(U_{1i}, \ldots, U_{qi})$$
$$X_{1i} = f_2(U_{1i}, \ldots, U_{qi})$$
$$. = .$$
$$. = .$$
$$. = .$$
$$X_{mi} = f_{m+1}(U_{1i}, \ldots, U_{qi})$$

Selection of the transformations that define the X and Y variables determines whether or not the model has the following properties.

1. The Y variable is a linear function of the quantity $\beta_0 + \beta_1 X_{1i} + \cdots + \beta_m X_{mi}$ and the random variable ε.

2. The variance of ε is constant over the full ranges of the X variables.

3. For any given combination of X values, the random variable ε is normally distributed.

4. The form of the model is consistent with known information concerning the relationships between the dependent variable and the various independent variables.

It is difficult to overemphasize the importance of the initial model formulation process. Whenever possible, the form of the initial model should be based on the analyst's general knowledge of the phenomenon being modeled and a detailed study of comparable modeling efforts with other similar data sets. Some practitioners routinely use plottings of their sample data to suggest the initial model form, while others follow a practice of using an initial model that contains a sufficient number of terms to express any possible relationship that might exist between the U variable being predicted and the predictor U variables. Either of these approaches tends to produce a regression equation that shows a very good fit to the set of sample data from which it was derived, but the equation typically provides poor predictions when applied to population elements not contained in the original sample. This poor predictive performance occurs because some of the relationships embedded in the equation reflect the characteristics of the particular sample from which it was derived rather than population properties. Such "overfitting" of the sample data can often be avoided through intelligent selection of the initial model.

C.4 FITTING SUBSET MODELS

After a complete initial model has been specified, the analyst will generally examine whether all terms in the model should be retained in the final regression equation. In general, this process involves fitting a number of *subset models* (i.e., models derived from the initial model by deleting certain independent variables) and comparing the relative performance of these models. A number of different approaches has been proposed for selecting the subset models to be fitted.[4] Three of the more widely known procedures are:

1. All possible regressions

2. Backwards elimination

3. Stepwise regression

The basic concepts involved in each of these techniques are briefly described in the following discussions.

---

[4] A thorough discussion of these procedures is contained in Chapter 6 of Draper and Smith (1981).

All Possible Regressions

This computationally intensive procedure fits every possible subset model. For an initial model involving three independent variables, eight subset models (including the full model) would be involved.

$$Y = \beta_0 + \varepsilon$$

$$Y = \beta_0 + \beta_1 X_1 + \varepsilon$$

$$Y = \beta_0 + \beta_2 X_2 + \varepsilon$$

$$Y = \beta_0 + \beta_3 X_3 + \varepsilon$$

$$Y = \beta_0 + \beta_1 X_1 + \beta_2 X_2 + \varepsilon$$

$$Y = \beta_0 + \beta_1 X_1 + \beta_3 X_3 + \varepsilon$$

$$Y = \beta_0 + \beta_2 X_2 + \beta_3 X_3 + \varepsilon$$

$$Y = \beta_0 + \beta_1 X_1 + \beta_2 X_2 + \beta_3 X_3 + \varepsilon \qquad \text{(C.11)}$$

The general relationship involved states that, for a linear model involving m independent variables, 2^m different subset regressions exist. Hence, for the example above, $m = 3$ and the number of different regressions to be fitted is 8. Even with a large data set, this is a trivial computational problem if modern computing equipment is available. However, if $m = 10$, the number of possible regressions is $2^{10} = 1024$ and, when $m = 15$, the number of subsets increases to 32,768. Even with exceptionally efficient computing equipment, this latter computation might be unacceptably expensive. In addition, the task of mentally assimilating and interpreting the output from such a calculation could suffice to ruin one's day. The computational inefficiency and laborious interpretation involved in the "all possible" regressions approach can be largely avoided by using a computer algorithm that produces so-called "best subsets" of regressions rather than all possible subsets. The user of such an algorithm specifies as input a value for k, the number of regressions of each size to be computed. The algorithm then fits the k "best" one-variable regressions, the k "best" two-variable regressions, and so on. (The meaning of "best" in this context is discussed in the following section.) An example of a "best subsets" algorithm is the method described by Furnival and Wilson (1974).

Backward Elimination

As a first step, the full initial regression model is fitted to the sample data. The backward elimination procedure then attempts to delete (one at a time) those variables that are not needed for satisfactory prediction of the dependent variable. After fitting of the initial model and selection of a critical value for the test statistic, the following hypothesis is tested for each regression coefficient (usually excluding β_0).

$$H_0: \quad \beta_i = 0 \qquad (i = 1, \ldots, m)$$

(This hypothesis can be tested with either t or F statistics.) If the null hypothesis is rejected in all cases, the procedure terminates and no smaller subset models are investigated. If the null hypothesis cannot be rejected in one or more of the tests, the variable associated with the least significant test statistic is deleted from the model to give a new candidate model, which is then exposed to the same deletion test procedure. The process continues until a model is obtained in which no variable can be deleted or until all variables have been deleted.

Stepwise Regression

The stepwise regression procedure is probably the most widely used method for subset regression analysis. An important conceptual difference in this method compared to others previously described involves the fact that the stepwise procedure will, in many cases, fail to fit the full initial model. (In such cases, many analysts separately fit the initial model so that its performance can be compared with the subset models generated by the stepwise procedure.) The stepwise algorithm can be applied to any subset model (including the initial full model). Consider a candidate subset model involving p parameters, including β_0 ($1 \le p \le m + 1$). (It is assumed that all subset models examined contain β_0.) Application of the stepwise algorithm to this model involves the following steps.

1.   The backward elimination algorithm is applied to see if any variable included in the candidate model can be deleted. If one or more such variables are present, the least significant one is deleted to form a new candidate model and the current iteration of the procedure is completed.

2.   If no variables can be deleted, $m - (p - 1)$ additional models are examined. Each of these models involves $p + 1$ parameters and is formed by adding an independent variable not contained in the current candidate model to the current candidate model. Within the group of $m - (p - 1)$ newly defined models, that model producing the minimum residual sum of squares is identified as the *expanded model*. This model includes one independent variable that is not contained in the current candidate model. The backward stepwise process is then used to test the significance[5] of the additional variable in the expanded

---

[5] Many of the computer programs that implement the stepwise procedure permit a different critical value of the test statistic to be used for the model expansion process from that used for model reduction

model. If this variable is significant, the expanded model is accepted as a new candidate model and the current iteration of the procedure is completed. If the additional variable is nonsignificant, the procedure terminates.

The stepwise procedure begins by applying the above algorithm to the model $Y = \beta_0$. Obviously, no variable can be deleted from this model, but step 2 of the algorithm often produces a new candidate model with one independent variable. The algorithm is then applied to this new candidate model, and this iteration will either terminate the procedure or produce a new candidate model containing two independent variables. From this point on, each iteration of the model can generally result in any one of the following.

1. Deletion of a variable to form a new candidate model.
2. Addition of a variable to form a new candidate model.
3. Termination of the procedure.

When the stepwise procedure terminates, all variables included in the final candidate model will be significant and no unincluded variable will show significance if added to the final candidate model.

Both the backward elimination and the stepwise procedure are much more economical of computer time than the all possible regressions approach. However, the all possible regressions method is the only one of the three that does examine all possible subset models. When all possible regressions are computed, the user is obviously confronted with the problem of selecting the "best" of these regressions. Some practitioners use the backward elimination and stepwise procedures as vehicles for avoiding such judgments by simply accepting the final candidate model as the best regression. However, experienced analysts generally examine the equations produced at each iteration of either process and often select, as the preferred regression, a model produced prior to the final iteration. It should be remembered that both the backward elimination procedure and the stepwise procedure project an unjustified image of statistical rigor. This arises from the fact that the decision-making significance tests always involve either the most significant variable not in the model or the least significant variable in the model. This "screening" that occurs prior to interpretation of the test statistic makes it generally impossible to evaluate the true significance level of the test.

C.5 COMPARING CANDIDATE MODELS

In the ideal regression analysis, the analyst specifies an initial model that, when fitted to the sample data, produces a regression equation composed entirely of statistically significant variables. In addition, plottings of the residuals from this model over predicted Y, and the independent variables show a random, constant variance pattern around a residual value of zero. In such a situation, the analyst will have fitted only one model and will generally adopt the calculated equation as the final regression without further ado. Since the sample data played no role in dictating the form of the model, the analyst can expect such sample statistics as R^2 (proportion of variation explained) and the residual mean square to be good indicators of the predictive performance of the final regression when it is applied in the population.

The only practical difficulty with the ideal regression analysis situation is its infrequency of occurrence with real-world data sets. All too commonly, the analyst will, for various reasons, be forced to fit a number of candidate models to the data set involved. Residual analysis will often rule out some of the candidate models for such reasons as heterogeneous variance or nonrandom relationships between the residuals and one or more independent variables. Usually, however, several candidate models will remain after dismissal of the equations with unacceptable residual patterns. These remaining candidate models may or may not have the same number of independent variables. One or more independent variables might be included in all the candidate models. On the other hand, each model could include only variables that occur in no other model. It will be assumed, for the moment, that all candidate models have the same dependent variable.

Several statistics have been suggested for use in comparing and evaluating candidate regression models. Formulas for computing some of the more widely used of these statistics follow. All formulas apply to the fitting of a p-parameter linear model (including a β_0 term) with a data set containing n observations where *TSS* denotes the corrected total sum of squares and *RSS* denotes the residual sum of squares.

1. The residual mean square.

$$RMS = RSS/(n - p) \tag{C.12}$$

2. The squared multiple correlation coefficient.

$$R^2 = 1 - \frac{RSS}{TSS} \tag{C.13}$$

3. The adjusted squared multiple correlation coefficient.

$$R_a^2 = 1 - (1 - R^2)\left(\frac{n - 1}{n - p}\right)$$

$$= 1 - RMS\left(\frac{n - 1}{TSS}\right) \tag{C.14}$$

4. Mallows C statistic.

$$C = \frac{RSS}{\hat{\sigma}^2} - (n - 2p) \tag{C.15}$$

where $\hat{\sigma}^2$ is the residual mean square obtained by fitting the full regression model of which the p parameter model being evaluated is a subset.

5. The *PRESS* (prediction sum of squares) statistic.

$$PRESS = \sum_{i=1}^{n} (Y_i - \hat{Y}_{ip}^*)^2 \qquad (C.16)$$

where

Y_i = observed value of Y for observation i

$\hat{Y}_{ip}^*$ = predicted value of Y for observation i as calculated from a regression equation derived through fitting the p parameter model to a data set obtained by deleting observation i from the original data set

Calculation of the *PRESS* statistic requires fitting of the p parameter model to each of n different data sets. Each of the regression equations obtained is used to calculate a single predicted value.

When these statistics are being used as indicators of "goodness" in candidate regressions, the analyst will be looking for large values of R^2 and R_a^2; while small values of *RMS*, *C*, and *PRESS* indicate regressions with desirable properties. Two different cases must be identified when considering these statistics as potential criteria for evaluating candidate regression models.

1. The models to be evaluated have the same number of variables (i.e., p is constant within the set of models being considered).

2. Each of the models to be evaluated has a different number of variables (i.e., p is different for each of the models being considered).

Case 1 is the simpler situation and is considered first. If all the candidate models have the same number of variables, the *RMS*, R^2, R_a^2, and *C* statistics are equivalent criteria (i.e., the model with the smallest *RMS* value will also have the smallest *C* value and the largest values for R^2 and R_a^2; the model with the second smallest *RMS* value will also have the second smallest *C* value and the second largest values for R^2 and R_a^2; etc.). It is difficult to directly compare the *PRESS* statistic to the other four criteria, and a ranking made with the *PRESS* statistic will, in general, differ from the common ranking obtained with the other four statistics. However, if the sample size is large, the *PRESS* statistic value should be close to the *RSS* value, in which case the ranking obtained with the *PRESS* statistic should be very close to the ranking given by the other four criteria.

If the set of candidate models to be evaluated contains models of different sizes, but, for one or more sizes, more than one model is present, the usual first step toward selecting a final model is to identify for each p ($p > 1$) the "best"

p-parameter equation where the definition of "best" can be based on any of the five statistics defined above. (The use of RMS, R^2, R_a^2, or C would produce identical selections. Selections produced by the $PRESS$ statistic could differ.) When this step has been completed, the case 2 situation defined above exists. Specifically, there are now several (possibly as many as m) candidate models in which each candidate model contains a different number of variables. Each of these models has been selected as the best model of its size using one of the selection criteria previously defined and has associated with it a value for each of the criterion statistics. At this point, it becomes useful to identify the criterion statistic values associated with the best p-parameter model as RMS_p, R_p^2, R_{ap}^2, C_p, and $PRESS_p$. For any set of candidate models, these values could be tabulated with the format shown in Table C.1.

For any set of candidate models, the analyst must decide how to use the values for one or more of the criterion statistics to select a single "best" value. No exact rules for making this selection are available, and the ultimate choice should reflect the analysts' subject matter knowledge as well as their analyses of the criterion statistic values. It must also be noted that analysts differ in their approaches to interpreting the criterion statistic values. Nevertheless, we attempt to briefly summarize the most common approaches to using these statistics. Selection guidelines for each of the criteria follow.

1. Residual Mean Square

The RMS_p statistic has been used fairly extensively as a selection criterion. Some analysts simply select as the final model the candidate regression with the smallest value of RMS_p. However, it has been pointed out (Hocking, 1976) that this practice is most appropriate when the objective of the analysis is parameter estimation or development of a model with good extrapolation properties. If the objective of the analysis is the development of a model that will provide

TABLE C.1

Format for Tabulating Criterion Statistics

Number of Parameters in Model (p)	Statistic Values				
	RMS_p	R_p^2	R_{ap}^2	C_p	$PRESS_p$
2	RMS_2	R_2^2	R_{a2}^2	C_1	$PRESS_1$
3	RMS_3	R_3^2	R_{a3}^2	C_2	$PRESS_2$
$\vdots$	$\vdots$	$\vdots$	$\vdots$	$\vdots$	$\vdots$
m	RMS_m	R_m^2	R_{am}^2	C_m	$PRESS_m$

good predictions (as is the case with most forestry regression analyses), the RMS_p statistic should probably be employed as follows.

(a) Plot the RMS_p values over p. For the larger values of p, the RMS_p values will generally fluctuate around a horizontal line. The RMS value associated with the line is denoted as $\hat{\sigma}^2$ since this value will usually be a satisfactory estimate of σ^2. (This assumes that the largest model contains all variables present in any of the smaller models.)

(b) Selection of the final model is accomplished by selecting the candidate model that represents the best compromise between (i) minimizing the size of the model, and (ii) having an RMS_p value that is reasonably close to the $\hat{\sigma}^2$ value.

2. Squared Multiple Correlation Coefficient

Since a decrease in R^2 never occurs whenever a model is expanded by the addition of another variable, it is seldom appropriate to use maximization of R^2 as a selection rule.[6] Instead, the model selected as best should (a) contain as few variables as possible, and (b) have an R^2 value that is not substantially less than R^2_{max}, where R^2_{max} is the maximum of the R^2_p values. If the largest model contains all variables present in other models, it is often useful to plot the R^2_p values over p. Typically, such a plotting shows the R^2_p values for large p lying close to an upper asymptote of R^2_{max}. As p decreases, however, there will be a point where the R^2_p values begin to decrease sharply. The model associated with the p value at which this decrease begins is often a good choice as the final model.

3. Adjusted Squared Multiple Correlation Coefficient

This statistic is essentially equivalent to RMS_p which is far easier to interpret. It is therefore recommended that RMS_p be used in preference to R^2_{ap} as a selection criterion. The R^2_{ap} statistic has been defined here because some best subset computer programs use maximization of R^2_{ap} as the selection criterion. Such a procedure is equivalent to selecting those subset regressions that have minimum RMS_p values.

4. Mallows C_p Statistic

Selection of a final regression with the C_p statistic is a matter of identifying the regression that offers the best compromise between (a) minimizing C_p, and (b) having a C_p value that is approximately equal to p. In some cases, the same regression will be optimal with respect to both objectives, and selection of the

---

[6] In theory, the change in R^2 resulting from addition of another variable could be zero. However, with realistic data sets, this situation occurs very infrequently.

final regression is straightforward. The statistical considerations involved in reaching a compromise between the two objectives are discussed by Draper and Smith (1981).

5. The *PRESS$_p$* Statistic

Model selection with the *PRESS$_p$* statistic is again a matter of reaching the best compromise between two sometimes conflicting considerations. The first is to select a model with small p, while the second involves choosing a final regression for which the *PRESS$_p$* value is not appreciably greater than *PRESS$_{min}$*, where *PRESS$_{min}$* is the minimum of the candidate regression *PRESS$_p$* values.

All of these criteria constitute attempts to deal with the problem of selecting the best of several (or, in some cases, many) candidate regression models without involving an excessive number of independent variables or obtaining a final model that has been overfitted. Historically, the R_p^2 statistic has almost certainly been the most widely used selection criterion. In recent years, the C_p statistic has become increasingly popular. The C_p value conveys considerable information concerning the properties of a particular regression equation. Many analysts find a plotting of C_p values over p for all candidate regressions to be a useful tool in selecting the final regression, since models with $C_p \approx p$ can be easily identified and their C_p values can then be compared. There is also considerable current interest in the use of the *PRESS$_p$* statistic as a selection criterion. This statistic has considerable intuitive appeal in cases where the objective of the analysis is prediction. However, the amount of computation required to produce *PRESS$_p$* statistics is somewhat intimidating, particularly with large data sets, and some analysts seem to feel that, for most problems, the information obtained does not justify the cost.

Situations sometimes arise in which the best regression must be selected from a set of candidate models with different dependent variables. For example, suppose the following models were fitted to data involving the variables X and Y.

$$Y = \beta_0 + \beta_1 X \tag{C.17}$$

$$\ln(Y) = \beta_0 + \beta_1 X \tag{C.18}$$

$$Y/X = \beta_0 + \beta_1(1/X) \tag{C.19}$$

None of the previously described criterion statistics can be validly used to compare the relative performance of the regression equations obtained by fitting the three models shown above, because each of those statistics is meaningful only for comparisons of regressions that involve the same dependent variable. An index for comparing the performance of regression models with different dependent variables has been suggested by Furnival (1961). This problem often arises in an analysis to develop individual tree volume or weight prediction equations since the most commonly used models involve several different transformations of stem content as the dependent variables.

The material previously presented in this Appendix constitutes a very brief introduction to current methods of linear regression analysis. An extensive body of literature concerning this topic exists in textbooks and articles in a variety of scientific journals. Thorough introductory discussions of the subject have been provided by Neter and Wasserman (1974), Hocking (1976), and Draper and Smith (1981). Numerous additional references are provided in each of these sources.

C.6 NONLINEAR REGRESSION MODELS

Although a detailed discussion of nonlinear regression methods is outside the scope of this book, some readers may find a brief introduction to the topic helpful. Conceptually, there is little difference between linear and nonlinear least-squares procedures since, in both cases, the objective is to determine the set of parameter estimates that minimizes the sum of the squared residuals. However, the mathematics involved in actual calculation of the nonlinear least-squares estimates is quite different from that for linear regression.

The basic linear regression model was defined in equation (C.1). This is referred to as a *linear model* because the dependent variable is a linear function of the parameters. It is important that this definition be clearly understood. As an illustration, consider the polynomial model

$$Y_i = \beta_0 + \beta_1 X_i + \beta_2 X_i^2 + \beta_3 X_i^3 + \varepsilon_i \qquad (C.20)$$

Although this model expresses a nonlinear relationship between Y and X, it is still a linear model because Y is a linear function of the parameters (i.e., the β_j values). On the other hand, in the model

$$Y_i = \beta_1 + \beta_2 X_{1i}^{\beta_3} + \varepsilon_i \qquad (C.21)$$

Y is not a linear function of the parameters, so that equation (C.21) is a nonlinear regression model.

In general, any nonlinear regression model can be represented as

$$Y_i = f(X_{1i}, X_{2i}, \dots, X_{mi}; \beta_1, \beta_2, \dots, \beta_k) + \varepsilon_i \qquad (C.22)$$

When predicted values of the parameters are available, predicted values of the response variable can be obtained as

$$\hat{Y}_i = f(X_{1i}, X_{2i}, \ldots, X_{mi}; \hat{\beta}_1, \hat{\beta}_2, \ldots, \hat{\beta}_k) \qquad \text{(C.23)}$$

so that, for a set of sample data with n observations,

$$Q = \sum_{i=1}^{n} \hat{\varepsilon}_i^2 = \sum_{i=1}^{n} (Y_i - \hat{Y}_i)^2$$

$$= \sum_{i=1}^{n} [Y_i - f(X_{1i}, X_{2i}, \ldots, X_{mi}; \hat{\beta}_1, \hat{\beta}_2, \ldots, \hat{\beta}_k)]^2 \qquad \text{(C.24)}$$

It is possible, for any given nonlinear model, to differentiate Q with respect to each of the parameters and obtain a set of normal equations. In the linear regression model case, the normal equations are linear equations that are, in general, easily solved for the parameter estimates. For any nonlinear model, the normal equations are nonlinear and solving them for the parameter estimates is, at best, a difficult task.

Because of the difficulties involved in solving the normal equations for a nonlinear model, a different approach is generally used to obtain the parameter estimates. This approach is always iterative and generally involves the following steps.

1. An initial set of parameter estimates is specified by the analyst. These may be based on knowledge from previous analyses or examination of the data set being analyzed.

2. Using the current set of parameter estimates, the current value of Q is calculated. In addition, the derivative of Q with respect to each parameter estimate is evaluated using the current parameter estimate values.

3. The derivatives calculated in step 2 are used to obtain new parameter estimate values, and a new value of Q is calculated with the new parameter estimates.

4. If the difference between the new value of Q and the current value of Q is less than a specified constant, the procedure terminates and the current parameter estimate values are accepted as the final estimates. If the difference exceeds the specified constant, the new parameter estimates become the current parameter estimates and the process begins again from step 2. (Statistics other than Q can be used for the termination test. Some programs, for example, base the termination test on the proportional changes in the parameter estimates.)

Several different algorithms have been developed to carry out the computations involved in step 3. Although the details of these algorithms are mathematically complex, their overall objective is fairly easy to grasp. If, during a given iteration of step 3, the derivative of Q with respect to $\hat{\beta}_j$ is positive, then Q can be made smaller by decreasing $\hat{\beta}_j$. If the derivative is negative, an increase in $\hat{\beta}_j$ will produce a decrease in Q. However, the current calculated values of the derivatives apply exactly only at the current values of the parameter estimates. Thus, the practical question involved is: Given the derivative values, by how much should each parameter estimate be changed in the current iteration? The principal differences among the various available nonlinear regression programs primarily reflect different approaches to dealing with this question.

Successful application of nonlinear regression techniques requires considerable sophistication on the part of the user. If a poor set of initial parameter estimates is selected or an unfortunate choice is made concerning the parameter estimate modification algorithm, the procedure may converge very slowly or it may not converge at all. In addition, if convergence does occur, it may be to a set of estimates that constitutes a local rather than a global minimum. Detailed discussions of nonlinear regression methods are available in Bard (1974) and Draper and Smith (1981). Two of the more widely used computer programs for implementing nonlinear regression analyses are described in Dixon (1979) and Helwig and Council (1979).

REFERENCES

Bard, Y. 1974. *Nonlinear parameter estimation.* Wiley, New York.

Dixon, W. J. (Ed.). 1979. *BMD biomedical computer programs, P series.* Univ. Calif. Press, Berkeley.

Draper, N. R., and H. Smith. 1981. *Applied regression analysis.* 2nd ed. Wiley, New York.

Furnival, G. M. 1961. An index for comparing equations used in constructing volume tables. *For. Sci.* 7:337–341.

Furnival, G. M., and R. W. Wilson. 1974. Regression by leaps and bounds. *Technometrics* **16**:499–511.

Helwig, J. T., and K. A. Council (Eds.). 1979. *SAS user's guide, 1979 edition.* SAS Institute, Raleigh, N.C.

Hocking, R. R. 1976. The analysis and selection of variables in linear regression. *Biometrics* **32**:1–51.

Neter, J., and W. Wasserman. 1974. *Applied linear statistical models.* Irwin, Homewood, Ill.

Index